Algebra Connections
California Edition

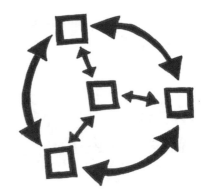

Managing Editors

Leslie Dietiker
Phillip and Sala Burton Academic High School
San Francisco, CA

Evra Baldinger
Phillip and Sala Burton Academic High School
San Francisco, CA

Contributing Editors

Carlos Cabana
San Lorenzo High School
San Lorenzo, CA

John Cooper
Del Oro High School
Loomis, CA

Mark Coté
Beaver Lake Middle School
Issaquah, WA

Joanne da Luz
The Life Learning Academy
San Francisco, CA

David Gulick
Phillips Exeter Academy
Exeter, NH

Patricia King
Holmes Junior High School
Davis, CA

Lara Lomac
Phillip and Sala Burton Academic
High School, San Francisco, CA

Bob Petersen
Rosemont High School
Sacramento, CA

Ward Quincey
Gideon Hausner Jewish Day School, Palo
Alto, CA

Barbara Shreve
San Lorenzo High School
San Lorenzo, CA

Michael Titelbaum
University of California
Berkeley, CA

Illustrator

Kevin Coffey
San Francisco, CA

Technical Manager

Bethany Armstrong
Davis, CA

Technical Assistants

Erica Andrews
Elizabeth Burke
Elizabeth Fong
Keith Lee

Eric Baxter
Carrie Cai
Rebecca Harlow
Michael Leong

Program Directors

Leslie Dietiker
Phillip and Sala Burton Academic High School
San Francisco, CA

Judy Kysh, Ph.D.
Departments of Mathematics and Education
San Francisco State University

Brian Hoey
Christian Brothers High School
Sacramento, CA

Tom Sallee, Ph.D.
Department of Mathematics
University of California, Davis

Consultants from San Lorenzo High School

Ashanti Branch	Laura Evans	Eric Price	Estelle Woodbury
Suzanne Cristofani	Lisa Jilk	Ana Ruiz	Dorothy Woods
Kristina Dance	Karen O'Connell	Hannah Witzemann	Lisa Wright

Assessment Contributors:

Evra Baldinger, Managing Editor
Phillip and Sala Burton Academic High School
San Francisco, CA

Carlos Cabana
San Lorenzo High School
San Lorenzo, CA

Mark Coté
Beaver Lake Middle School
Issaquah, WA

Leslie Dietiker
Phillip and Sala Burton Academic High School
San Francisco, CA

Laura Evans
San Lorenzo High School
San Lorenzo, CA

Judy Kysh, Ph.D.
Departments of Mathematics and Education
San Francisco State University

Contributing Editors of the Parent Guide:

Bev Brockhoff
Glen Edwards Middle School
Lincoln, CA

Elizabeth Coyner
Christian Brothers High School
Sacramento, CA

Brian Hoey
Christian Brothers High School
Sacramento, CA

Patricia King
Holmes Junior High School
Davis, CA

Bob Petersen, Managing Editor
Rosemont High School
Sacramento, CA

Editor of Extra Practice:

Bob Petersen
Rosemont High School
Sacramento, CA

Technical Manager of Parent Guide:

Rebecca Harlow
Stanford University
Stanford, CA

2 3 4 5 6 7 8 9   10 09 08

Printed in the United States of America   California Edition   ISBN-13: 978-1-60328-000-6

A Note to Students:

Welcome to a new year of math! In this course, you will be exposed to a powerful set of mathematical tools called algebra. As a set of tools, algebra is the foundation of higher mathematics. In fact, future courses will build from what you learn here. While you learn algebra, we also hope you become used to a new way of thinking: a way of investigating new situations, studying relationships, and figuring  out what strategies can be used to solve problems. Learning to think this way is useful in mathematical contexts, other academic disciplines, and situations outside the classroom.

In meeting the challenges of algebra, you will not be working alone. During this course you will collaborate with other students as a member of a study team. Working in a team means speaking up and interacting with others. You will explain your ideas, listen to what others have to say, and ask questions if there is something you do not understand. In algebra, a single problem can often be solved several ways. You will see problems in different ways than your teammates do. Each of you has something to contribute while you work on the lessons in this course.

Together, your team will complete problems and activities that will help you develop mathematical ideas and methods. Your teacher will support you as you work, but will not take away your opportunity to think and investigate for yourself. Each topic will be revisited many times and connected to other topics. If something is not clear to you the first time you work with it, you will have more chances to build your understanding as the course continues.

Learning math this way has a significant advantage: as long as you actively participate, make sure everyone in your study team is involved, and ask good questions, you will find yourself understanding mathematics at a deeper level than ever before. By the end of this course, you will have a powerful set of mathematical tools at your disposal. You will see how these tools connect with each other so that you can use them to solve new problems. With your teammates you will meet mathematical challenges you would not have known how to approach before.

In addition to the support provided by your teacher and your study team, CPM has also created online resources to help you, including help with homework, a parent guide, and extra practice. You will find these resources and more at www.cpm.org.

We wish you well and are confident that you will enjoy learning algebra!

Sincerely,
The CPM Team

Algebra
Connections
Table of Contents

Student Edition

Chapter 7 Linear Relationships

Chapter 8 Quadratics

CHAPTER 1

Welcome to Algebra! What is algebra? This chapter will introduce you to many of the big ideas you will explore and the ways you will be working during this course. You will apply your current mathematical knowledge to solve problems, some of which you will revisit later in the course to solve using new algebraic tools.

This chapter will also introduce you to the five Ways of Thinking that are threaded throughout the course. They are: **justifying** (explaining and verifying your ideas), **generalizing** (predicting behavior for any situation), **making connections** (connecting your ideas to other ways of seeing or to past or future learning), **reversing thinking** (solving problems "backward and forward"), and **applying and extending** (applying your knowledge to new contexts and extending it to help solve new problems).

Guiding Questions

Think about these questions throughout this chapter:

What is algebra?

How can I solve a problem that I have never seen before?

How can I organize my work?

How can I describe my process?

Finally, this chapter is about problem solving. During this chapter, you will use a variety of problem-solving strategies that will remain useful throughout this course, including:

Guessing and Checking	Collecting Data	Finding Patterns
Drawing a Graph	Working Backward	

Chapter Outline

Section 1.1 This section will include several problems and activities that use many of the big ideas of algebra. Each one will require your study team to work together and use various problem-solving strategies.

Section 1.2 This section introduces another problem-solving strategy that will help you solve a complex problem called "The Apartment." You will also have opportunities to reflect on and write about your mathematical understanding by creating a Learning Log.

1.1.1 What stories can a graph tell?

Interpreting Graphs

You will focus on several challenges during this unit that will require you to use different problem-solving strategies. While all of the problems are solvable with your current math skills, some will be revisited later in the course so that you can apply new algebraic tools to solve them. Each problem also introduces you to an important concept of algebra that you will study in this course.

1-1.   GETTING TO KNOW YOU, Part One

How can a graph tell a story? Today you will find your team members and then will work together to write a story for a graph.

Your Task: Your teacher will give you one part of a graph. Find the students in the class who have the other pieces of the same graph. When you find all of the students whose graph parts belong with yours, sit down together as a team.

As a team, come up with a story that could be represented by your team's graph. Think carefully about each part of the graph. Once your team agrees on a story, make sure every member of the team can describe each part of the story and explain its connection to the corresponding part of the graph.

To help you work together today, each member of the team has a specific job, assigned by your first name (or by your last name if any team members have the same first name).

Team Roles

Resource Manager – If your name comes first alphabetically:

- Make sure that the team has tape.

- Ask the teacher when the **entire** team has a question. *"No one has an idea? Should I ask the teacher?"*

- Make sure your team cleans up by delegating tasks. You could say, *"I will put away the _____ while you _____ ."*

Facilitator – If your name comes second alphabetically:

- Start the team's discussion of the graph by asking, *"What could this graph be about?… What are some ideas?"*

- Help the team agree on a story: *"Do we agree on all of the parts of our story?"*

Recorder/Reporter – If your name comes third alphabetically:

- Tape the graph pieces together on a piece of paper to form the graph.

- Take notes for the team. The notes should include phrases like, *"For part one…"* and explanations like, *"Because part one is not so steep…"*

Task Manager – If your name comes fourth alphabetically:

- Remind the team to stay on task and not to talk to students in other teams. You can suggest, *"Let's move on to another part of the graph."*

- Listen for reasons and challenge your teammates to justify their thinking. *"But why do you think that?"*

1-2.   GETTING TO KNOW YOU, Part Two

Suppose the graph at right represents
something about the four students in your
team. But what is the graph about? Decide
what information the *x*- and *y*-axes could
represent so that each point represents a
different member of your team. **Justify** your
statements.

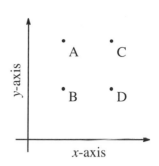

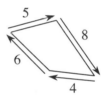

METHODS AND MEANINGS

MATH NOTES

The Perimeter and Area of a Figure

The **perimeter** of a figure is the
distance around the exterior (outside)
on a flat surface. It is the total length
of the boundary that encloses the
interior (inside) region. See the
example at right.

Perimeter = $5 + 8 + 4 + 6 = 23$ units

The **area** indicates the number of
square units needed to fill up a region
on a flat surface. For a rectangle, the
area is computed by multiplying its
length and width. The rectangle at
right has a length of 5 units and a width
of 3 units, so the area of the rectangle
is 15 square units.

Area = $5 \cdot 3 = 15$ square units

1-3.   MATHOGRAPHY

Write a letter about yourself that will help your teacher get to know you as an individual, addressing each of the general topics below (in bold). Choose a few of the suggested questions to get you started.

About You: By what name do you like to be called? What are your interests, talents, and hobbies? What are you proud of? With whom do you live? What languages do you speak? When is your birthday? What are you like as a member of a team? In what ways are you excited about working in a team? In what ways are you nervous about it?

You as a Math Student: Describe your memories as a math student from kindergarten until now. What experiences in math have you liked? Why? How do you feel about taking Algebra? Have you ever worked in a team in a math class before? What kinds of math do you imagine yourself doing in Algebra class?

1-4.   DIAMOND PROBLEMS

Finding and using a pattern is an important problem-solving skill you will use in algebra. The patterns in Diamond Problems will be used later in the course to solve other types of algebraic problems.

Look for a pattern in the first three diamonds below. For the fourth diamond, explain how you could find the missing numbers (?) if you know the two numbers (#).

Copy the Diamond Problems below onto your paper. Then use the pattern you discovered to complete each one.

a.   b.   c.   d.   e.

Algebra Connections

1-5.   The area of the rectangle at right is 24 square units. On graph paper, draw and label all possible rectangles with an area of 24 square units. Use only whole numbers for the dimensions (measurements).

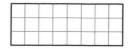

Area = 24 square units

a.   Find the perimeter of each of these rectangles. You may want to refer to the Math Notes box for this lesson for more information on the perimeter of a figure.

b.   Of these rectangles, which has the largest perimeter? Which has the smallest perimeter? Describe these shapes. Remember to use complete sentences.

1-6.   CAR COMPARISON

The following three graphs describe two cars, A and B.

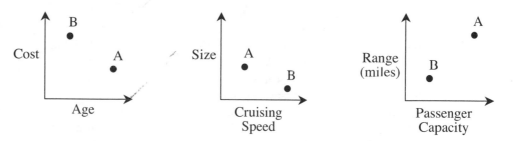

Decide whether each of the following statements is true or false. Explain your reasoning.

a.   The newer car is more expensive.

b.   The slower car is larger.

c.   The larger car is newer.

d.   The cheaper car carries more passengers.

1.1.2 How can I name a point?

Using the (x, y) Coordinate Plane

Today you will use a **coordinate system** to refer to the locations of specific points in the form (x, y). By the end of this lesson, be sure you and your teammates know the answers to the following target questions:

How can you plot a point using its (x, y) coordinates?

How can you name a point on the graph?

How can you describe a pattern formed by points?

1-7. THE EUCALYPTUS GROVE

Some communities in Mozambique plant eucalyptus tree farms because their tall, straight trunks make great poles for building homes. While touring his farm, Etube (pronounced "eh-**too**-bay") noticed that some of the trees have a deadly disease. He created a coordinate system, shown in the diagram below, to keep track of where the infected trees are. The farm's roads are shown as the x- and y-axes in the diagram, and Etube's house is located where the two roads intersect. Each section of the farm (known as a **quadrant**) has 12 rows of 12 trees. The trees marked with a ✪ show signs of disease – the tops are turning brown!

a. The tree marked A, located at the point (–3, 6), is diseased. In (x, y) form, list the locations of all of the other diseased trees shown on the diagram.

b. On a piece of graph paper, neatly draw and label x- and y-axes to represent the roads intersecting at Etube's house. Place points or symbols on your graph to represent the diseased trees.

Etube just learned that the trees at (–8, 2) and (5, –7) are also diseased. Add these trees to your diagram.

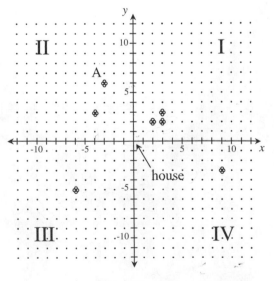

Problem continues on next page →

Algebra Connections

1-7.   *Problem continued from previous page.*

      c.   In (x, y) form, what is the location of Etube's house? This is also called the **origin** of a graph.

      d.   Etube is standing at the farmhouse looking out at Quadrant I and sees that the tree at $(3, 2)$ is diseased. However, he notices that he cannot see the tree at $(6, 4)$ because it is blocked by the tree at $(3, 2)$.

          In (x, y) form, write down the locations of two other trees that he cannot see from his house because they are hidden behind the tree at $(3, 2)$. What do the locations of these trees have in common? When looking at the coordinates, what pattern(s) do you notice?

      e.   While standing at his house, can Etube see the diseased tree at $(9, -3)$? If so, explain how you know. If not, name any trees that block its view. How can you be sure that these trees hide the tree at $(9, -3)$? Be sure to **justify** your team's conclusion.

      f.   The tree disease is passed each day when the leaves of a diseased tree touch the leaves of a healthy tree that grows next to it, as shown on the diagram at right. (Note that the disease cannot pass between trees on opposite sides of the road because their leaves do not touch.) Etube knows that the tree at $(-8, 2)$ is diseased. In (x, y) form, write the locations of four trees that will be infected by that tree on the first day.

      g.   In Quadrant I, three trees are diseased. Write the locations (x, y) of the trees that will be infected by these three trees by the end of the first day.

      h.   Etube noticed that there is one diseased tree in Quadrant III. The disease is spreading rapidly, and he is worried because the tree medicine will not arrive for four more days. How many trees in Quadrant III will still be healthy after the fourth day? How do you know? Use your diagram, keep track of the diseased trees, and **justify** your response.

1-8.   Reflect on how you used the coordinates (the x- and y-values) to find and refer to points on the graph during today's lesson. Revisit the target questions, reprinted below, and share your conclusions in a class discussion.

          How can you plot a point using its (x, y) coordinates?

          How can you name a point on the graph?

          How can you describe a pattern formed by points?

METHODS AND MEANINGS

Axes, Quadrants, and Coordinates

The *x*- and *y*-axes help define points on a graph (called a "Cartesian Plane"). The **x-axis** is horizontal, while the **y-axis** is vertical. The *x*- and *y*-axes divide the graphing area into four sections called **quadrants**. Written as an **ordered pair**, a point is named by its **coordinates** (x, y), with the *x*-coordinate written first.

4-quadrant graph:

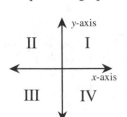

1st-quadrant graph:

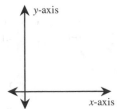

1-9.   In the graph at right, points A, B, and C represent three different students.

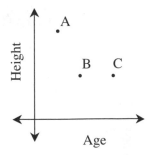

a.   Which student is oldest? Explain how you decided.

b.   What can you say about student B compared to students A and C? Tell as much as you can and **justify** your statements.

1-10.   Compute each of the following sums and differences.

a. $-7 + (-2)$ b. $3 + (-4)$ c. $-2 - 5$ d. $-1 + 5$

e. $4 - (-2)$ f. $-7 - (-8)$

1-11.   Using whole numbers only, draw every possible rectangle with an area of 18 square units on graph paper. Write $A = 18$ un^2 inside each figure. Label the dimensions (length and width) of each rectangle.

1-12.   Latisha is determined to do well in school this year. Her goal is to maintain at least an 85% average in all of her courses.

    a.   Latisha started with two scores: 72% and 89%. Confirm that the average of these two scores is 80.5%. Show your work.

    b.   Latisha's third score is 90%. Use her scores from part (a) to figure out her average now. Be sure to show your work.

1-13.   In Algebra, you will need to be able to work with numbers, words, and geometric representations. Use these representations to answer the following problems.

    a.   Draw and shade a figure that represents 100%. Label 100% below it. Then describe the figure in words.

    b.   Similarly, draw and shade figures that represent 50%, 25%, and 150%. Label each figure and describe it in words.

    c.   Draw and shade a figure that represents "one-third." How can this figure be represented with a number?

    d.   Describe what the diagram at right represents using words and numbers.

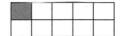

1-14.   Use the graph at right to answer the following questions about quadrants and coordinates of points.

    a.   What are the coordinates of the two points in Quadrant II (where the x-value is negative and the y-value is positive)?

    b.   What are the coordinates of the two points in Quadrant IV (where the x-value is positive and the y-value is negative)?

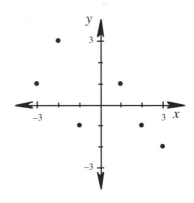

1.1.3 How can I use data to solve a problem?

Collecting, Organizing, and Analyzing Data

Computing batting averages, performing scientific experiments, and polling people during elections are just a few examples of how data can provide useful information when it is collected and analyzed. In this lesson you will be collecting and organizing data to determine the potential danger of riding a roller coaster.

1-15. NEWTON'S REVENGE

Have you heard about Newton's Revenge, the new roller coaster? It's so big, fast, and scary that people are already starting to talk. Some people are worried about the tunnel that thrills riders with its very low ceiling.

The closest the ceiling of the tunnel ever comes to the seat of the roller-coaster car is 200 cm. Although no accidents have been reported yet, rumors have been spreading that very tall riders have broken their arms as they went through the tunnel with their arms raised over their heads. Unfortunately, due to these rumors, many tall people have stopped riding the coaster.

Your Task: Consider how you could determine whether the tunnel is actually safe for any rider, no matter how tall. Discuss the questions below with your team. Be ready to share your responses with the rest of the class.

Discussion Points

What is this problem about? What is it asking you to do?

What information can help you answer this question?

How can you get the information you need?

1-16.   One way to determine if the roller coaster is safe is to collect and analyze data.

a.   Collect data from each member of your team.

Each member of the team needs to be measured twice. First, have one team member stand and have another team member measure his or her height. Second, have the same student sit in a chair or desk, raise his or her arms so that they are stretched as far as possible above his or her head, and measure the distance from the seat of the chair to his or her fingertips. All measurements should be in centimeters.

Student Name	Height (cm)	Reach (cm)

Each person should record the team's data in a table like the one above.

b.   Send one person up to record your team's data on the class table. Then add the rest of the class data to your own table.

c.   Each person should put his or her initials on a sticky dot, then graph his or her own *height vs. reach* point on the class graph.

1-17.   Use the class graph to answer the questions below.

a.   Are there any dots that you think show *human error*? That is, are there any dots that appear to be graphed incorrectly or that someone may have measured incorrectly? Explain why or why not.

b.   Is a person's reach related to his or her height? That is, what seems to be true about the reach of taller people? Explain.

c.   Since a person's reach depends on his or her height, we call the reach the **dependent** quantity and the height the **independent** quantity. Examine the class graph of the data from problem 1-16. On which axis was the independent data represented? On which axis was the dependent data represented?

d.   Is there a trend in the data? How can you **generalize** the trend?

1-18.   Everyone is complaining about how the teacher made the class graph!

    a.   Jorge is confused about how the teacher decided to set up the graph. *"Why is it a 1st-quadrant graph instead of a 4-quadrant graph?"* Answer Jorge's question. In general, how should you decide what kind of graph to use?

    b.   Lauren is annoyed with the *x*-axis. *"Why didn't the teacher just use the numbers from the table?"* she whined. *"Why count by twenties?"* What do you think?

    c.   Hosai thinks that the graph is TOO BIG. *"The dots are all mashed together! Why did the teacher begin both the x- and y-axes at zero? Anyone that short would never be allowed on the roller coaster. Why not just start closer to the smallest numbers on the table?"* she asked. What do you think?

    d.   Sunita says the graph is TOO SMALL! *"If we're supposed to be using this data to check if the coaster is safe for really tall people, the graph has to have room to graph tall people's dots too."* Do you agree? If so, how much room do you think is needed?

1-19.   Using all of your ideas from problem 1-18, make your own graph that will help you determine whether the ride is safe for very tall people. For example, the basketball player Yao Ming is 7 feet 6 inches (about 228.6 cm) tall. Is the roller coaster is safe for him? Explain.

1-20.   Is the roller coaster safe for all riders? Prepare a poster that shows and **justifies** your team's answer to this question. Every team poster should include:

    •   A large, clear graph.

    •   A complete, clear, and convincing explanation of why your team thinks the ride is or is not safe for all riders.

METHODS AND MEANINGS

Adding and Subtracting Integers

An **integer** is any positive or negative whole number or zero. Look at the examples of integers and non-integers below:

$$-1001 \quad 56 \quad 0 \quad -2$$

examples of integers

$$\tfrac{1}{2} \quad 2.1 \quad \pi \quad 8.3$$

examples of non-integers

The diagram at right shows that $-1+1=0$. One way to think of this concept is to think of an elevator. If you start one floor below ground (-1) and travel up one floor $(+1)$, you end up on the ground floor (which can be represented with zero).

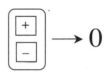

One useful strategy that works when adding and subtracting integers is to draw a diagram and eliminate zeros. Study the examples below:

Example 1: $5 - 8 = 5 + (-8) = -3$

Example 2: $-2 + 7 = 5$

Example 3: $-6 - 1 = -6 + (-1) = -7$

1-21. Copy these Diamond Problems and use the pattern you discovered earlier, shown at right, to complete each of them. Some of these may be challenging!

a.

b.

c.

d.

e.

f.

g.

h.

1-22. Compute without a calculator.

a. $-15 + 7$ b. $8 - (-21)$ c. $-12 - (-4)$ d. $-9 + (-13)$

e. $-50 - 30$ f. $3 - (-9)$ g. $-75 - (-75)$ h. $(-3) + 6$

i. $9 + (-14)$ j. $28 - (-2)$ k. $-3 + (-2) + 5$ l. $3 + 2 + 5$

1-23. The area of each rectangle below is shown in the middle of the rectangle. For each figure, find the missing length or width.

a.

A = 60 un²

8

b.
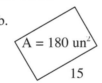
A = 180 un²

15

c.
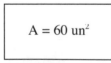
A = 231 un²   14

1-24. Compute without a calculator.

a. $427 - (-3)$ b. $-50 + (-150)$

1-25. In Algebra, you will need to be able to work with numbers, words, and geometric representations. Use these representations to answer the following questions.

a. Write another fraction that is equivalent to $\frac{4}{5}$. Draw diagrams to show that they are equal.

b. Find the equivalent decimal for both fractions. Was rounding your answer necessary?

c. Find the equivalent percent for both fractions.

1-26.   On graph paper, draw all of the possible rectangles with an area of 16 square units. Use only whole-number lengths (no decimals). What are the dimensions of the rectangle with the smallest perimeter?

1-27.   The area of a rectangle is 450 square inches. If the length of the rectangle is 24 inches, what is the width?

1-28.   Latisha earned an 85% today. Her previous scores were 72%, 89%, and 90%. Calculate her new average.

1-29.   Estimate the areas of Montana and California using the grid below. Which state has the greatest area? Compare the area of Montana to the area of California. Explain how you estimated the area of each state.

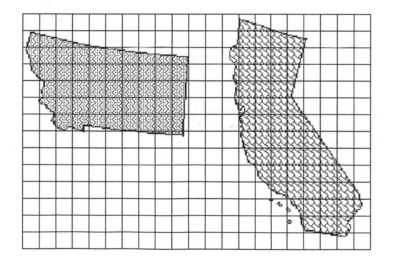

1-30.   The diamond at right represents the pattern you found in problem 1-4.

    a.   Complete these Diamond Problems.

    i.   1 / ½

    ii.   10 / 7

    iii.   5 / ⅓

    iv.   8 / −6

    b.   Create two new Diamond Problems of your own.

1.1.4 How can I generalize a pattern?

Finding and Generalizing Patterns

Often, mathematics is described as "the study of patterns." Today you will preview future work with patterns by studying two tile patterns and using them to make predictions. As you work on these patterns, consider the following questions:

How do I see the pattern?

How is it changing?

Is there another way to find a solution?

1-31.   GROWING, GROWING, GROWING

Copy the tile pattern shown below onto graph paper.

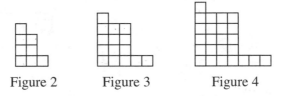

Figure 2   Figure 3   Figure 4

a.   Draw the 1st, 5th, and 6th figures on your paper.

b.   How is the pattern changing?

c.   What would the 100th figure look like? How many tiles would it have? How can you **justify** your prediction?

1-32.   Examine this new tile pattern. Copy it onto your paper.

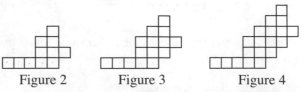

Figure 2   Figure 3   Figure 4

a.   Draw the 1st, 5th, and 6th figures on your paper.

b.   Michael knows that one of the figures in this tile pattern has 79 tiles. What is its figure number? There are <u>many</u> ways to figure this out – be sure to listen to each person's ideas about how to find a solution. Be prepared to explain how you answered this question.

1-33.   For either the pattern in problem 1-31 or the pattern in problem 1-32, prepare a team transparency or poster with your description of the pattern and your prediction. Every team transparency or poster should include:

- Clear drawings of figures from your pattern.

- An explanation of the pattern you found.

- Your prediction. (Make sure your reasoning is clear!)

METHODS AND **M**EANINGS

Fractions, Decimals, and Percents

Fractions, decimals, and percents are different ways to represent the same number.

Below are some ways to convert a number from one of these representations to another.

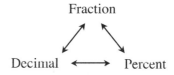

Percent to decimal:

Since "percent" means "out of 100," divide the percent by 100.

$29.6\% = 29.6 \div 100 = 0.296$

Decimal to percent:

Reverse the process: Multiply the decimal by 100.

$0.68 = (0.68)(100) = 68\%$

Fraction to percent:

Find an equivalent fraction that has 100 in the denominator. The numerator is the percent.

$\frac{3}{5} = \frac{60}{100} = 60\%$

Percent to fraction:

Since "percent" means "out of 100," place the percent in a fraction over 100. Simplify as needed.

$48\% = 0.48 = \frac{48}{100} = \frac{12}{25}$

Fraction to decimal:

Since a fraction implies division, divide the numerator by the denominator.

$\frac{7}{8} = 7 \div 8 = 0.875$

Decimal to fraction:

Write and reduce the fraction that has the same meaning of the decimal. For example, since 0.4 is "four-tenths":

$0.4 = \frac{4}{10} = \frac{2}{5}$

1-34.   Copy the axes below onto your paper. Place and
        label a point on the graph for each of the products
        listed below.

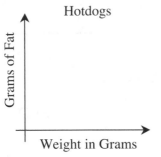

a.   Dog-Eat-Dog has a
     supreme hotdog
     that weighs 80
     grams and has 40
     grams of fat.

b.   Hot Doggies has a
     diet hotdog that
     weighs 50 grams and has only 9 grams of fat.

c.   Dog-alicious has a cheap hotdog that weighs 40
     grams and has 30 grams of fat.

1-35.   Copy and complete each sequence below. Using words, not numbers, describe how
        the patterns work. (For example, write, "Double the previous number.")

a.   1, 3, 6, 10, ___, ___

b.   1, $\frac{1}{2}$, $\frac{1}{4}$, $\frac{1}{8}$, ___, ___

c.   1, 3, 9, 27, ___, ___

d.   8, 7, 5, 2, ___, ___

e.   49, 47, 52, 50, 55, ___, ___

1-36.   Recall the Diamond Problem pattern that you found in
        problem 1-4, which is represented in the diamond at right.
        Copy and complete the Diamond Problems below using the
        same pattern.

a.   b.   c.   d.

1-37.   Copy the number line below onto your paper. Locate the following numbers by
         placing the lowercase letters *a* through *e* on the number line corresponding to the
         values given below. Part (a) is done for you.

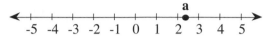

a. $2\frac{1}{3}$ b. -2.7 c. $\frac{1}{2}$

d. -0.2 e. $33\frac{1}{3}\%$ of 12

1-38.   Draw and shade a diagram to represent $\frac{2}{3}$. Label your diagram with the fraction.
         Would 0.66 or 0.67 be a more appropriate decimal equivalent? Explain why.

1-39.   Susan's apartment is shown at right.
         Assuming that all rooms are
         rectangular, find the quantities
         described below. All measurements are
         in feet.

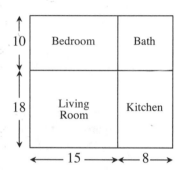

         a.   Find the area of her living room.

         b.   Find the area of her entire
               apartment.

         c.   How much larger than her
               bedroom is her living room?

1.2.1 How can I solve it?

Solving Problems with Guess and Check

In this lesson, you will work with your team to find a strategy for solving a complex problem. It will be important for you to find ways to organize your work so that other people can follow your process.

1-40.   THE APARTMENT

Your architecture firm has been hired to design an apartment building. Each of the apartments in the building will be laid out as shown at right so that each room is rectangular.

The building's owners have given you the following specifications.

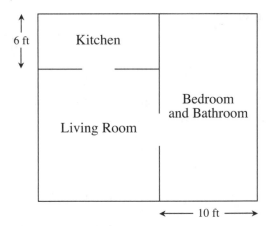

- The living room of an apartment must have an area of 180 square feet.

- The shorter side of the kitchen must be 6 feet to make room for counter space.

- The shorter width of the bedroom and bath must be 10 feet so that a dresser and king-sized bed will fit.

- The entire area of each apartment must be exactly 450 square feet.

Your Task: Find the possible dimensions for every room in the apartment. Be prepared to **justify** your answer (show how you know it works), and show all of your work in a way that someone who is not in your team can read and understand it.

Discussion Points

How can you start?

How can you organize your work?

How can you use the results from one guess
to make your next guess better?

1-41.   Charles decided to start this problem by making a guess. He guessed that everything would come out right if one side of the living room were 10 feet.

a.   Does it matter which side of the living room is 10 feet long? Why or why not? Find the area of the entire apartment twice: once if the base of the living room is 10 feet long, and again if the height of the living room is 10 feet long. Do the results come out the same?

b.   Is Charles' guess correct? That is, can one of the sides of the living room be 10 feet long? Explain.

c.   As you checked Charles' guess, did you organize your work so that anyone could read and understand your thinking? If not, try to find a way to reorganize your work to make it clear.

d.   As a team, try another guess for a dimension of the living room. Organize your work to check if that guess is correct.

1-42.   One way to organize your work in this kind of problem is by using a table. The table can be structured something like this:

Length of _____	• ?	Total Area

a.   Use this method to check the rest of your guesses for this problem.

b.   Continue guessing and checking until you find correct room dimensions. Once you have an answer, organize your work so that it shows the dimensions of all of the rooms and can be read and understood by someone who is not in your team. Be ready to present to the class both your final answer and the different guesses that you tried along the way.

Further Guidance
section ends here.

1-43.   LEARNING LOGS

Throughout this course, you will be asked to reflect on your
understanding of mathematical concepts in a Learning Log. Your
Learning Log will contain explanations and examples to help you
remember what you have learned throughout the course. It is
important to write each entry of the Learning Log in your own
words so that later you can use your Learning Log as a resource
to refresh your memory. Your teacher will tell you where to write your Learning
Log entries. Remember to label each entry with a title and a date so that it can be
referred to later.

In this first Learning Log entry, describe what you know about the Guess and Check
problem-solving method. For example, what does a Guess and Check problem look
like? What does the solution look like? How does the method work? Title this
entry "Guess and Check" and include today's date.

METHODS AND MEANINGS

MATH NOTES

Multiplication and Division of Integers

When multiplying and dividing integers, an even number of
negative integers gives a positive result, and an odd number of
negative integers gives a negative result. Some examples:

$$(-4) \cdot (-8) = 32 \qquad (-60) \div (-15) = 4 \qquad (-5) \cdot (-2) \cdot (-4) = -40$$

$$(-6) \cdot (5) = -30 \qquad (12) \div (4) = 3 \qquad (-3) \cdot (5) \cdot (-4) = 60$$

1-44.   Copy and complete each of the Diamond Problems below.
          The pattern used in the Diamond Problems is shown at
          right.

a.   b.   c.   d.

e.   f.   g.   h.

1-45.   Latisha's friend Brandee forgot to make up a
          test and had these scores: 80%, 92%, 91%,
          75%, 89%, 84%, 0%, and 85%.

          a.   Calculate Brandee's average. Does this
               average score really represent her
               abilities? Why or why not?

          b.   Brandee persuaded her teacher, Ms.
               Juarez, to allow her to make up the
               missed test. Brandee received a 78%.
               Calculate her new average.

          c.   What difference did the 0% score make? Does this new average represent
               Brandee's ability more accurately?

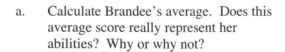

1-46.   While organizing his bookshelf, Michael noticed that he had eight more science-
          fiction novels than spy novels. If he owns 26 science-fiction and spy novels, how
          many of each type of novel does he own? Explain how you found your solution.

1-47.   Explain what the graph at right represents. What
          information does it convey?

1-48.   Copy the axes at right and put a dot for each student
described below.

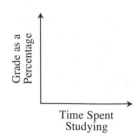

a.   Student A, who studies hard but gets only
average grades.

b.   Student B, who studies little but gets good grades.

1-49.   Try these problems without a calculator first. Then use a calculator to check your
answer.

a. $\quad -16 + 7$

b. $\quad 10 - (-24)$

c. $\quad (3)(-9)$

d. $\quad -9 + (-11)$

e. $\quad -49 - 36$

f. $\quad -56 \div (-7)$

g. $\quad 15 \div (-3)$

h. $\quad -7 \div 7$

i. $\quad (-6) \cdot 9$

j. $\quad (-5)(-5)$

k. $\quad (-6) \cdot (43)$

l. $\quad 27 - (-3) - 4$

1.2.2 How can I organize my work?

More Guess and Check

As you continue your focus on Guess and Check today, organize your work so that you can find
your solutions methodically.

While you work, use the following focus questions to help guide your team's discussion:

What is the problem about?

What is the relationship between the quantities involved?

How can you use the results from one guess to make a better guess?

1-50.   BULL'S-EYE!

Jaime was throwing darts at a target. When his dart landed in the
center of the target (the "bull's-eye"), he earned 7 points. However,
when his dart landed on the outside ring, he earned 2 points. After
50 throws, his score was reported to be 160 points. Jaime
wanted to know how many bull's-eyes he had hit, but his friend did
not know. How many bull's-eyes did Jaime hit?

1-51.   Your teacher will assign your team one of the following problems. Use Guess and Check to solve your problem, and then prepare a presentation to share your solution and method with the class. Use the focus questions from the lesson introduction to help you get started.

   a.   Adele, Amanda, and Alisa are sisters who are raising funds to go on a scouting trip. Adele sold twice as many cookies as Amanda. Alisa sold the same number as Amanda. Their uncle also donated $15, but he did not want any cookies. Together they raised $655. How much money did each sister raise?

   b.   Rachel fenced off an area in the shape of a rectangle for her dog. She used 48 feet of fencing material, and the rectangle is 6 feet longer than it is wide. What are the dimensions (length and width) of the rectangle?

   c.   At track practice, each runner usually carries a lap counter. Hector and McQuisten want to make their coach think that they have run farther than they actually have, so they decide to share a lap counter. Hector runs twice as far as McQuisten does. When both are finished running, the lap counter reads 48 laps. How many laps did Hector actually run?

   d.   When the football game started, there were twice as many Philly students as Comstock students. Five minutes into the game, busses arrived, bringing an additional 600 Philly students to the game. Total attendance for the game was 3552 students. How many students attended from each school?

   e.   Shaunice has 36 feet of fence to put around her rectangular flowerbed. How long and how wide will the flowerbed have to be so that she has 72 square feet of area to plant flowers?

1-52.   Present to the class your team's method and solution to one of the parts of problem 1-51. As you listen to other teams' presentations, ask questions like, *"How did you know what columns to use?"*, *"How did you know what to guess?"*, and *"Does it matter which order the columns are in?"*

1-53.   Explain in your Learning Log how you can use the results of a guess to choose your next guess. How can you tell if you should make your next guess much different than or very close to your last guess? Title this entry "Choosing Good Guesses" and include today's date.

METHODS AND MEANINGS

Word-Problem Vocabulary

There are some vocabulary words that occur frequently in word problems. Examine these words and their meanings below.

Twice
• 2

This means "times two" or "double." For example, if Erica has *twice* as many dimes as she has quarters, then if she has 6 quarters, she has $6 \cdot 2 = 12$ dimes.

Sum
+

This is the result of adding. If a problem states that the *sum* of the number of pencils and pens is 10, that means that the number of pencils plus the number of pens is 10.

Product
( )( )

This is the result of multiplying. If a problem states that the *product* of two numbers is 96, that means that you multiply the first number by the second number to get 96.

More Than
+

This description tells you that something is a certain quantity greater than something else. This phrase is similar to phrases like "greater than" and "higher than." For example, if Erica has 8 *more* rabbits *than* pigs, and if she has 10 pigs, then she has $10 + 8 = 18$ rabbits. "More than" implies addition.

Less Than
–

This description works much like "more than" (above). This phrase is similar to phrases like "fewer than" and "shorter than." If Erica has 5 pounds *less* dog food *than* cat food, and if she has 11 pounds of cat food, then she has $11 - 5 = 6$ pounds of dog food. "Less than" implies subtraction.

Times More Than
( )( )

This description tells you that some quantity is a multiple of some other quantity. If Erica has 7 *times more* flour *than* sugar, and she has 3 pounds of sugar, then she has $7 \cdot 3 = 21$ pounds of flour. "Times more than" implies multiplication.

1-54.   Solve the problem below using Guess and Check. State your solution in a sentence.

Todd is 10 years older than Jamal. The sum of their ages is 64. How old are Todd and Jamal?

1-55.   Solve the problem below using Guess and Check. State your solution in a sentence.

Jabari is thinking of three numbers. The greatest number is twice as big as the least number. The middle number is three more than the least number. The sum of the three numbers is 75. Find the numbers.

1-56.   Copy the pattern at right and continue the pattern for successive powers of 3.

$3^1 = 3$
$3^2 = 9$
$3^3 = \underline{\quad}$
$3^4 = \underline{\quad}$

a.   In a sentence or two, describe a pattern formed by the units digits (the "ones") of the numbers in the pattern.

b. $3^1 = 3$. List the next three powers of 3 for which the ones place is a 3.

$\vdots$

$3^9 = \underline{\quad}$

1-57.   Copy and complete each of the Diamond Problems below. The pattern used in the Diamond Problems is shown at right.

a.

b.

c.

d.

1-58.   The area of a rectangle is 24,396 square centimeters. If the width is 38 centimeters, what is the length? How do you know?

1.2.3 How can I solve it?

More Guess and Check

Today you will continue your work on solving word problems with Guess and Check. As you work with your teammates, use the following focus questions to help focus your team's discussion:

What is the problem about?

What is the relationship between the quantities involved?

How can you use the results from one guess to make a better guess?

1-59.   HELPING THE HOMELESS

A study team decided to volunteer at the local soup kitchen to help feed the homeless people in their neighborhood. While the team cooked the soup, Rose noticed that the number of cans of tomato paste was five more than twice the number of cans of noodles. Afterward, the team recycled 44 cans that were emptied into the soup.

a.   How many cans of each ingredient did the team use?

b.   Later, Rose learned that a can of tomato paste costs $0.70 while a can of noodles costs $0.50. How much did it cost to make the soup?

1-60.   Tamar was daydreaming during Social Studies class and only wrote down the following information: Mexico has 70 million more citizens than Canada; the United States has three times the number of citizens as Mexico; and there are 430 million citizens in Mexico, Canada, and the United States combined. Based on this information, how many citizens live in Canada?

1-61.   When setting the price of admission tickets for the amusement park, Tabitha wants the price for a two-child, two-adult family to be $100. She also wants the adult tickets to cost $8.00 more than twice the cost of a child's ticket. How much should a child's ticket cost?

1-62.   One side of a triangle is 3 inches shorter than twice the length of the shortest side. The third side is 5 inches longer than the shortest side. If the perimeter is 110 inches, find the lengths of all three sides.

1-63.    A pet shop has 15 animals, all cats and birds. If the animals have a total of 32 legs, how many birds are there?

1-64.   What questions do you still have about the Guess and Check solution process? In your Learning Log, write some questions you have about how to solve a word problem using Guess and Check. Title this entry "Questions about Guess and Check" and label it with today's date.

1-65.   Solve the problem below using Guess and Check. State your solution in a sentence.

The perimeter of a triangle is 76 centimeters. The second side is twice as long as the first side. The third side is four centimeters shorter than the second side. How long is each side?

1-66.   The pattern below is composed of nested squares.

   a.   Draw the next figure in the pattern.

   b.   Find the area of the shaded region for the figure you drew in part (a).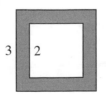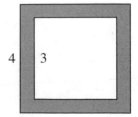

1-67.   Examine the tile pattern at right.

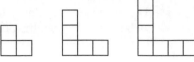

Figure 1   Figure 2   Figure 3

    a.   On your paper, sketch
       Figures 4 and 5.

    b.   How does the pattern grow?
       Explain how you know.

    c.   How many tiles will there be in Figure 100? Explain how you know.

1-68.   Look at each graph below and write a story or description about what each graph
    shows.

a.
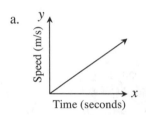

b.
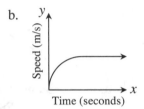

c.
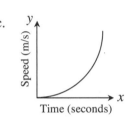

1-69.   Enrollment in math
    courses at Kennedy
    High School in
    Bloomington,
    Minnesota, is shown in
    the pie chart at right. If
    there are 1000 students
    enrolled in math
    courses, approximately
    how many students are
    enrolled in Algebra? In
    Geometry? In Calculus?

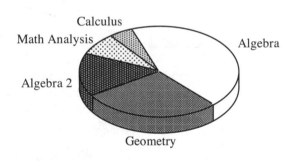

Chapter 1 Closure   What have I learned?

Reflection and Synthesis

The activities below offer you a chance to reflect on what you have learned during this chapter. As you work, look for concepts that you feel very comfortable with, ideas that you would like to learn more about, and topics you need more help with. Look for **connections** between ideas as well as **connections** with material you learned previously.

①   TEAM BRAINSTORM

With your team, brainstorm a list for each of the following three topics. Be as detailed as you can. How long can you make your list? Challenge yourselves. Be prepared to share your team's ideas with the class.

Topics: What have you studied in this chapter? What ideas and words were important in what you learned? Remember to be as detailed as you can.

Problem Solving: What did you do to solve problems? What different strategies did you use?

Connections: How are the topics, ideas, and words that you learned in previous courses are **connected** to the new ideas in this chapter? Again, make your list as long as you can.

MAKING CONNECTIONS

The following is a list of the vocabulary used in this chapter. Make sure that you are familiar with all of these words and know what they mean. Refer to the glossary or index for any words that you do not yet understand.

area	average	coordinates
dimensions	equivalent	graph
Guess and Check	integers	less than
more than	pattern	perimeter
product	quadrants	sum
table	twice	x- and y-axes

Make a concept map showing all of the **connections** you can find among the key words and ideas listed above. To show a **connection** between two words, draw a line between them and explain the **connection**, as shown in the example below. A word can be **connected** to any other word as long as there is a **justified connection**. For each key word or idea, provide a sketch of an example.

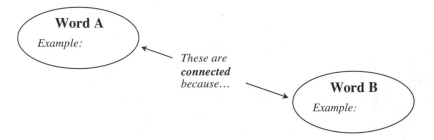

Your teacher may provide you with vocabulary cards to help you get started. If you use the cards to plan your concept map, be sure either to re-draw your concept map on your paper or to glue the vocabulary cards to a poster with all of the **connections** explained for others to see and understand.

While you are making your map, your team may think of related words or ideas that are not listed above. Be sure to include these ideas on your concept map.

③ SUMMARIZING MY UNDERSTANDING

This section gives you an opportunity to show what you know about certain math topics or ideas. Your teacher will give you directions for exactly how to do this. Your teacher may give you a "GO" page to work on. "GO" stands for "Graphic Organizer," a tool you can use to organize your thoughts and communicate your ideas clearly.

WHAT HAVE I LEARNED?

This section will help you evaluate which types of problems you have seen with which you feel comfortable and those with which you need more help. This section will appear at the end of every chapter to help you check your understanding. Even if your teacher does not assign this section, it is a good idea to try these problems and find out for yourself what you know and what you need to work on.

Solve each problem as completely as you can. The table at the end of this closure section has answers to these problems. It also tells you where you can find additional help and practice on problems like these.

CL 1-70. In (x, y) form, write the coordinates of each point (*A* through *F*) circled on the graph at right.

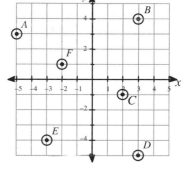

CL 1-71. On graph paper, draw and label *x*- and *y*-axes. Find and label the following points:

G(3, 2)   H(1, 4)   I(−2, −1)

J(4, −2)   K(−5, 1)

CL 1-72. Solve the following problem using Guess and Check. Show your guesses in an organized way.

Alex hangs each pair of pants and each shirt on a separate hanger. He has 51 hangers in his closet all holding clothes. Every time he buys 1 pair of pants he also buys 2 shirts. How many shirts does Alex own?

CL 1-73. On graph paper, draw at least six different-sized rectangles that have an area of 64 square units. Then find the perimeter of each rectangle.

CL 1-74. Copy and complete each of the Diamond Problems below. The pattern used in the Diamond Problems is shown at right.

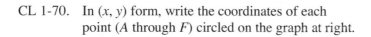

a.

b.

c.

d.

e.

f.

CL 1-75.   Copy the pattern below onto graph paper. Draw the 1ˢᵗ and 5ᵗʰ figures on your paper.

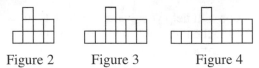

Figure 2   Figure 3   Figure 4

   a.   How many tiles are in each figure?

   b.   Describe how the pattern is changing.

   c.   How many tiles would the 6ᵗʰ figure have? the 10ᵗʰ figure?

CL 1-76.   Check your answers using the table at the end of this section. Which problems do
you feel confident about? Which problems were hard? Have you worked on
problems like these in math classes you have taken before? Use the table to make a
list of topics you need help on and a list of topics you need to practice more.

⑤   HOW AM I THINKING?

This course focuses on five different **Ways of Thinking**: reversing thinking,
justifying, generalizing, making connections, and applying and extending
understanding. These are some of the ways in which you think while trying to make
sense of a concept or to solve a problem (even outside of math class). During this
chapter, you have probably used each Way of Thinking multiple times without even
realizing it!

This closure activity will focus on one
of these Ways of Thinking: **making
connections**. Read the description of
this Way of Thinking at right.

Think about the **connections** that you
have made during this chapter. When
have you linked one idea with another?
What **connections** have you made with
ideas that you learned in a previous
math class? You may want to flip
through the chapter to refresh your
memory about the problems that you
have worked on. Discuss any of the
connections you have made with the
rest of the class.

Once your discussion is complete,
practice thinking this way by making a
concept map as described in closure
activity #2, *Making Connections*.

> ### Making Connections
>
> You often think this way when you
> try to show how one idea relates to
> or links with another idea. For
> example, when you catch yourself
> thinking, *"This reminds me of
> something…"*, you are making a
> connection.
>
>

Answers and Support for Closure Activity #4
What Have I Learned?

Problem	Solution			Need Help?	More Practice
CL 1-70.	a. (−5, 3) b. (3, 4) c. (2, −1) d. (3, −5) e. (−3, −4) f. (−2, 1)			Lesson 1.1.2 Math Notes box	Problems 1-7, 1-14, 1-34, and 1-48
CL 1-71.				Lesson 1.1.2 Math Notes box	Problems 1-7, 1-14, 1-34, and 1-48
CL 1-72.	Alex owns 34 shirts.			Problems 1-41 and 1-42	Problems 1-50, 1-51, 1-54, 1-55, 1-59, 1-60, 1-61, 1-62, 1-63, and 1-65
CL 1-73.	Multiple answers are possible. Rectangles with integer sides have dimensions 1 by 64, 2 by 32, 4 by 16, and 8 by 8. However, to get more than four rectangles with different dimensions, you need to also use non-integer lengths, such as $\frac{1}{2}$ by 128 or $\frac{1}{3}$ by 192.			Lesson 1.1.1 Math Notes box	Problems 1-5, 1-11, 1-23, 1-26, 1-27, and 1-58

Problem	Solution	Need Help?	More Practice

CL 1-74.

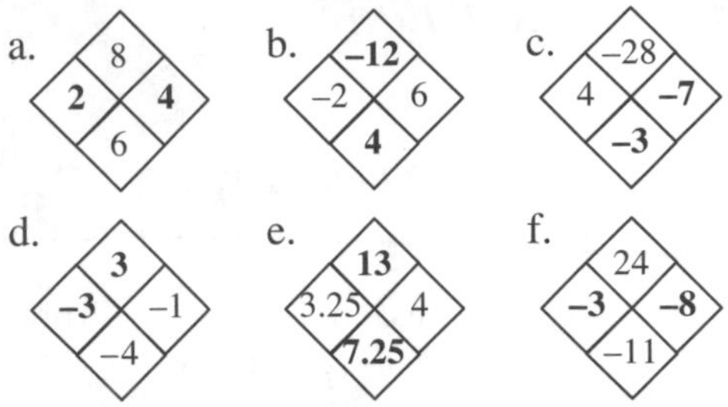

a.

b.

c.

Need Help? Problem 1-4

More Practice: Problems 1-21, 1-30, 1-36, 1-44, and 1-57

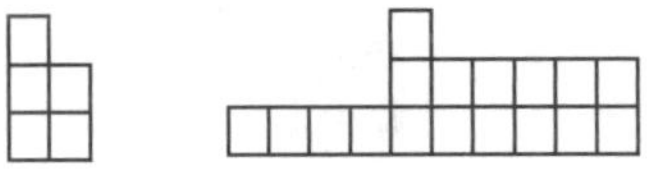

d.

e.

f.

CL 1-75.

Figure 1   Figure 5

Need Help? Lesson 1.1.4

More Practice: Problems 1-31, 1-32, and 1-67

a.   5, 8, 11, 14, 17

b.   Each figure has three more tiles than the one before it.

c.   The 6th figure would have 20 tiles. The 10th figure would have 32 tiles.

CHAPTER 2   Variables and Proportions

This chapter begins with a focus on the use of variables in algebra (such as x and y). You will use tools called "algebra tiles" to explore how and where to use variables. Since this topic lays the foundation for simplifying expressions and solving equations, it will be revisited and built upon repeatedly throughout the course.

In the second part of this chapter, you will develop methods to solve problems that involve proportional relationships. For example, if you want to know how many people at your school are left-handed, how can you use the information from your class to make a prediction? Questions like these will rely on your intuition about proportions.

In this chapter, you will learn:

➢ What a variable is.

➢ How to write and simplify algebraic expressions.

➢ How to compare two complicated algebraic expressions.

➢ How to solve for a variable if you know that two expressions are equal.

➢ How to solve problems involving proportional relationships.

Guiding Questions

Think about these questions throughout this chapter:

What is a variable?

What can I do with a variable?

How can I solve for a variable?

How many different ways can I write an expression?

What's the relationship?

Chapter Outline

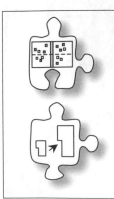

Section 2.1 This section introduces algebra tiles to develop the symbolic manipulation skills of combining like terms and solving linear equations. A special focus will be placed on the meaning of "minus" and how to make "zero."

Section 2.2 You will use your intuition about proportional relationships to find new ways to solve proportional problems.

2.1.1 What is a variable?

....

Exploring Variables and Combining Like Terms

In "The Apartment," problem 1-40, the length and width of each room was unknown. Similarly, the height of the tallest person who could ride the roller coaster safely in "Newton's Revenge," problem 1-15, was unknown. When using Guess and Check, you guessed the value of something that was unknown in order to solve for it.

In Algebra and in future mathematics courses, you will work with unknown quantities that can be represented using **variables**. Today, manipulatives called "algebra tiles" will be introduced to help you and your teammates answer some important questions, such as "What is a variable?" and "How can we use it?"

2-1.   Your teacher will distribute a set of algebra tiles for your team to use during this course. As you explore the tiles, address the following questions with your team. Be prepared to share your responses with the class.

- How many different shapes are there? What are all of the different shapes?

- How are the shapes different? How are they the same?

- How are the shapes related? Which fit together and which do not?

2-2.   Draw a picture of each size of tile on your paper.

a.   The algebra tiles will be referred to by their areas. Since the smallest square has a length of 1 unit, its area is 1 square unit. Thus, the name for this tile is "one" or a "unit tile." Can you use the unit tile to find the other lengths? Why or why not?

b.   Name the other tiles using their areas. Be sure to use what you know about the area of a rectangle and the area of a square.

2-3.   JUMBLED PILES

Your teacher will show you a jumbled pile of algebra tiles and will challenge you to name all of them. What is the best description for the collection of tiles? Is your description the best possible?

2-4. Build each collection of tiles represented below. Then name the collection using a simpler algebraic expression, if possible. If it is not possible to simplify the expression, explain why not.

a. $3x + 5 + x^2 + y + 3x^2 + 2$

b. $2x^2 + 1 + xy + x^2 + 2xy + 5$

c. $2 + x^2 + 3x + y^2 + 4y + xy$

d. $3y + 2 + 2xy + 4x + y^2 + 4y + 1$

2-5. In your Learning Log, explain what a variable is in your own words. Describe each type of tile with a diagram that includes each dimension and an area label. Explain when tiles can and cannot be combined. Be sure to include examples to support your statements. Title this entry "Variables" and include today's date.

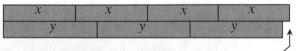

2-6. Suppose you put one of your x-tiles and two unit tiles with another pile of three x-tiles and five unit tiles. What is in this new pile? Write it as a sum.

2-7.   Suppose one person in your team has two x^2-tiles, three x-tiles, and one unit tile on his desk and another person has one x^2-tile, five x-tiles, and eight unit tiles on her desk. You decide to put all of the tiles together on one desk. What is the name for this new group of tiles?

2-8.   Copy the following figures onto your paper. Then find the area and perimeter of each shape. Assume that all corners are right angles. Show all work.

a.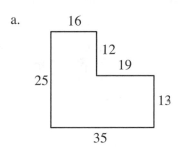

b.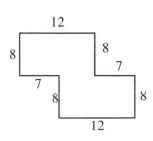

2-9.   Find the perimeter of the entire rectangle shown at right (that is, the outside boundary of the figure). Notice that the areas of two of the parts have been labeled inside the rectangle. Also find the total area. Remember to show all work leading to your solution.

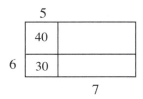

2-10.   One meaning of the word **evaluate** is to find the value of an expression. To evaluate, replace a variable with a number and calculate the result. For example, when you are asked to evaluate the expression $4x - 2$ when $x = -7$, you would put –7 in place of the variable and calculate: $4 \cdot (-7) - 2 = -30$.

Evaluate the expressions below for the given values of x and y.

a. $\frac{6}{x} + 9$ if $x = 3$

b. $8x - 3 + y$ if $x = 2$ and $y = 1$

c. $2xy$ if $x = 5$ and $y = -3$

d. $2x^2 - y$ if $x = 3$ and $y = 8$

2-11.   Use Guess and Check to solve the following problem. Write your solution as a sentence.

A cable 84 meters long is cut into two pieces so that one piece is 18 meters longer than the other. Find the length of each piece of cable.

2.1.2   What's the perimeter?

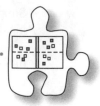

. . . .

Simplifying Expressions by Combining Like Terms

While Lesson 2.1.1 focused on the area of algebra tiles, today's lesson will focus on the perimeter. What is perimeter? How can you find it? By the end of this lesson, you will be able to find the perimeter of strange shapes formed by multiple tiles.

Your class will also focus on multiple ways to find perimeter, recognizing that there are different ways to "see," or recognize, perimeter. Sometimes, with complex shapes, a convenient shortcut can help you find the perimeter more quickly. Be sure to share any insight into finding perimeter with your teammates and with the whole class.

While working today, ask yourself and your teammates these focus questions:

How did you see it?

How can you write it?

Is your expression as simplified as possible?

2-12.   Your teacher will provide a set of algebra tiles for your team to use today. Separate one of each shape and review its name (area). Then find the *perimeter* of each tile. Decide with your team how to write a simplified expression that represents the perimeter of each tile. Be prepared to share the perimeters you find with the class.

2-13.   For each of the shapes formed by algebra tiles below:

- Use tiles to build the shape.

- Sketch and label the shape on your paper and write an expression that represents the perimeter.

- Simplify your perimeter expression as much as possible.

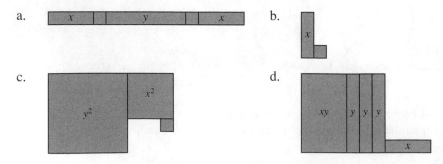

2-14.   Calculate the perimeter of the shapes in problem 2-13 if the length of each x-tile is 3 units and the length of each y-tile is 8 units. Show all work.

2-15.   EXTENSION

The perimeter of the shape at right is 32 units.
Find possible values for x and y. Is there more
than one possible solution? If so, find another
solution. If not, explain how you know there is
only one solution.

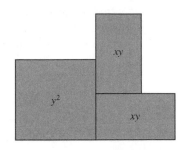

2-16.   In your Learning Log, create your own shape using three different-
shaped tiles. Draw the shape and show how to write a simplified
expression for its perimeter. Label this entry "Finding Perimeter
and Combining Like Terms" and include today's date.

LOOKING DEEPER

Commutative Properties

MATH NOTES

The **Commutative Property of Addition** states that when *adding* two
or more number or terms together, order is not important. That is:

$$a + b = b + a \qquad \text{For example, } 2 + 7 = 7 + 2$$

The **Commutative Property of Multiplication** states that when *multiplying*
two or more numbers or terms together, order is not important. That is:

$$a \cdot b = b \cdot a \qquad \text{For example, } 3 \cdot 5 = 5 \cdot 3$$

However, *subtraction* and *division* are <u>not</u> commutative, as shown below.

$$7 - 2 \neq 2 - 7 \text{ since } 5 \neq -5$$

$$50 \div 10 \neq 10 \div 50 \text{ since } 5 \neq 0.2$$

Review & Preview

2-17.   Simplify each algebraic expression below, if possible. If it is not possible to
simplify the expression, explain why not.

a. $3y + 2y + y^2 + 5 + y$

b. $3y^2 + 2xy + 1 + 3x + y + 2x^2$

c. $3xy + 5x + 2 + 3y + x + 4$

d. $4m + 2mn + m^2 + m + 3m^2$

2-18.   Remember that one meaning of the word "evaluate" is to replace a variable with a number and to calculate the result. For example, when asked to evaluate the expression x^2 when $x = -2$, the solution would be $(-2)^2 = 4$.

Evaluate the expressions below for the given values.

a. $-4d + 3$ if $d = -1$

b. $k - m$ if $k = 4$ and $m = -10$

c. $\frac{t}{w}$ if $t = 6$ and $w = -3$

d. $x^2 + y^2$ if $x = 7$ and $y = 5$

2-19.   The diagram at right is the floor plan of Randy's apartment. All measurements are in feet. Use the diagram to answer the following questions.

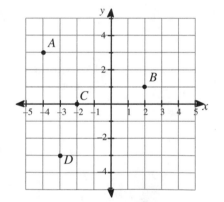

a.   What are the dimensions (length and width) of Randy's living room?

b.   Randy's friends are coming to visit him soon. He plans to keep them out of his bedroom. Find the area of each of the other three rooms he will have to clean.

c.   What is the total area of the rooms he will have to clean?

2-20.   Examine the graph at right.

a.   In (x, y) form, name the coordinates of points A, B, C, and D.

b.   On graph paper, draw a set of axes like the ones shown at right. Then plot points $E(5, 2)$, $F(-3, -1)$, $G(0, -4)$, and $H(2, -3)$.

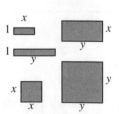

2-21.   If the tiles have the dimensions shown at right, what is the name of the tile collection below? (That is, what is the total area of all of the pieces?) Write the expression algebraically, using x, x^2, y, y^2, and xy.

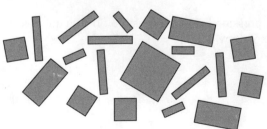

Algebra Connections

2.1.3 What does "minus" mean?

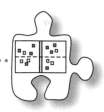

Writing Algebraic Expressions

In this section, you will look at algebraic expressions and see how they can be interpreted using an expression mat. To achieve this goal, you first need to understand the different meanings of the "minus" symbol, which is found in expressions such as $5 - 2$, $-x$, and $-(-3)$.

2-22.   What does " $-$ " mean? Find as many ways as you can to describe this symbol and discuss how these descriptions differ from one another. Share your ideas with the class and record the different uses in your Learning Log. Title this entry "Meanings of Minus" and include today's date.

2-23.   USING AN EXPRESSION MAT

Your introduction to algebra tiles in Lessons 2.1.1 and 2.1.2 involved only positive values. Today you will look at how you can use algebra tiles to represent "minus." Below are several tiles with their associated values. Note that the shaded tiles are positive and the unshaded tiles are negative (as shown in the diagram at right, which will appear throughout the text as a reminder).

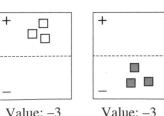

 $= 5$  $= -3$ $= 3x$ $= -2y$

"Minus" can also be represented with a new tool called an **expression mat**, shown at right. An expression mat is an organizing tool that will be used to represent expressions. Notice that there is a positive region at the top and a negative (or "opposite") region at the bottom.

Using the expression mat, the value -3 can be shown in multiple ways, two of which are shown at right.

Note that in these examples, the left-hand diagram uses negative tiles in the "+" region, while the right-hand diagram uses positive tiles in the "−" region.

Value: −3   Value: −3

a.   Build two different representations for $-2x$ using an expression mat.

b.   Similarly, build $3x - (-4)$. How many different ways can you build $3x - (-4)$?

2-24.   During your discussion of problem 2-23, did you see all of the different ways to represent "minus"? Discuss how you could use an expression mat to represent the different meanings discussed in class.

2-25.   BUILDING EXPRESSIONS

Use the expression mat to create each of the following expressions with algebra tiles. Find at least two different representations for each expression. Sketch each representation on your paper. Be prepared to share your different representations with the class.

a. $-3x + 4$ b. $-(y - 2)$

c. $-y - 3$ d. $5x - (3 - 2x)$

2-26.   In problem 2-25, you represented algebraic expressions with algebra tiles. In this problem, you will need to **reverse** your thinking in order to write an expression from a diagram of algebra tiles.

Working with a partner, write algebraic expressions for each representation below. Start by building each problem using your algebra tiles.

a. 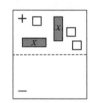   b. 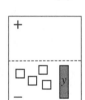   c. 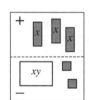   d.

2-27.   Patti, Emilie, and Carla are debating the answer to part (d) of problem 2-26. Patti wrote $2 - 1 + 2x - 3$. Carla thinks that the answer is $2x + 2 - 4$. Emilie is convinced that the answer is $2x - 2$. Discuss with your team how each person might have arrived at her answer. Who do you think is correct? When you decide, write an explanation on your paper and **justify** your answer.

2-28.   Reflect on what you have learned from today's lesson as you answer the following question in your Learning Log. Title this entry "Representing Expressions on an Expression Mat" and include today's date.

Using an expression mat, find two different ways to represent $x - 1 - (2x - 3)$. Sketch the different representations and write a few sentences to describe the differences in the ways you built each representation.

METHODS AND MEANINGS

Evaluating Expressions and the Order of Operations

The word **evaluate** indicates that the value of an expression should be calculated when a variable is replaced by a numerical value.

For example, when you evaluate the expression $xy - 4x + 7$ when $x = 6$ and $y = -5$, the result is:

$$(6)(-5) - 4(6) + 7 \Rightarrow -30 - 24 + 7 \rightarrow -47$$

When evaluating a complex expression, you must remember to use the **order of operations**. As illustrated in the example below, the order of operations is:

First, evaluate any groups of operations that are defined by **parentheses** or other grouping symbols.

$$15 \div 3 \cdot 4 - (8 - 6)^2 + 6$$

Next, evaluate any **exponents** (such as any numbers that are squared).

$$15 \div 3 \cdot 4 - (2)^2 + 6$$

Then, evaluate any **multiplication** or **division** operations from left to right.

$$15 \div 3 \cdot 4 - 4 + 6$$

Finally, evaluate any **addition** or **subtraction** operations from left to right. In this example, the expression $15 \div 3 \cdot 4 - (8 - 6)^2 + 6$ has the value of 22.

$$20 - 4 + 6$$

$$22$$

2-29.   Copy and simplify the following expressions by combining like terms. Using or drawing sketches of algebra tiles may be helpful.

a. $2x + 3x + 3 + 4x^2 + 10 + x$

b. $4x + 4y^2 + y^2 + 9 + 10 + x + 3x$

c. $2x^2 + 30 + 3x^2 + 4x^2 + 14 + x$

d. $20 + 5xy + 4y^2 + 10 + y^2 + xy$

2-30. Read the Math Notes box for this lesson. Then evaluate each expression below.

   a. For $y = 2 + 3x$ when $x = 4$, what does y equal?

   b. For $a = 4 - 5c$ when $c = -\frac{1}{2}$, what does a equal?

   c. For $n = 3d^2 - 1$ when $d = -5$, what does n equal?

   d. For $v = -4(r - 2)$ when $r = -1$, what does v equal?

   e. For $3 + k = t$ when $t = 14$, what does k equal?

2-31. Decide if each statement below is true or false. Explain how you know and name any properties you use.

   a. $-19 + 7 = -7 + 19$
                          b. $\frac{4}{5} \cdot 1 = \frac{4}{5}$

   c. $\frac{3}{2} \cdot \frac{2}{3} = 1$
                              d. $5 \cdot 7 - 5 \cdot \frac{1}{5} = 34$

2-32. Use Guess and Check to solve the following problem. Write your answer in a complete sentence.

Susan is buying three different colors of tiles for her kitchen floor. She is buying 25 more red tiles than beige tiles, and three times as many navy-blue tiles as beige tiles. If Susan buys 435 tiles altogether, how many tiles of each color does she buy?

2-33. Without a calculator, compute the value of each expression below.

   a. $-14 + (-31)$
                             b. $-(-8) - (-2)$

   c. $\frac{-16}{-8}$
                                 d. $-11 \cdot 24$

   e. $\frac{1}{2} - \frac{3}{4}$
                                 f. $46 \div (-23)$

2.1.4 What makes zero?

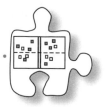

Using Zero to Simplify Algebraic Expressions

Today you will continue your work with rewriting algebraic expressions. As you work with your team, ask yourself and your teammates these focus questions:

How did you see it?

How can you write it?

Is your expression as simplified as possible?

2-34.   LIKELY STORY!

Imagine the following situations:

- You baby-sit your neighbor's baby and stuff the $15 you earned into your purse. When you get home, the $15 is nowhere to be found. It must have fallen out of your purse.

- The Burton Pumas football team completes a pass and gains 12 yards. But on the very next play, the quarterback holds onto the ball too long and gets sacked, losing 12 yards.

- You are at the beach. You dig a hole in the sand and place the sand you remove in a pile next to your hole. Someone comes along and pushes the pile back into the hole.

What do each of these situations have in common? Can you represent each of them using symbols? How?

2-35.   How can you represent zero with tiles on an expression mat? With your team, try to find at least two different ways to do this (and more if you can). Be ready to share your ideas with the class.

2-36.   Gretchen used seven algebra tiles to build the expression shown below.

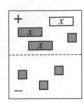

a.   Build this collection of tiles in your own expression mat and write its value.

b.   Represent this same value three different ways, each time using a *different number* of tiles. Be ready to share your representations with the class.

2-37.   Build each expression below so that your representation does not match those of your teammates. Once your team is convinced that together you have found four different, valid representations, sketch your representation on your paper and be ready to share your answer with the class.

a. $-3x + 5 + y$ b. $-(-2y + 1)$ c. $2x - (x - 4)$

2-38.   Write the algebraic expression shown on each expression mat below. Build the model and then simplify the expression by removing as many tiles as you can *without changing the value* of the expression. Finally, write the simplified algebraic expression.

a.

b.

2-39.   Simplify each of the following expressions by building it on your expression mat and removing zeros. Your teacher will give you instructions about how to represent your work on your paper.

a. $3x - (2x + 4)$ b. $7 - (4y - 3) + 2y - 4$

2-40.   In your Learning Log, describe the different ways you can represent zero using your expression mat. Include an example and be sure to draw the tiles. Title this entry "Using Zeros to Simplify" and include today's date.

LOOKING DEEPER

Associative and Identity Properties

The **Associative Property of Addition** states that when *adding* three or more number or terms together, grouping is not important. That is:

$$(a+b)+c = a+(b+c) \qquad \text{For example, } (5+2)+6 = 5+(2+6)$$

The **Associative Property of Multiplication** states that when *multiplying* three or more numbers or terms together, grouping is not important. That is:

$$(a \cdot b) \cdot c = a \ (b \cdot c) \qquad \text{For example, } (5 \cdot 2) \cdot 6 = 5 \cdot (2 \cdot 6)$$

However, *subtraction* and *division* are <u>not</u> associative, as shown below.

$$(5-2)-3 \neq 5-(2-3) \text{ since } 0 \neq 6$$

$$(20 \div 4) \div 2 \neq 20 \div (4 \div 2) \text{ since } 2.5 \neq 10$$

The **Identity Property of Addition** states that adding zero to any expression gives the same expression. That is:

$$a+0 = a \qquad \text{For example, } 6+0 = 6$$

The **Identity Property of Multiplication** states that multiplying any expression by one gives the same expression. That is:

$$1 \cdot a = a \qquad \text{For example, } 1 \cdot 6 = 6$$

2-41.   Read the Math Notes box above and for Lesson 2.1.2. Then examine the work below that shows one way to simplify the expression $3x + 8 + (x+10)$. Decide which property was used for each step.

Expression	What property was used?
$3x + 8 + (x+10)$	Original expression
$(3x + 8 + x) + 10$	a.
$(3x + x + 8) + 10$	b.
$(4x + 8) + 10$	Added like terms
$4x + (8 + 10)$	c.
$4x + 18$	Added like terms

2-42.   Can zero be represented by any number of tiles? Using only the unit tiles (in other words, only the 1 and –1 tiles), determine if you can represent zero on an expression mat with the number of tiles below. If you can, draw an expression mat demonstrating that it is possible. If it is not possible, explain why not.

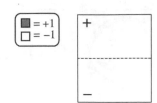

   a.   2 tiles   b.   6 tiles   c.   3 tiles

2-43.   Without a calculator, compute the value of each expression below.

   a. $-3+6$ b. $(-2)(-9)$

   c. $-4-9-11$ d. $-12-18$

   e. $\frac{3}{4}(-8)$ f. $(-2)(-2)(2)$

   g. $7+(-19)$ h. $-15 \div 15$

2-44.   Write and simplify the algebraic expression shown in each expression mat below.

   a. 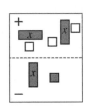   b.   c.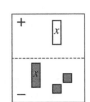

2-45.   When writing an expression for part (a) of problem 2-44, Ricardo wrote $2x-3-(x+1)$ while Francine wrote $-3+2x-(x+1)$. Francine states that their expressions are equivalent. Is Francine's conclusion true or false? Use algebraic properties to **justify** your conclusion.

2-46.   Copy and complete each of the Diamond Problems below. The pattern used in the Diamond Problems is shown at right.

   a.   b.   c.   d.

2.1.5 How can I simplify the expression?

Using Algebra Tiles to Simplify Algebraic Expressions

Which is greater: 58 or 62? That question might seem easy, because the numbers are ready to be compared. However, if you are asked which is greater, $2x + 8 - x - 3$ or $6 + x + 1$, the answer is not so obvious! In this lesson, you and your teammates will investigate how to compare two algebraic expressions and decide if they are equal.

2-47. For each expression below:

- Use an expression mat to build the expression.

- Find a different way to represent the same expression using tiles.

a. $7x - 3$

b. $-(-2x + 6) + 3x$

2-48. COMPARING EXPRESSIONS

Two expressions can be represented at the same time using an **expression comparison mat**. The expression comparison mat puts two expression mats side-by-side so you can compare them and see which is greater. For example, in the picture at right, the expression on the left represents −3, but the expression on the right represents −2. Since $-2 > -3$, the expression on the right is greater.

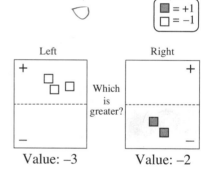

Build the expression comparison mat shown at right. Write an expression representing each side of the expression mat.

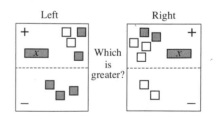

a. Can you simplify each of the expressions so that fewer tiles are used? Develop a method to simplify both sides of the expression comparison mats. Why does it work? Be prepared to **justify** your method to the class.

b. Which side of the expression comparison mat do you think is greater (has the largest value)? Agree on an answer as a team. Make sure each person in your team is ready to **justify** your conclusion to the class.

2-49. As Karl simplified some algebraic expressions, he recorded his work on the diagrams below.

- Explain in writing what he did to each expression comparison mat on the left to get the expression comparison mat on the right.

- If necessary, simplify further to determine which expression mat is greater. How can you tell if your final answer is correct?

a.

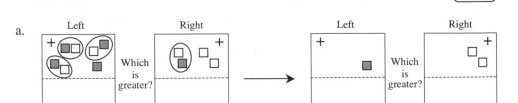

b.

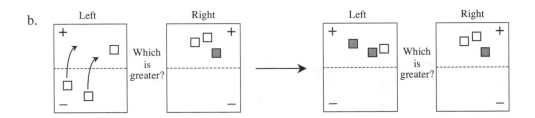

c.

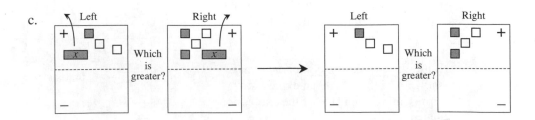

2-50.   Use Karl's "legal" simplification moves to determine which side of each expression
comparison mat below is greater. Record each of your "legal" moves on the Lesson
2.1.5A Resource Page by drawing on it the way Karl did in problem
2-49. After each expression is simplified, state which side is greater
(has the largest value). Be prepared to share your process and
reasoning with the class.

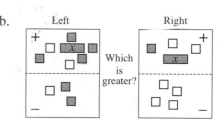

a.

b.

2-51.   In your Learning Log, explain each of the types of "legal" moves
that you can use to simplify and compare expressions. For each
type of "legal" move, sketch an example. Title this entry "Legal
Moves for Simplifying and Comparing Expressions" and include
today's date.

Ⓜ ETHODS AND MEANINGS

Combining Like Terms

MATH NOTES

Combining tiles that have the same
area to write a simpler expression
is called **combining like terms**.
See the example shown at right.

$$x^2 + 2x + 2$$

When you are not working with actual tiles, it can help to picture the tiles in
your mind. You can use these images to combine the terms that are the same.
Here are two examples:

Example 1: $2x^2 + xy + y^2 + x + 3 + x^2 + 3xy + 2$ ⟹ $3x^2 + 4xy + y^2 + x + 5$

Example 2: $3x^2 - 2x + 7 - 5x^2 + 3x - 2$ ⟹ $-2x^2 + x + 5$

A **term** is an algebraic expression that is a single number, a single variable,
or the product of numerals and variables. The simplified algebraic
expression in Example 2 above contains three terms. The first term
is $-2x^2$, the second term is x, and the third term is 5.

2-52.   Simplify the following expressions by combining like terms, if possible.

a. $x + x - 3 + 4x^2 + 2x - x$ b. $8x^2 + 3x - 13x^2 + 10x^2 - 25x - x$

c. $4x + 3y$ d. $20 + 3xy - 3 + 4y^2 + 10 - 2y^2$

2-53.   Copy and complete each of the Diamond Problems below. The
pattern used in the Diamond Problems is shown at right.

a.   b.   c.   d.

2-54.   The two lines at right represent the
growing profits of Companies A and B.

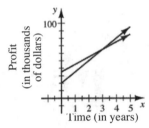

a.   Sketch this graph on your paper. If Company A
started out with more profit than Company B,
determine which line represents A and which
represents B. Label the lines appropriately.

b.   In how many years will both companies have the same profit?

c.   Approximately what will that profit be?

d.   Which company's profits are growing more quickly? How can you tell?

2-55.   Use your mental-math skills to compute the following percentages.

a.   100% of 832   b.   50% of 832

c.   25% of 832   d.   10% of 832

2-56.   Evaluate each expression to find y.

a. $y = 2 + 4.3x$ when $x = -6$ b. $y = (x - 3)^2$ when $x = 9$

c. $y = x - 2$ when $x = 3.5$ d. $y = 5x - 4$ when $x = -2$

2.1.6 Which is greater?

. . . .

Using Algebra Tiles to Compare Expressions

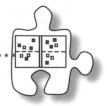

Can you always tell whether one algebraic expression is greater than another? In this lesson, you will compare the values of two expressions, practicing the different simplification strategies you have learned so far.

2-57.   WHICH IS GREATER?

Write an algebraic expression for each side of the expression comparison mats given below. Use the "legal" simplification moves you worked with in Lesson 2.1.5 to determine which expression on the expression comparison mat is greater.

a.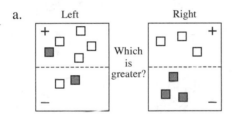

b.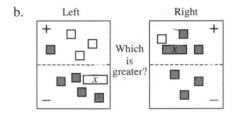

c.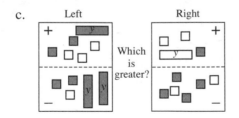

d.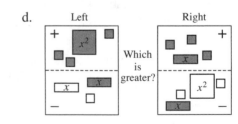

e.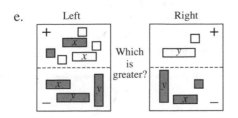

f.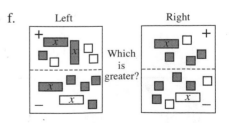

2-58.   Build the expression comparison mat shown below with algebra tiles.

a.   Simplify the expressions using the "legal" moves that you developed in Lesson 2.1.5.

b.   Can you tell which expression is greater? Explain in a few sentences on your paper. Be prepared to share your conclusion with the class.

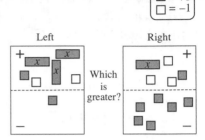

METHODS AND MEANINGS

Simplifying an Expression

Three common ways to simplify or alter expressions on an expression mat are illustrated below.

- Removing an equal number of opposite tiles that are in the same region. For example, the positive and negative tiles in the same region at right combine to make zero.

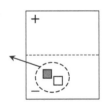

- Flipping a tile to move it out of one region into the opposite region (i.e., finding its opposite). For example, the tiles in the "–" region at right can be flipped into the "+" region.

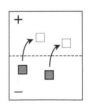

- Removing an equal number of identical tiles from both the "–" and the "+" regions. This strategy can be seen as a combination of the two methods above, since you could first flip the tiles from one region to another and then remove the opposite pairs.

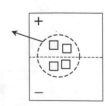

2-59.   One of the Ways of Thinking for this course is **justifying**. This is how you think
         when you support conclusions with valid reasoning, such as with an algebraic
         property. For example, when you want to convince someone that $8x + (2x - 3)$ is
         equivalent to $(8x + 2x) - 3$, you can support your claim with the Associative
         Property of Addition.

         Determine if the following statements are true or false. If true, **justify** your
         conclusion by stating the appropriate algebraic property. If false, explain how you
         know.

         a. $(8751)(38190) = (38190)(8751)$ b. $27^{1/3} + 0 = 27^{1/3}$

         c. $3 - 5 = 5 - 3$ d. $19.479 \cdot 1 = 19.479$

2-60.   Cairo wants to create a graph that represents the heights and bases of all rectangles
         that have an area of 36 square units. He started by drawing the rectangles A, B, C,
         and D below. Examine the dimensions (length and width) of each rectangle.

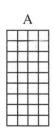
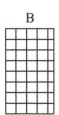
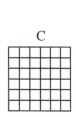
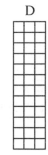

         a.   Copy the graph at right onto graph
               paper. Then match the letter of
               each rectangle above with a point
               on the graph. Which point is not
               matched?

         b.   What are the base, height, and
               area for the unmatched point?

         c.   Why should the unmatched point
               not be on Cairo's graph?

         d.   Find the dimensions of three more
               rectangles that have areas of 36 square
               units. At least one of your examples should have dimensions that are not
               integers. Place a new point on the graph for each new rectangle you find.

         e.   Connect all of the points representing an area of 36 square units. Describe the
               resulting graph.

2-61.   Find a simplified algebraic expression for each expression mat below.

a. 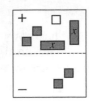   b. 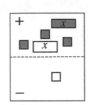   c.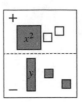

2-62.   One of Teddy's jobs at home is to pump gas for his family's sedan and truck. When he fills the truck up with 12 gallons of gas, he notices that it costs him $26.28.

a.   How much does one gallon of gas cost? Explain how you found your answer.

b.   How much will it cost him to fill up the sedan if it needs 15 gallons of gas? Show your work.

c.   When Teddy filled up the tank on his moped, it cost $8.76. How much gas did his moped need? Explain how you know.

2-63.   Decide if each of the statements below is sometimes true, always true, or never true. **Justify** your conclusion. If the statement is not always true, produce a counterexample (an example that shows the statement can or must be false) to help support your claim.

a.   If $y = 3$, then $2y = 6$.

b.   If $x + 3 = 9$, then $x = 2$.

c.   If the product of two numbers is positive (meaning more than zero), then both numbers must be positive.

d.   If $a + b = b$, then $a = 0$.

e.   If a and b are both odd integers, then ab is even.

f.   If x is greater than zero, then $-x$ is less than zero.

g.   If a is **prime** (meaning that a is an integer greater than 1 and has no other factors besides 1 and itself), then $(a + 1)$ is not prime.

h.   If x is greater than y, and both x and y are not zero, then $\frac{1}{y}$ is greater than $\frac{1}{x}$.

2.1.7 How can I write it?

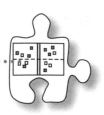

Simplifying and Recording Work

Today you will continue to compare expressions as you strengthen your simplification strategies. At the same time, you will work with your class to find ways to record your work so that another student can follow your strategies.

2-64. Use algebra tiles to build the expressions below on an expression comparison mat. Use "legal" simplification moves to determine which expression is greater, if possible. If it is not possible to tell which expression is greater, explain why.

a. Which is greater: $3x - (2 - x) + 1$ or $-5 + 4x + 4$?

b. Which is greater: $2x^2 - 2x + 6 - (-3x)$ or $-(3 - 2x^2) + 5 + 2x$?

c. Which is greater: $-1 + 6y - 2 + 4x - 2y$ or $x + 5y - (-2 + y) + 3x - 6$?

2-65. RECORDING YOUR WORK

Although using algebra tiles can make some things easier because you can "see" and "touch" the math, it can be difficult to remember what you did to solve a problem unless you take good notes.

Use the simplification strategies you have learned to determine which expression on the expression comparison mat at right is greater. Record each step as instructed by your teacher. Also record the simplified expression that remains after each move. This will be a written record of how you solved this problem. Discuss with your team what the best way is to record your moves.

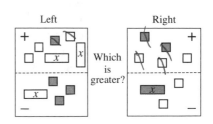

2-66. While Athena was comparing the expressions shown at right, she was called out of the classroom. When her teammates needed help, they looked at her paper and saw the work shown below. Unfortunately, she had forgotten to explain her simplification steps.

Can you help them figure out what Athena did to get each new set of expressions?

Left Expression	Right Expression	Explanation
$3x + 4 - x - (-2) + x^2$	$-1 + x^2 + 4x - (4 + 2x)$	Original expressions
$3x + 4 - x - (-2)$	$-1 + 4x - (4 + 2x)$	
$3x + 4 - x + 2$	$-1 + 4x - 4 - 2x$	
$2x + 6$	$2x - 5$	
6	-5	
Because $6 > -5$, the left side is greater.		

2-67. For each pair of expressions below, determine which is greater, carefully recording your steps as you go. If you cannot tell which expression is greater, state, "Not enough information." Make sure that you record your result after each type of simplification. For example, if you flip all of the tiles from the "−" region to the "+" region, record the resulting expression and indicate what you did using either words or symbols. Be ready to share your work with the class.

a.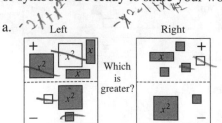

b.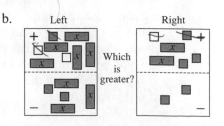

c. Which is greater: $5 - (2y - 4) - 2$ or $-y - (1 + y) + 4$?

d. Which is greater: $3xy + 9 - 4x - 7 + x$ or $-2x + 3xy - (x - 2)$?

METHODS AND MEANINGS

Solving Problems with Guess and Check

By now you should have seen several ways to organize information as you solve a problem using Guess and Check. One way to organize each guess and its results is using a table. An example of this work is shown below.

Problem: The base of a rectangle is three centimeters more than twice the height. The perimeter is 60 centimeters. Find the base and height of the rectangle.

height

base

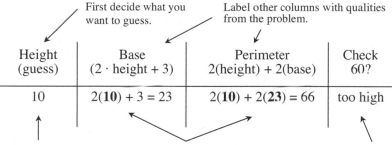

First decide what you want to guess.

Label other columns with qualities from the problem.

Height (guess)	Base (2 · height + 3)	Perimeter 2(height) + 2(base)	Check 60?
10	2(**10**) + 3 = 23	2(**10**) + 2(**23**) = 66	too high
8	2(**8**) + 3 = 19	2(**8**) + 2(**19**) = 54	too low
9	2(**9**) + 3 = 21	2(**9**) + 2(**21**) = 60	correct

Make a guess.

Use the relationships stated in the problem to determine the values of the other qualities (such as base and perimeter).

Check to see if your answer is correct. Then revise your guess and try again until you find the correct answer.

2-68.   Solve this problem using Guess and Check. You may want to review the Math
         Notes box for this lesson. Write your solution in a sentence.

         The number of students attending the Fall play was 150 more than the number of
         adults attending. Student tickets cost $3, and adult tickets cost $5. A total of $4730
         was collected. How many students attended the play?

2-69.   Sylvia simplified the
         expressions on the
         expression comparison mat
         shown at right. Some of
         her work is shown. Are all
         of her moves "legal"?
         Explain.

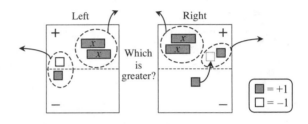

2-70.   Examine the tile pattern at right.

         a.   On graph paper, draw Figures 4 and 5.

         b.   What would Figure 10 look like?
               How many tiles would it have?
               What about Figure 100?

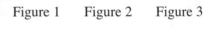

               Figure 1   Figure 2   Figure 3

         c.   Cami has a different tile pattern. She decided to represent the number of tiles
               of her pattern in a table, as shown below. Can you use the table to predict how
               many tiles would be in Figure 5 of her tile pattern? How many tiles would
               Figure 8 have? Explain how you know.

Figure Number	1	2	3	4
Number of Tiles	5	9	13	17

2-71.   Examine the shape made with algebra tiles at right.

         a.   Write an expression that represents the perimeter
               of the shape. Then evaluate your expression for
               $x = 6$ and $y = 10$ units.

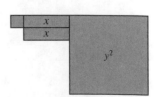

         b.   Write an expression that represents the area of the
               shape. What is the area if $x = 6$ and $y = 10$ units?

2-72.   CALCULATOR CHECK

Use your scientific calculator to compute the value of each expression in the left-hand column below. Match each result to an answer in the right-hand column.

a. $-3 + 16 - (-5)$

b. $(3 - 5)(6 + 2)$

c. $17(-23) + 2$

d. $5 - (3 - 17)(-2 + 25)$

e. $(-4)(-2.25)(-10)$

f. $-1.5 - 2.25 - (-4.5)$

g. $\frac{4-5}{-2}$

1. -16

2. 327

3. 0.5

4. 18

5. -90

6. 0.75

7. -389

2.1.8 What if both sides are equal?

Using Algebra Tiles to Solve for x

Can you always tell whether one algebraic expression is greater than another? In this section, you will continue to practice the different simplification strategies you have learned so far to compare two expressions and see which one is greater. However, sometimes you do not have enough information about the expressions. When both sides of an equation are equal, you can learn even more about x. As you work today, focus on these questions:

How can you simplify?

How can you get x alone?

Is there more than one way to simplify?

Is there always a solution?

2-73.   WHICH IS GREATER?

Build each expression represented below with the tiles provided by your teacher. Use "legal" simplification moves to determine which expression is greater, if possible. If it is not possible to determine which expression is greater, explain why it is impossible. Be sure to record your work on your paper.

a.

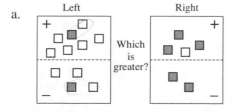

b.   Which is greater: $x + 1 - (1 - 2x)$
      or $3 + x - 1 - (x - 4)$?

2-74.   WHAT IF BOTH SIDES ARE EQUAL?

If the number 5 is compared to the number 7, then it is clear that 7 is greater. However, what if you compare x with 7? In this case, x could be smaller, larger, *or equal to* 7.

Examine the expression comparison mat below.

a.   If the left expression is smaller than the right expression, what does that tell you about the value of x?

b.   If the left expression is greater than the right expression, what does that tell you about the value of x?

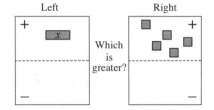

c.   What if the left expression is equal to the right expression? What does x have to be for the two expressions to be equal?

2-75.   SOLVING FOR X

Later in the course, you will learn more about situations like parts (a) and (b) in the preceding problem, called "inequalities." For now, assume that the left expression and the right expression are equal in order to learn more about x. The two expressions will be brought together on one mat to create an **equation mat**, as shown in the figure below. The double line down the center of an equation mat represents the word "equals." It is a wall that separates the left side of an equation from the right side.

a.   Obtain the "Equation Mat" resource page from your teacher. Build the equation represented by the equation mat at right using algebra tiles. Simplify as much as possible and then solve for x. Be sure to record your work.

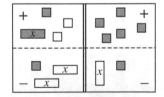

b.   Build the equation $2x - 5 = -1 + 5x + 2$ using your tiles by placing $2x - 5$ on the left side and $-1 + 5x + 2$ on the right side. Then use your simplification skills to simplify this equation as much as possible so that x is alone on one side of the equation. Use the fact that both sides are equal to solve for x. Record your work.

2-76.   Now **apply** this new solving skill by building, simplifying, and solving each equation below for x. Record your work.

a. $3x - 7 = 2$

b. $1 + 2x - x = x - 5 + x$

c. $3 - 2x = 2x - 5$

d. $3 + 2x - (x + 1) = 3x - 6$

e. $-(x + 3 - x) = 2x - 7$

f. $-4 + 2x + 2 = x + 1 + x$

 METHODS AND MEANINGS

MATH NOTES

Using an Equation Mat

An **equation mat** can help you visually represent an equation with algebra tiles.

The double line represents the "equals" sign (=).

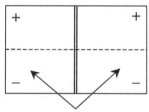

For each side of the equation, there is a positive and a negative region.

For example, the equation $2x - 1 - (-x + 3) = 6 - 2x$ can be represented by the equation mat at right. (Note that there are other possible ways to represent this equation correctly on the equation mat.)

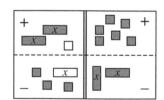

2-77.   WHICH IS GREATER?

For each expression comparison mat below, simplify and determine
which side is greater.

a.
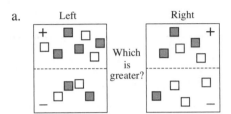

b.
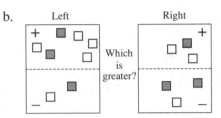

2-78.   Use Guess and Check to solve the problem below. Then state your solution in a
sentence.

Mairé is thinking of two numbers. When she adds them, she gets 40. When she
multiplies them, she gets 351. Help her younger sister, Enya, figure out the
numbers.

2-79.   Simplify each expression below as much as possible.

a. $3y - y + 5x + 3 - 7x$

b. $-1 - (-5x) - 2x + 2x^2 + 7$

c. $6x + 2 - 1 - 4x - 3 - 2x + 2$

d. $\frac{2}{3}x - 3y + \frac{1}{3}x + 2y$

2-80.   Plot the points (0, 0), (3, 2), and (6, 4) on graph paper. Then draw a line through the
points. Name the coordinates of three more points on the same line.

2-81.   Mr. Dexter's teams earned the following scores on a quiz: 15, 20, 19, 20, 16, 20, 14,
18, and 17.

a.   What is the mean (average score)?

b.   What is the median (middle score)?

c.   What is the mode (the score that occurs most often)?

2.1.9   What is *x*?

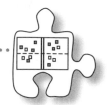

More Solving Equations

Today you will explore more equations on the equation mat and will examine all of the tools you have developed so far to solve for *x*. While you are working on these problems, be prepared to answer the following questions:

How can you simplify?

Can you get the variable alone?

Is there more than one way to simplify?

Is there always a solution?

2-82.   On your paper, write the equation represented in each diagram below. For each equation, simplify as much as possible and then solve for *x* or *y*. Be sure to record your work on your paper.

$\blacksquare = +1$
$\square = -1$

a.
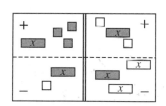

b.
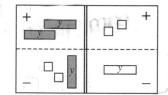

2-83.   IS THERE A SOLUTION?

While solving homework last night, Richie came across three homework questions that he thinks have no solution. Build each equation below and determine if it has a solution for *x*. If it has a solution, find it. If it does not have a solution, explain why not.

$\blacksquare = +1$
$\square = -1$

a.
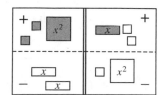

b.
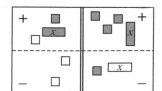

c.
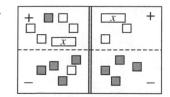

2-84.   Continue to develop your equation-solving strategies by solving each equation below
(if possible). Remember to build each equation, simplify as much as possible, and
solve for x or y. There are often multiple ways to solve equations, so remember to
justify that each step is "legal." If you cannot solve for x, explain why not. Be sure
to record your work.

a. $-x + 2 = 4$

b. $4x - 2 + x = 2x + 8 + 3x$

c. $4y - 9 + y = 6$

d. $9 - (2 - 3y) = 6 + 2y - (5 + y)$

2-85.   In your Learning Log, explain when you can solve for x in an
equation and when you cannot. Be sure to give an example of each
situation. Title this entry "Solutions of an Equation" and include
today's date.

2-86. Translate the equation mat at right into an equation. Remember that the double line represents "equals."

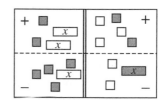

2-87. Ling wants to save $87 for tickets to a rock concert. If she has $23 now and will save $4 per week, how long will it take her to get enough money to buy the tickets? Make a Guess and Check table to help you solve this problem.

2-88. On graph paper, plot the points (0, 0), (–2, 1), and (2, –1). Then draw a line through them. Name the coordinates of three more points on the same line that have integer coordinates.

2-89. Copy and complete each of the Diamond Problems below. The pattern used in the Diamond Problems is shown at right.

a.

b.

c.

d.

2-90. Evaluate the expressions below for the given values.

a. $6m + 2n^2$ for $m = 7$ and $n = 3$

b. $\frac{5x}{3} - 2$ for $x = -18$

c. $(6x)^2 - \frac{x}{5}$ for $x = 10$

d. $(k - 3)(k + 2)$ for $k = 1$

2.2.1 How can I solve it?

···

Solving Problems With Proportional Intuition

In Chapter 1, you looked at ways to organize your algebraic thinking using graphs and tables. In the first part of this chapter, you used algebra tiles to model combining like terms and solving equations. Today you will examine proportional situations. What proportional tools do you already have? What new ways can you and your team find to solve proportional problems?

2-91.   PROPORTIONAL RELATIONSHIPS

Solve the five problems (a) through (e) below. Don't estimate! Instead, use the information to find an answer that is as accurate as possible. There are many different strategies you can use, so be sure to give reasons as you discuss your ideas with your team. To help **justify** your ideas, make sure both to *show* and to *explain* your work. For example:

- Label all numbers with what they represent. For example, don't just write "5"; instead, write "5 pounds."

- Give reasons for each action. For example, if you decided to add 10, say why. (Why did you add? Why 10?)

- Organize your work so that others will understand what you did and why you did it that way.

a.   Mr. Douglas made a copy of the triangle shown at right, but he accidentally enlarged it! The longest side of the new copy had a length of 32 cm. How long are the two shorter legs?

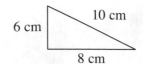

b.   Ferroza's pet ferret eats so much that she has to buy ferret food in bulk. Five pounds cost $17.50. How much would 30 pounds cost? How much would 33 pounds cost?

Problem continues on next page →

2-91.   *Problem continued from previous page.*

c.   Oscar often cleans his teachers' overhead transparencies. He can clean 17 transparencies in 10 minutes. At this rate, how long would it take him to clean 75 transparencies? Now **reverse** the problem: How many transparencies could Oscar clean in one hour?

d.    The Math Club is having a tamale sale! The school has 1600 students, but the club members are not sure how many tamales to make. One day during lunch, the club asked random students if they would buy a tamale. They found that 15 out of 80 students surveyed said they would definitely buy a tamale. How many tamales should the Math Club expect to sell?

e.   When he was little, Miguel could not sleep without his Captain Terrific action figure – it looked so life-like because it was a perfect scale model. The actor who plays Captain Terrific on television is 216 cm tall. Miguel's doll is 10 cm tall.

   i.   If the doll's neck is 0.93 cm long, how long is the actor's neck?

   ii. If the actor's head has a circumference of 30 cm, what is the circumference of the doll's head?

2-92.   The five problems above are all examples of situations that involve **proportional relationships**. In your Learning Log, write your observations about what all five of these problems have in common. Title this entry "Proportional Relationships" and label it with today's date.

2-93.   Find the perimeter and area of Jacob's swimming pool shown in the diagram below. Be sure to show all of your work.

18 m

6 m

11 m

9 m

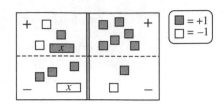

2-94.   On your paper, write the equation
          represented in the equation mat at
          right. Simplify as much as possible
          and then solve for x.

2-95.   For each equation below, draw a
          picture of the tiles in an equation mat,
          simplify, and solve for x. Record
          your work.

          a. $2x - 7 = -x + 2$ b. $-2 - 3x = x + 6$

2-96.   Copy and simplify the following expressions by combining like terms.

          a. $y + 2x - 3 + 4x^2 + 3x - 5y$ b. $2x - 6x^2 + 9 - 1 - x - 3x$

          c. $2y^2 + 30x - 5y^2 + 4x - 4y - y$ d. $-10 + 3xy - 3xy + y^2 + 10 - y^2$

2-97.   Ferroza can buy a 24-ounce bag of ferret food for $1.19, or
          she can buy a 36-ounce bag for $2.89. Which is the better
          deal? **Justify** your conclusion.

2-98.   Since the beginning of school, Steven has been saving money to buy a new MP3
          player. His bank balance is represented by the graph below.

          a.   According to the graph, about how
                much money had Steven saved after 2
                weeks of school?

          b.   About how much money did Steven
                probably have after 4 weeks of school?
                How can you tell?

          c.   If he keeps saving at the same rate, how
                much will he have saved by Week 7?
                Explain how you know.

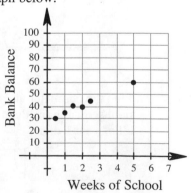

2.2.2 How can I organize my work?

. . . .

Sharing Proportion-Organizing Strategies

In Lesson 2.2.1, you solved problems using proportional reasoning (that is, you used the fact that each situation was proportional to solve the problem). Today you will work with two more proportional situations. This time, your focus will be on how to organize your work and how to explain your reasoning.

2-99.   Solve these proportion problems and be ready to present your method. Remember to label all numbers and explain (in words or symbols) the reasons for your work. Be sure to organize your ideas in a way that will help others see what you did.

   a.   Toby uses seven tubes of toothpaste every ten months. How many tubes would he use in five years? In two years? How long would it take him to use 100 tubes?

   b.   Mr. Douglas is at it again! The little trapezoid below on the left got enlarged in the photocopying machine and turned into the big trapezoid on the right. How long are the missing sides of the shapes (x and y)?

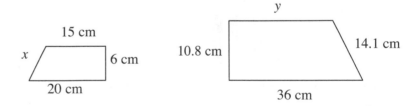

2-100.   Look back at the proportion problems you solved today and yesterday. Share your strategies with the class.

   a.   Did you always organize your work the same way? What different organizational strategies did you or your classmates use?

   b.   What did all of the problems yesterday and today have in common?

2-101.   In your Learning Log, show at least two examples of ways to organize your work when solving problems that require proportional reasoning. Title this entry "Solving Proportion Problems" and include today's date.

METHODS AND MEANINGS

Similar Figures

Photocopy-enlargement problems like Mr. Douglas's (see part (a) of problem 2-91 and part (b) of problem 2-99) involve figures that are similar. In plain English, "similar" means "close to the same." But in mathematics, **similar** means that two figures have the same shape but are not necessarily the same size.

Below are examples of some shapes that are similar and other shapes that are not similar.

These pairs of shapes <u>are</u> similar: **These pairs are <u>not</u> similar:**

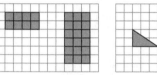   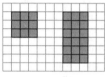   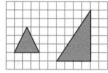

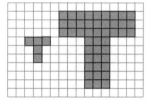   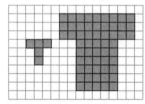

2-102.   Use proportional reasoning to solve the following problems.

a.   A typical small bag of colored candies has about 135 candies in it, 27 of which are blue. At this rate, how many blue candies would you expect in a pile of 1000 colored candies?

b.   Ten calculators cost $149.50. How much would 100 cost? 1000? 500?

c.   Tickets to 50 home baseball games would cost $1137.50. How much would it cost to get tickets for all 81 home games? How many games could you go to for $728?

2-103.   At the annual dog show, Chantel noticed that there were three more Schnauzers than Scotties. She also realized that the number of Wirehaired Terriers was three less than twice the number of Schnauzers. If there were 78 dogs in all (counting Schnauzers, Scotties, and Wirehaired Terriers), how many Schnauzers were there?

2-104.   Write the equation represented in the equation mat below.

a.   Simplify both sides as much as possible, and then solve for x.

b.   Evaluate both the left side and the right side using your solution from part (a). Remember that if your solution is correct, both sides should have the same value.

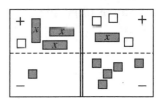

2-105.   For the following equations, draw a picture of the tiles in an equation mat, use "legal" moves to simplify, and then solve for x. Record your work.

a. $-3x + 7 = x - 1$ b. $1 + 2x - 3 = 4x - 2$

2-106.   To bake 100 of his favorite cookies, Mr. Wallis needs 350 grams of sugar.

a.   How many grams of sugar would he need to bake 10 cookies? What about 20 cookies? Show all work.

b.   To help him know how much sugar to use when baking cookies, Mr. Wallis started to make a table, as shown at right. Copy and complete his table on your paper.

Cookies	Sugar (g)
100	350
10	
20	
2	
1	
5	
	700
	1400

2-107.   Read the Math Notes box for this lesson, entitled "Similar Figures." Then draw your own example of two figures that are **similar**.

2.2.3 How can I use proportional relationships?

Using Proportional Relationships

How many books in the Library of Congress are science fiction? How many people will vote for your favorite candidate in the next election? How many fish are in the ocean?

To answer questions about huge quantities, it is sometimes best to start by thinking in terms of small quantities. Today you will use proportional relationships to make predictions about large collections of people and things. During today's work, consider:

How are these related?

How can you use this information to make a prediction?

2-108.   COUNTING CANDIES

Can you use the number of candies in a small bag to predict the number of candies in a large bag? To answer this, follow the directions from your teacher and discuss these questions:

- Using the small bag of candy, what could you predict about the large bag?

- Could you also use the large bag of candy to make a prediction about the small bag? Why or why not?

a.   Decide what you will predict about the large bag. For example, you could try to predict the number of red candies in the large bag.

b.   Collect data from the small bag. What should you measure?

c.   Use your data and proportional reasoning to make a prediction about the large bag.

d.   As a class, find a way to determine if your prediction was fairly accurate. If it was not close to being accurate, what do you think happened?

2-109.   Kenny can make 12 origami (folded-paper) cranes in 4 minutes. He read a story about a girl who made 1000 cranes, and was curious about how long it would take him to make that many (assuming he worked without stopping).

a.   If Kenny works at a constant rate, how many cranes could Kenny fold in 8 minutes? 20 minutes? What about in 1 hour? Show how you calculated each answer.

b.   When he was done, Kenny made a graph of his progress, shown at right. According to the graph, approximately how long would it take him to fold 100 cranes? What about 0 cranes?

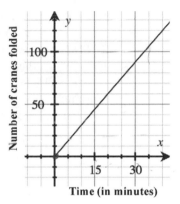

c.   This situation is an example of **direct variation**, because as the time Kenny folds increases, the number of cranes increases in direct proportion. Explain why the graph of a direct variation situation has to be linear (a line), like the one shown at right.

2-110.   How many people are in your math class? How many of those people are left-handed? Use this information to make predictions about other groups of people.

a.   How many students are in your grade? About how many of those students would you expect to be left-handed?

b.   How many students are in your entire school? About how many of those students would you expect to be left-handed?

c.   Now **reverse** the process: The Kennedy Middle School Left-Handers' Club has counted 270 left-handed students in their school. About how many students do you think there are at Kennedy Middle School?

d.   Across town, Grand Prairie High has 1060 *right*-handed students. About how many students would you expect there to be at Grand Prairie High?

2-111.   Where else does the idea of a proportional relationship between part and whole appear? Read the Math Notes box following this problem and explain how one part of the Sierpinski Triangle is similar to the whole triangle.

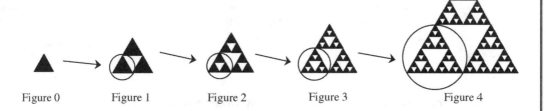

LOOKING DEEPER

MATH NOTES

Fractals

Fractals are geometric structures developed by repeating a process over and over. A famous example of a fractal is the **Sierpinski Triangle**, shown below. To create this design, make three copies of a triangle and place them into a larger triangle, as shown in Figure 1. Then repeat the process by taking the large triangle of Figure 1 and copying it in the same arrangement, shown in Figure 2. If this process is continued infinitely, the result is the Sierpinski Triangle.

Figure 0 → Figure 1 → Figure 2 → Figure 3 → Figure 4

Review & Preview

2-112. When baking cookies for his class of 21 students, Sammy needed two eggs. Now he wants to bake cookies for the upcoming science fair. If he expects 336 people to attend the science fair, how many eggs will he need?

2-113. The graph below shows distances traveled by Car A and Car B. Car A is represented by the line containing point A, and Car B is represented by the line containing point B. Use the graph to answer the following questions.

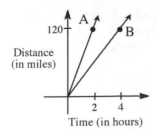

a. Which car is traveling faster? How can you tell?

b. Find the coordinates of point A and point B.

c. How fast did Car A travel (in miles per hour)? How fast did Car B travel?

d. Does the distance Car A has traveled vary directly with the time? Why or why not?

2-114.   Solve the equations below for x and check your solutions.

    a. $-3 + x = -2x + 6$ b. $5 - x = 3x + 1$

    c. $-4x = 2x + 9$ d. $-(x - 3) = -4x$

2-115.   Simplify the following expressions.

    a. $x + 3x - 3 + 2x^2 + 8x - 5$ b. $3y + 14y^2 - 6y^2 - 9y + 1 - y - 3y$

    c. $2y^2 + 30xy - 2y^2 + 4y - 4x$ d. $x - 0.2x$

2-116.   Mr. Wallis has done it again! He has started to create more tables to help him figure out things like how many gallons of gas it takes to travel a certain number of miles or how many minutes it takes to walk a certain number of blocks. Use proportional reasoning to complete his tables below.

a.

# of Books	Days
2	10
10	50
	60
3	
1	
$\frac{1}{5}$	
	365

b.

Minutes	Blocks
10	25
5	12.5
1	
20	
30	
	0
	35

c.

Miles	Gallons
280	14
140	7
	21
20	
100	
1000	
	17.5

Chapter 2 Closure   What have I learned?

Reflection and Synthesis

The activities below offer you a chance to reflect on what you have learned during this chapter. As you work, look for concepts that you feel very comfortable with, ideas that you would like to learn more about, and topics you need more help with. Look for **connections** between ideas as well as **connections** with material you learned previously.

①   TEAM BRAINSTORM

With your team, brainstorm a list for each of the following three topics. Be as detailed as you can. How long can you make your list? Challenge yourselves. Be prepared to share your team's ideas with the class.

Topics: What have you studied in this chapter? What ideas and words were important in what you learned? Remember to be as detailed as you can.

Problem Solving: What did you do to solve problems? What different strategies did you use?

Connections: What topics, ideas, and words that you learned *before* this chapter are **connected** to the new ideas in this chapter? Again, make your list as long as you can.

The following is a list of the vocabulary used in this chapter. The words that appear in bold are new to this chapter. Make sure that you are familiar with all of these words and know what they mean. Refer to the glossary or index for any words that you do not yet understand.

algebra tiles	area	**combining like terms**
equal	**equation**	**equation mat**
equivalent	**evaluate**	**expression**
expression comparison mat	**expression mat**	**greater**
minus	**negative**	**opposite**
order of operations	**proportional**	**simplify**
solution	**solve**	sum
term	**variable**	**zero**

Make a concept map showing all of the **connections** you can find among the key words and ideas listed above. To show a **connection** between two words, draw a line between them and explain the **connection**, as shown in the example below. A word can be **connected** to any other word as long as there is a **justified connection**. For each key word or idea, provide a sketch of an example.

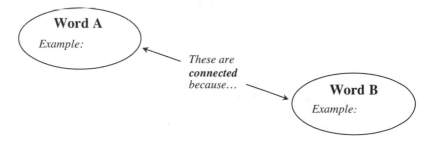

Your teacher may provide you with vocabulary cards to help you get started. If you use the cards to plan your concept map, be sure either to re-draw your concept map on your paper or to glue the vocabulary cards to a poster with all of the **connections** explained for others to see and understand.

While you are making your map, your team may think of related words or ideas that are not listed above. Be sure to include these ideas on your concept map.

③   SUMMARIZING MY UNDERSTANDING

This section gives you an opportunity to show what you know about certain math topics or ideas. Your teacher will give you directions for exactly how to do this. Your teacher may give you a "GO" page to work on. "GO" stands for "Graphic Organizer," a tool you can use to organize your thoughts and communicate your ideas clearly.

④   WHAT HAVE I LEARNED?

This section will help you evaluate which types of problems you have seen with which you feel comfortable and those with which you need more help. This section appears at the end of every chapter to help you check your understanding. Even if your teacher does not assign this section, it is a good idea to try the problems and find out for yourself what you know and what you need to work on.

Solve each problem as completely as you can. The table at the end of this closure section has answers to these problems. It also tells you where you can find additional help and practice on problems like these.

CL 2-117. Examine the expression mat at right.

a.   Copy the expression mat onto your paper.

b.   Write an expression for the tiles as they appear.

c.   On your drawing, circle all of the zeros that you can find to simplify the expression.

d.   Write the completely simplified expression.

CL 2-118. Zeke lives 30 miles from his aunt, Zelda, and is riding his bike home from her house. Interpret the graph to tell a story about what could have happened on his ride home.

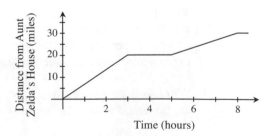

CL 2-119. Write expressions for each side of the expression comparison mat. Use "legal" moves to simplify and determine which is greater.

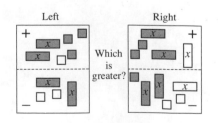

CL 2-120. Solve the following problem using Guess and Check. Show your guesses in an organized way.

Ralph and Alphonse are shooting marbles. Ralph has five more marbles than Alphonse, and they have a total of 73 marbles. How many marbles does each of them have?

CL 2-121. Simplify each expression with or without algebra tiles. Record your steps.

a. $3 + 7x - (2 + 9x)$

b. $6 - (3x - 4) + 7x - 11$

CL 2-122. Copy the pattern below onto graph paper. Draw Figures 1 and 5 on your paper.

a.   How many tiles are in each figure?

b.   How is the pattern changing?

c.   How many tiles would Figure 6 have?

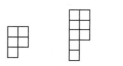

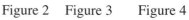

Figure 2   Figure 3   Figure 4

CL 2-123. Silvia has a picture from her trip to the Grand Canyon. The photo is 4 inches tall by 6 inches wide.

a.   She would like to make a larger photo for her wall that is as big as possible. The widest the enlarged photo can be is 48 inches. How tall will the enlarged photo be?

b.   Silvia also wants a wallet-sized photo to carry around and show her friends that is 1.5 inches tall. How wide will the wallet-sized photo be?

CL 2-124. Evaluate $6x - (3y + 7) - xy$ when $x = 5$ and $y = 3$.

CL 2-125. Simplify the expression below by combining like terms:

$$3x^2 + 10 - y^2 + 4x - 8x^2 - 5y - 8 + y^2 + 3$$

CL 2-126. Solve this equation to find x: $2 - (3x - 4) = 2x - 9$.

CL 2-127. Check your answers using the table at the end of the closure section. Which problems do you feel confident about? Which problems were hard? Use the table to make a list of topics you need help on and a list of topics you need to practice more.

HOW AM I THINKING?

This course focuses on five different **Ways of Thinking**: reversing thinking, justifying, generalizing, making connections, and applying and extending understanding. These are some of the ways in which you think while trying to make sense of a concept or to solve a problem (even outside of math class). During this chapter, you have probably used each Way of Thinking multiple times without even realizing it!

This closure activity will focus on one of these Ways of Thinking: **justifying**. Read the description of this Way of Thinking at right.

Think about the topics that you have learned during this chapter. When did you need to convince someone that your thinking was correct? What types of **justification** did you need to use? You may want to flip through the chapter to refresh your memory about the problems that you have worked on. Discuss any ideas you have with the rest of the class.

Once your discussion is complete, analyze how **justifications** work below.

Justifying

You often think this way when you try to convince yourself or someone else that an idea or solution is correct. Often, a justification is the answer to the questions "Why?" or "How do you know for sure?" When you catch yourself thinking, "*I think this is true because…*," you are justifying.

a. While simplifying the expressions shown in the expression comparison mat at right, the four members of a study team made the following statements. Which students **justified** their statements? And were the **justifications** convincing? Explain why or why not.

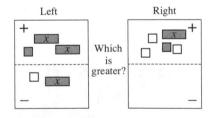

Rosalita: "I think we can take the positive unit tile and negative unit tile away from the left side because they make zero."

Anthony: "I think we can take an x-tile away from both sides."

Barry: "I don't think we can tell which side is greater because there are more x-tiles on the left side than on the right."

Deshawn: "I think we can remove a positive and negative unit tile from the "+" region on the right side because they are opposites, so they make zero."

Continues on next page →

Algebra Connections

⑤ *Continued from previous page.*

b. Your teammate needs help understanding why $-(-2x-3) = 2x+3$. She thinks that $-(-2x-3) = 2x-3$. **Justify** why $-(-2x-3) = 2x+3$ so that she is convinced.

c. Examine the tile pattern below. What do you think Figure 0 must look like? **Justify** why your Figure 0 fits the pattern.

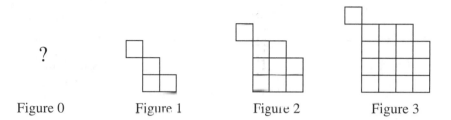

?			
Figure 0	Figure 1	Figure 2	Figure 3

Answers and Support for Closure Activity #4
What Have I Learned?

Problem	Solution	Need Help?	More Practice
CL 2-117.	b. $2x - x + 3 - 2 - (x - x + 2 - 1)$ c. one possible answer: d. x	Problem 2-23, Lesson 2.1.6 Math Notes box	Problems 2-26, 2-36, 2-38, 2-39, 2-42, 2-44, and 2-59
CL 2-118.	There are many possible stories for this graph. Make sure your story explains the changes in speed and the stops and starts in the graph. Zeke travels 20 miles during the first 3 hours and then rests for 2 hours. Then he travels 10 miles in the next 3 hours and reaches his house after 8 hours.	Lesson 1.1.3	Problems 2-98 and 2-113 (also problems 1-6, 1-9, 1-20, 1-47, 1-48, and 1-68)
CL 2-119.	Left: $-1 + 2x + 3 - (2x - 2) = 4$ Right: $2x + 2 - x - (2x - x - 2 + 1) = 3$ The left expression is greater than the right expression.	Problem 2-48, Lesson 2.1.6 Math Notes box	Problems 2-49, 2-50, 2-57, 2-58, 2-65, 2-66, 2-67, 2-69, 2-73, and 2-77

Problem	Solution	Need Help?	More Practice
CL 2-120.	Ralph has 39 marbles, and Alphonse has 34 marbles.	Lesson 2.1.7 Math Notes box	Problems 2-11, 2-32, 2-68, 2-78, 2-87, and 2-103
CL 2-121.	a. $-2x+1$ b. $4x-1$	Lesson 2.1.4, Lesson 2.1.6 Math Notes box	Problems 2-38, 2-39, 2-44, and 2-59
CL 2-122.	a. 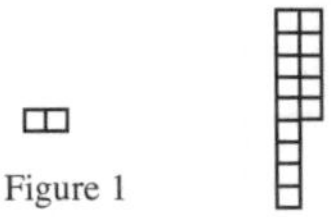 Figure 1 Figure 5 b. Each figure has three more tiles than the one before it. c. Figure 6 would have 17 tiles.	Lesson 1.1.4	Problem 2-70 (also problems 1-31, 1-32, and 1-67)
CL 2-123.	a. The picture would be 32 inches tall. b. The picture would be 2.25 inches wide.	Lessons 2.2.1 and 2.2.3	Problems 2-91, 2-99, 2-102, 2-106, 2-108, 2-109, 2-110, 2-112, and 2-116
CL 2-124.	$6 \cdot 5 - (3 \cdot 3 + 7) - 5 \cdot 3 = -1$	Lesson 2.1.3 Math Notes box	Problems 2-10, 2-18, 2-30, 2-56, and 2-90
CL 2-125.	$-5x^2 + 4x - 5y + 5$	Lesson 2.1.1, Lesson 2.1.5 Math Notes box	Problems 2-4, 2-17, 2-29, 2-52, 2-79, 2-96, and 2-115
CL 2-126.	$x = 3$	Problems 2-74 and 2-75, Lesson 2.1.8 Math Notes box	Problems 2-76, 2-82, 2-83, 2-84, 2-95, 2-105, and 2-114

3

Graphs and Equations

CHAPTER 3   Graphs and Equations

In this chapter you will **extend** your understanding of the use of variables in algebra (such as *x* and *y*). You will learn about tools (such as graphing calculators) that will help you explore how variables affect tile patterns, tables, and graphs. You will also continue to develop your ability to solve equations, started in Chapter 2, and will begin a study of the multiple representations of data. You will study the **connections** between graphing and solving equations in Chapter 4.

In this chapter, you will learn:

> ➤ How to find a rule from a table.

> ➤ How to represent a situation using a table, a rule, and a graph.

> ➤ How to graph linear and parabolic rules using an appropriate scale.

> ➤ What it means for something to be the solution to an equation and also what it means for an equation to have no solution.

> ➤ How to determine the number of solutions to an equation.

Guiding Questions

Think about these questions throughout this chapter:

What is a variable?

What is the pattern?

How many different ways can I represent it?

How can I solve it?

How can I check my answer?

Chapter Outline

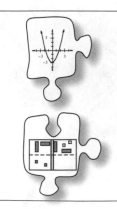

Section 3.1   In this section, you will learn the graphing mechanics that you will need throughout the rest of this course. You will also learn how to create tables, write rules, and draw graphs to represent situations and patterns.

Section 3.2   Section 3.2 will **extend** the work you did in Section 2.2. You will learn how to solve linear equations without using algebra tiles and will learn the significance of solutions.

3.1.1 What is the rule?

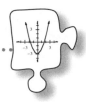

Extending Patterns and Finding Rules

You have been learning how to work with variables and how to find values for variables in equations. In this section, you will learn how to **extend** patterns and how to **generalize** your pattern with a rule. As you work with your team, use these questions to focus your ideas:

How is the pattern growing?

What is the rule?

Is there another way to see it?

How can you tell if your rule is correct?

3-1. Some people describe mathematics as "the study of patterns." For each tile pattern below, draw Figure 1 and Figure 5 on graph paper. First try it individually, and then consult with your team. What does Figure 100 look like? Explain how you know.

a.

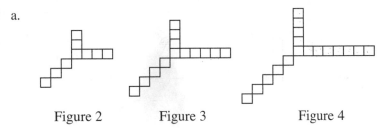

Figure 2   Figure 3   Figure 4

b.

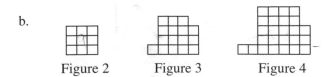

Figure 2   Figure 3   Figure 4

3-2. FINDING RULES FROM TABLES

How can you describe the rule that governs a pattern or table? Obtain the Lesson 3.1.1A Resource Page from your teacher and find the tables below. Then, as a class, find the pattern, fill in the missing parts, and **extend** each table with at least two more $x \rightarrow y$ pairs that fit the pattern. Then **generalize** the pattern's rule in words.

a.

IN (x)	OUT (y)
	C
L	N
	F
Q	
W	Y

Rule:

b.

IN (x)	OUT (y)
easy	
	light
hot	cold
up	down
left	

Rule:

c.

IN (x)	OUT (y)
△	⬠
⬠	
	⬡
⬡	⬡
⯃	

Rule:

d.

IN (x)	OUT (y)
8	17
−2	
	9
12	25
10	21

Rule:

e.

IN (x)	OUT (y)
100	51
4	
6	4
30	16
	31

Rule:

f.

IN (x)	OUT (y)
4	16
−1	1
	9
12	
−6	

Rule:

3-3. Obtain the Lesson 3.1.1B Resource Page from your teacher. For each $x \rightarrow y$ table given, find the pattern and fill in the missing entries. Then write the rule for the pattern in words. Be sure to share your thinking with your teammates.

a.

IN (x)	OUT (y)
	8
0	−2
−4	−10
10	18
−2	
	198
0.5	

Rule:

b.

IN (x)	OUT (y)
3	−9
10	
−1	3
	6
0	
	−36
−5	15

Rule:

c.

IN (x)	OUT (y)
0.5	
	37
2	5
−10	101
−5	
0	1
	50

Rule:

Problem continues on next page →

3-3. *Problem continued from previous page.*

d.

IN (x)	OUT (y)
6	
11	5
	−4
23	17
−7	
	40
−4	−10

Rule:

e.

IN (x)	OUT (y)
2	6
4	20
10	110
−3	
	30
7	56
1	

Rule:

f.

IN (x)	OUT (y)
−8	
10	53
3	18
0	
	8
19	
4	23

Rule:

LOOKING DEEPER

Patterns in Nature

MATH NOTES

Patterns are everywhere, especially in nature. One famous pattern that appears often is called the Fibonacci Sequence, a sequence of numbers that starts 1, 1, 2, 3, 5, 8, 13, 21, …

The Fibonacci numbers appear in many different contexts in nature. For example, the number of petals on a flower is often a Fibonacci number, and the number of seeds on a spiral from the center of a sunflower is, too.

To learn more about Fibonacci numbers, search the Internet or check out a book from your local library. The next time you look at a flower, look for Fibonacci numbers!

3-4. **WHICH IS GREATER?**

Write the algebraic expressions shown below. Use "legal" simplification moves to determine which expression in the expression comparison mat is greater.

a.

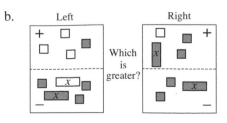

b.

3-5.   Evaluate the expressions below for the given values.

   a. $3(2x+1)$ for $x = -8$ b. $\frac{x-6}{4} - 1$ for $x = -14$

   c. $-2m^2 + 10$ for $m = -6$ d. $k \cdot k \div k \cdot k \div k$ for $k = 9$

3-6.   At the fair, Kate found a strange machine with a
        sign on it labeled, "Enter a number." When she
        pushed the number 15, the machine displayed 9.
        When she entered 23, the machine displayed 17.
        Perplexed, she tried 100, and the machine
        displayed 94.

   a.   What is the machine doing?

   b.   What would the machine display if she
         entered 77?

3-7.   Ms. Nguyen needs to separate $385 into three parts to pay some debts. The second
        part must be five times as large as the first part. The third part must be $35 more
        than the first part. How much money must be in each part?

3-8.   GO GOLDEN GOPHERS!

        The graph below describes the
        distance two cars have traveled after
        leaving a football game at the
        University of Minnesota.

   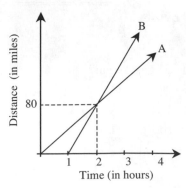

   a.   Which car was traveling faster? How
         can you tell?

   b.   The lines cross at (2, 80). What does
         this point represent?

   c.   Assuming that Car A continued to travel
         at a constant rate, how far did Car A
         travel in the first 4 hours?

3.1.2 How can I make a prediction?

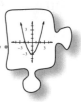

Using Tables, Graphs, and Rules to Make Predictions

In Lesson 3.1.1, you wrote rules for patterns found in $x \rightarrow y$ tables. In this lesson, you will focus on using variables to write algebraic rules for patterns and contextual situations. You will use a graph to help predict the output for fractional x-values and will then use a rule to predict the output when the input is too large and does not appear on the graph.

While working today, focus on these questions:

How can you write the rule without words?

What does x represent?

How can you make a prediction?

3-9. SILENT BOARD GAME

During Lesson 3.1.1, you created written rules for patterns that had no tiles or numbers. You will now write algebraic rules using a table of jumbled in/out numbers. Focus on finding patterns and writing rules as you play the Silent Board Game. Your teacher will put an incomplete $x \rightarrow y$ table on the overhead or board. Study the input and output values and look for a pattern. Then write the rule in words and symbols that finds each y-value from its x-value.

3-10.   JOHN'S GIANT REDWOOD, Part One

John found the data in the table below about his
favorite redwood tree. He wondered if he could use it
to predict the height of the tree at other points of time.
Consider this as you analyze the data and answer the
questions below. Be ready to share (and **justify**) your
answers with the class.

Number of Years after Planting	3	4	5
Height of Tree (in feet)	17	21	25

a.   How tall was the tree 2 years after it was
      planted? What about 7 years after it was
      planted? How do you know?

b.   How tall was the tree the year it was planted?

c.   Estimate the height of the tree 50 years after it was planted. How did you
      make your prediction?

3-11.   John decided to find out more about his favorite redwood tree by graphing the data.

a.   On the Lesson 3.1.2B Resource Page provided by your teacher, plot the points
      that represent the height of the tree over time. What does the graph look like?

b.   Does it make sense to connect the points? Explain your thinking.

c.   According to the graph, what was the height of the tree 1.5 years after it was
      planted?

d.   Can you use your graph to predict the height of the redwood tree 20 years after
      it was planted? Why or why not?

3-12.   John is still not satisfied. He wants to be able to predict
the height of the tree at any time after it was planted.

a.   Find John's table on your resource page and
      extend it to include the height of the tree in the
      0th year, 1st year, 2nd year, and 6th year.

b.   If you have not already, use the ideas from the Silent Board Game to write an
      algebraic rule for the data in your table. Be sure to work with your team and
      check that the rule works for all of the data.

c.   Use your rule to check your prediction in part (c) of problem 3-10 for how tall
      the tree will be in its 50th year. How close was your prediction?

3-13.   Write the equation represented in each diagram below on your paper. For each part, simplify as much as possible and then solve for x. Be sure to record your work on your paper.

a.

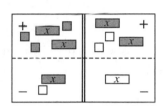

b.

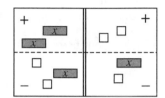

3-14.   Evaluate the following expressions given the values below.

a. $ab + bc + ac$ for $a = 2$, $b = 5$, and $c = 3$

b. $\frac{20 - x^2}{y - x}$ for $x = -2$ and $y = 6$

3-15.   Copy and simplify the following expressions by combining like terms.

a. $x + 3x - 3 + 2x^2 + 8 - 5x$ b. $2x + 4y^2 - 6y^2 - 9 + 1 - x + 3x$

c. $2x^2 + 30y - 3y^2 + 4xy - 14 - x$ d. $20 + 3xy - 3xy + y^2 + 10 - y^2$

3-16.   Use the order of operations to simplify the following expressions.

a. $5 - 2 \cdot 3^2$ b. $(-2)^2$

c. $18 \div 3 \cdot 6$ d. -2^2

e. $(5 - 3)(5 + 3)$ f. $24 \cdot \frac{1}{4} \div -2$

g.   Why are your answers for parts (b) and (d) different?

3-17.   Mrs. Swanson gives out only one type of candy for Halloween. The local discount store sells six pounds of butterscotch candies for $7.50. Use proportional reasoning to determine the information below. Be sure to explain your answer and organize your reasoning.

a.   What is the cost of 18 pounds of butterscotch candies?

b.   What is the cost of 10 pounds of butterscotch candies?

3.1.3 What is a graph and how is it useful?

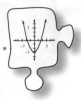

Using the Graphing Calculator and Identifying Solutions

In the last two lessons, you examined several patterns and learned how to represent the patterns in a table and with a rule. For the next few days, you will learn a powerful new way to represent a pattern and make predictions.

As you work with your team today, use these focus questions to help direct your discussion:

What is the rule?

How can you represent the pattern?

3-18.   Find the "Big Cs" pattern shown at right on the Lesson 3.1.3 Resource Page provided by your teacher.

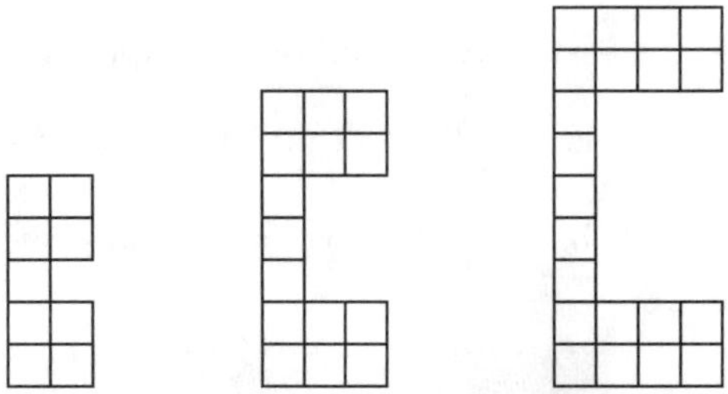

Figure 1   Figure 2   Figure 3

a.   Draw Figure 0 and Figure 4 on the grid provided on the resource page.

b.   On the resource page, represent the number of tiles in each figure with:

   - An $x \rightarrow y$ table.

   - An algebraic rule.

   - A graph.

c.   How many tiles will be in Figure 5? **Justify** your answer in at least two different ways.

d.   What will Figure 100 look like? How many tiles will it have? How can you be sure?

3-19.   Use the graphing technology provided by your teacher to analyze the pattern further and make predictions.

a.   Enter the information from your $x \rightarrow y$ table for problem 3-18 into your grapher. Then plot the points using a window of your choice. What do you notice?

b.   Find another $x \rightarrow y$ pair that you think belongs in your table. Use your grapher to plot the point. Does it look correct? How can you tell?

c.   Imagine that you made up 20 new $x \rightarrow y$ pairs. Where do you think their points would lie if you added them to the graph?

3-20.   In the same window that contains the data points, graph the algebraic equation for
          the pattern from problem 3-18.

          a.   What do you notice? Why did that happen?

          b.   Charles wonders about connecting the points
                 of the "Big Cs" data. When the points are
                 connected with an unbroken line or curve,
                 the graph is called **continuous**. If the graph
                 of the tile pattern is continuous, what does
                 that suggest about the tile pattern? Explain.

          c.   Jessica prefers to keep the graph of the tile-pattern data as separate points.
                 This is called a **discrete** graph. Why might a discrete graph be appropriate for
                 this data?

3-21.   If necessary, re-enter your data from the "Big Cs" pattern into your grapher. Re-
          enter the rule you found in problem 3-18 and graph the data and rule in the same
          window.

          For the following problems, **justify** your conclusions with the *graph*, the *rule*, and
          the *figure* (whenever practical). Your teacher may ask your team to present your
          solution to one of these problems. Be sure to justify your ideas using all three
          representations.

          a.   Frangelica thinks that Figure 6 in the "Big Cs" pattern has 40 tiles. Decide
                 with your team whether she is correct and **justify** your answer by using the
                 rule, drawing Figure 6, and adding the point to your graph of the data. Be
                 prepared to show these three different ways to **justify** your conclusion.

          b.   Giovanni thinks that the point (16, 99) belongs in the table for the "Big Cs"
                 pattern. Decide with your team whether he is correct and **justify** your
                 conclusion by examining the graph and the rule.

          c.   Jeremiah is excited because he has found another
                 rule for the "Big Cs" pattern! He thinks that
                 $y = x + 8$ also works. Prove or disprove Jeremiah's
                 claim. Be prepared to convince the class that your
                 conclusion is correct.

          d.   LaTanya has been thinking hard and has found
                 another rule for the same pattern! She is sure that
                 $y = 3(2x + 1)$ is also correct. Prove or disprove
                 LaTanya's position in as many ways as you can.

3-22.   Look back at the prediction you made in problem 3-18 for Figure 100 in the "Big
          Cs" pattern. Decide now if your prediction was correct and be ready to defend your
          position with all of the math tools you have.

METHODS AND MEANINGS

Discrete and Continuous Relationships

When a graph of data is limited to a set of separate, non-connected points, that relationship is called **discrete**. For example, consider the relationship between the number of bicycles parked at your school and the number of bicycle wheels. If there is one bicycle, it has two wheels. Two bicycles have four wheels, while three bicycles have six wheels. However, there cannot be 1.3 or 2.9 bicycles. Therefore, this data is limited because the number of bicycles must be a whole number, such as 0, 1, 2, 3, and so on.

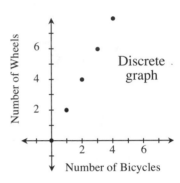

When graphed, a discrete relationship looks like a collection of unconnected points. See the example of a discrete graph above.

When a set of data is not confined to separate points and instead consists of connected points, the data is called **continuous**. "John's Giant Redwood," problem 3-10, is an example of a continuous situation because even though the table focused on integer values of years (1, 2, 3, etc.), the tree still grows between these values of time. Therefore, the tree has a height at any non-negative value of time (such as 1.1 years after it is planted).

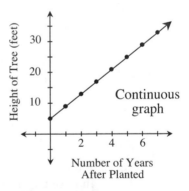

When the data for a continuous relationship is graphed, its points are connected to show that the relationship also holds true for all of the points between the table values. See the example of a continuous graph above.

Note: In this course, tile patterns will represent elements of continuous relationships and will be graphed with a continuous line or curve.

3-23.   On your paper, write the equation represented at right. Simplify as much as possible and then solve for x.

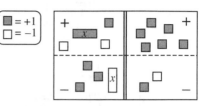

3-24.   Find the value of x that makes each equation below true.

a. $x + 7 = 2$

b. $-5 = \frac{1}{2}x$

c. $3x = -45$

d. $2 = -x$

e. $-5 = \frac{x}{2}$

f. $x^2 = 9$ (*all* possible values for x)

3-25.   For the following equations, draw a picture of the tiles on an equation mat, simplify, and solve for the variable. Record your work.

a. $3c - 7 = -c + 1$

b. $-2 + 3x = 2x + 6 + x$

3-26.   Solve this problem using Guess and Check. Write your solution in a sentence.

West High School's population is 250 students fewer than twice the population of East High School. The two schools have a total of 2858 students. How many students attend East High School?

3-27.   Solve the following problems using the order of operations. Show your steps. Verify your answers with your calculator.

a. $(-4)(-2) - 6(2 - 5)$

b. $23 - (17 - 3 \cdot 4)^2 + 6$

c. $14(2 + 3 - 2 \cdot 2) \div (4^2 - 3^2)$

d. $12.7 - 18.5 + 15 + 6.3 - 1 + 28.5$

3-28.   Copy the table below onto your paper and use your pattern skills to complete it.

IN (x)	2	10	0	7	–3		–10	100	x
OUT (y)	–6	–30	0			15			

    a.   Explain in words what is done to the input value, x, to produce the output value, y.

    b.   Write the process you described in part (a) in algebraic symbols.

3-29.   Write the equation represented in the equation mat at right.

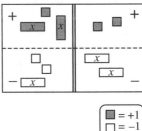

    a.   Simplify as much as possible and solve for x.

    b.   Evaluate both the left side and the right side using your solution from part (a). Remember that if your solution is correct, both sides should have the same value.

3-30.   For the following equations, draw a picture of the tiles in an equation mat, use "legal" moves to simplify, and solve for the variable. Record your work.

    a. $-3x + 7 = -x - 1$ b. $1 - 2p + 5 = 4p + 6$

3-31.   Combine like terms in each part below.

    a.   Liha has three x^2-tiles, two x-tiles, and eight unit tiles, while Makulata has five x^2-tiles and two unit tiles. At the end of class, they put their pieces together to give to Ms. Singh. Write an algebraic expression for each student's tiles and find the sum of their pieces.

    b.   Simplify the expression $4x + 6x^2 - 11x + 2 + x^2 - 19$.

    c.   Write the length of the line below as a sum. Then combine like terms.

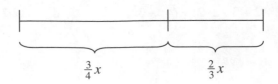

3.1.4 How should I graph?

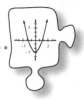

Completing Tables and Drawing Graphs

In Lesson 3.1.3, you used a graphing tool to represent all of the $x \rightarrow y$ pairs that follow a particular rule. Today you will learn how to make your own graphs for rules and how to recognize patterns that occur in graphs.

3-32.   CLASS GRAPH

Your teacher will give your team some x-values. For each x-value, calculate the corresponding y-value that fits the rule $y = -5x + 12$. Then mark the point you have calculated on the class graph.

3-33.   Use the rule $y = 2x + 1$ to complete parts (a) through (c) below.

a.   Make a table like the one below and use the rule provided above to complete it.

IN (x)	−4	−3	−2	−1	0	1	2	3	4
OUT (y)									

b.   Examine the numbers in the table. What are the greatest x- and y-values in the table? What are the smallest x- and y-values? Use this information to set up x- and y-axes that are scaled appropriately.

c.   Plot and connect the points on a graph. Be sure to label your axes and write numbers to indicate scale.

3-34.   Calculate the y-values for the rule $y = -3x + 1$ and complete the table below.

IN (x)	−4	−3	−2	−1	0	1	2	3	4
OUT (y)									

a.   Examine the x- and y-values in the table. Is it possible to use the same set of axes as problem 3-33? If so, graph and connect these points on the axes from problem 3-33. If not, plot and connect the points on a new set of axes.

b.   What does your graph look like? Describe the result.

c.   How is this graph similar to the graph in problem 3-33? How is it different?

3-35.   Calculate the *y*-values for the rule $y = x^2$ and complete the table below.

IN (x)	−4	−3	−2	−1	$-\frac{1}{2}$	0	$\frac{1}{2}$	1	2	3	4
OUT (y)											

a.   Examine the *x*- and *y*-values in the table. Use this information to set up a new set of *x*- and *y*-axes that are scaled appropriately. Plot and connect the points on your graph, and then label your graph with its rule.

b.   This graph is an example of a **parabola**. Read about parabolas in the Math Notes box below. Where is the vertex of the parabola you graphed in part (a)?

METHODS AND MEANINGS

MATH NOTES

Parabolas

One kind of graph you will study in this class is called a **parabola**. Two examples of parabolas are graphed at right. Note that parabolas are smooth "U" shapes, not pointy "V" shapes.

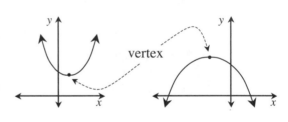

The point where a parabola turns (the highest or lowest point) is called the **vertex**.

3-36.   Complete a table like the one provided in problem 3-33 for the rule $y = x + 2$. Plot and connect the points on graph paper. Be sure to label the axes and include the scale.

Algebra Connections

3-37.   Use your pattern skills to copy and complete the table below.

IN (x)	2	10	6	7	−3		−10	100	x
OUT (y)	5	21	13			−15			

a.   Explain in words what is being done to the input value, x, to produce the output value, y.

b.   Write the process you described in part (a) in algebraic symbols.

3-38.   For the following equations, draw a picture of the tiles in an equation mat like the one shown at right. Then use "legal" moves to simplify and solve for the variable. Record your work.

a. $-2 + x = -x + 2$

b. $2 + 3x = x + 7$

3-39.   Evaluate each expression below.

a.   For $y = 5 + 8x$ when $x = 4$, what does y equal?

b.   For $a = 3 - 5c$ when $c = -0.5$, what does a equal?

c.   For $n = 2d^2 - 5$ when $d = -2$, what does n equal?

d.   For $v = -3(r - 3)$ when $r = -1$, what does v equal?

3-40.   Peggy Sue decided to enter her famous "5-Alarm Chili" at her local chili-cooking contest. Normally, she needs five tomatoes to make enough chili for her family of seven.

a.   How many tomatoes should she expect to use to make her famous recipe for 100 people?

b.   When she gets to the contest, she realizes that she only packed 58 tomatoes. How many people can she expect to feed?

3.1.5 How can I graph it?

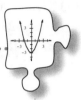

Graphs, Tables, and Rules

In Lesson 3.1.4, you practiced setting up the correct axes to graph data from a table. Today you will graph a rule by first making a table, and then by plotting the points from your table on a graph. You will also continue to find patterns in tables and graphs.

3-41.   SILENT BOARD GAME

Your teacher will put an incomplete $x \to y$ table on the board or overhead. Try to find the pattern (rule) that gets each y-value from its x-value. Find and write the rule for the pattern you find.

3-42.   GOOD TIPPER

Mr. Wallis needs your help. He is planning on taking his new girlfriend out to dinner and wants to be prepared to give a tip at the end of the meal. He knows that with any miscalculation, he may leave too little or too much, which might change her view of him and jeopardize their relationship. Therefore, he would like to create a "tip table" that would help him quickly determine how much tip to leave.

a.   Create a table like the one shown below. What are reasonable values of x? Mr. Wallis needs a tip table that will help him quickly determine a tip for a bill that may occur after a nice dinner for two. Discuss this with your team and then choose eight values for x.

Dinner Bill (in dollars)								
Amount of Tip (in dollars)								

b.   Mr. Wallis is planning to leave a 15% tip. That means that for a bill of $10, he would leave a $1.50 tip. Determine the tip for all of the values in your table from part (a). This is Mr. Wallis's tip table.

c.   Use the tip table to estimate the tip quickly if the bill is $36. What if the bill is $52.48?

Problem continues on next page →

Algebra Connections

3-42.   *Problem continued from previous page.*

d.   Mr. Wallis is worried that he may not be able to quickly estimate using his table for unusual amounts, such as $52.48. He would like a graph to help him determine a 15% tip for *all possible* dollar amounts between $10 and $100. With your team, determine how to set up axes and then graph the points from the tip table. Use the questions below to help guide your discussion.

- Should the tip be graphed on the *x*-axis or the *y*-axis? Read the Math Notes box for this lesson about **dependent** and **independent variables** to help you decide.

- Which quadrants are useful for this graph? Why?

- What are the greatest and smallest values of *x* and *y* that must fit on the graph? How can you scale your axes to create the most effective graph for Mr. Wallis?

e.   Use your tip graph from part (d) to test your estimations in part (c). Which representation (table or graph) helped to find the most accurate tip? Which was easiest to use? Explain.

3-43.   ONE OF THESE POINTS IS NOT LIKE THE OTHERS

a.   Plot and connect the points in the table below.

IN (x)	−2	4	1	6	−5	0
OUT (y)	−6	−2	−3	2	−9	−4

b.   Identify the point that does not appear to fit the pattern.

c.   Correct the point found in part (b) above so it fits the pattern.

3-44.   Copy and complete the table below for the rule $y = \frac{1}{2}x + 6$.

IN (x)	−4	−3	−2	−1	0	1	2	3	4
OUT (y)									

a.   Graph and connect the points from your table on graph paper. Remember to label the graph with its rule.

b.   Does the point (10, 12) lie on this graph? How can you tell?

METHODS AND MEANINGS

Independent and Dependent Variables

When one quantity (such as the height of a redwood tree) depends on another (such as the number of years after the tree was planted), it is called a **dependent variable**. That means its value is determined by the value of another variable. The dependent variable is usually graphed on the *y*-axis.

If a quantity, such as time, does not depend on another variable, it is referred to as the **independent variable**, which is graphed on the *x*-axis.

For example, in problem 3-42, you compared the amount of a dinner bill with the amount of a tip. In this case, the tip depends on the amount of the dinner bill. Therefore, the tip is the dependent variable, while the dinner bill is the independent variable.

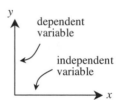

Review & Preview

3-45. Create an *x*→*y* table using at least eight points from the graph at right. Write the rule for the pattern in the table.

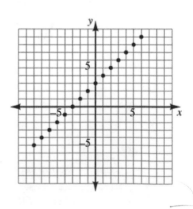

3-46. For each rule below, make a table of *x*- and *y*-values. Then graph and connect the points from your table on graph paper using an appropriate scale. Label each graph with its equation.

a. $y = -2x + 7$

b. $y = 11x$

3-47. On graph paper, draw Figure 0 and Figure 4 for
the pattern at right.

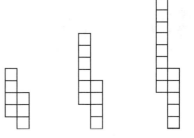

Figure 1   Figure 2   Figure 3

a. Represent the number of tiles in each
figure in an $x \to y$ table. Let x be the
figure number and y be the total
number of tiles.

b. Use the table to graph the pattern.

c. Without drawing Figure 5, predict
where its point would lie on the graph.
Justify your prediction.

3-48. Use your pattern skills to copy and complete the table below.

IN (x)	2	10	6	7	−3		−10	100	x
OUT (y)	2	6	4			15			

a. Explain in words what is done to the input value, x, to produce the output
value, y.

b. Write the process you described in part (a) in algebraic symbols.

3-49. For the following equations, simplify and solve for the variable. Record your work.

a. $2x - 7 = -2x + 1$

b. $-2x - 5 = -4x + 2$

3.1.6 What makes a complete graph?

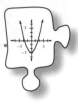

Complete Graphs

Over the past several days you have learned to make graphs from tables, then graphs from rules.
Today you will continue to study graphs by deciding what needs to go into a graph to make it
complete.

3-50. **SILENT BOARD GAME**

Your teacher will put an incomplete $x \rightarrow y$ table on the board or overhead. Try to find
the pattern (rule) that gets each y-value from its x-value. Find and write the rule for
the pattern you find.

3-51. Examine the following
graphs and answer the
question associated with
each one. What do you
notice?

Note: This stoplight icon will appear
periodically throughout the text.
Problems with this icon display
common errors that can be made. Be
sure not to make the same mistakes
yourself!

a. What are the
coordinates of
point A?

b. Where will the
line be when
$x = 5$?

c. What is t
when $k = 1$?

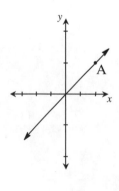

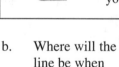
No y value

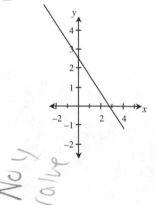

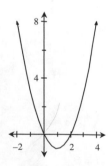

3-52. On your own graph paper, graph $y = -3x + 2$. Then, as a class,
decide what needs to be included to make a graph complete. Copy
the qualities of a complete graph as a Learning Log entry. Title this
entry "Qualities of a Complete Graph" and include today's date.

3-53.   Make your own complete graph for each of the following rules:

    a. $y = -x + 1$ b. $y = 0.5x + 2$ c. $y = x^2 - 4$

3-54.   Examine the graphs from problem 3-53.

    a.   How are they different? Be as specific as you can.

    b.   Label the (x, y) coordinates on each of your graphs for the point where each graph crosses the y-axis. These points are called **y-intercepts**.

    c.   Label the (x, y) coordinates on each of your graphs for the point or points where each graph crosses the x-axis. These points are called **x-intercepts**.

3-55.   Complete a table for the rule $y = x^2 + 2$. Then plot and connect the points on a graph. Be sure to label the axes and include the scale. Use negative, positive, and zero values for x.

3-56.   Complete a table for the rule $y = -x + 3$. Then plot and connect the points on a graph. Be sure to label the axes and include the scale. Use negative, positive, and zero values for x.

3-57.   On graph paper, draw Figure 0 and Figure 4 for the pattern below. Describe Figure 100 in detail.

    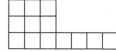   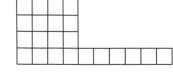

        Figure 1   Figure 2   Figure 3

3-58.   Write an expression that represents the perimeter of the shape built with algebra tiles at right. Then find the perimeter if $x = 3$ units and $y = 7$ units.

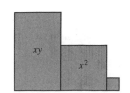

3-59.   For the following equations, draw a picture of the tiles on an equation mat, use "legal" moves to simplify, and then solve for the variable. Record your work.

    a. $3x - 7 + 3 + 2x = -x + 2$ b. $-2k + 5 + (-k) + 1 = 0$

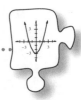

3.1.7 What is wrong with this graph?

Identifying Common Graphing Errors

In this chapter you have used rules to find *y*-values to go with *x*-values in tables. Then you graphed the *x*→*y* pairs you found. Today you will be examining how rules, tables, and graphs can be used to represent new situations. You will also learn how to avoid common graphing errors. As you work, revisit the following questions:

What *x*-values should go in my table?

How can I correct this error?

How should I scale my graph?

3-60.   Ms. Cai's class is studying the "dented square" shape shown at right. This shape is formed by removing a square with side length 1 from a larger square. Her students decided to let *x* represent the side length of the large square and *y* represent the perimeter of the entire shape.

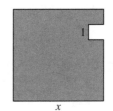

a.   What is the perimeter of the "dented square?" That is, what rule could help you find the perimeter for any value of *x*?

b.   Make a table for the rule Ms. Cai's class found. Make sure the *x*-values you use are appropriate for this situation. What are the possible *x*-values?

c.   Make a graph from your *x*→*y* table.

d.   Do you think the points on your graph should be connected? **Justify** your answer.

3-61.   GOOFY GRAPHING

Now Ms. Cai's class is studying a tile pattern. Her students
decided to represent the pattern with the $x \rightarrow y$ table at right.

x	y
2	8
3	17
5	35
6	44

a.   Ms. Cai wants her class to graph the data in this table.
Write (x, y) coordinates for each point that needs to be
plotted.

b.   When Ms. Cai's students started to graph this data, they made mistakes right
from the beginning. The diagrams below show how some of Ms. Cai's
students set up their axes. Your teacher will assign your team one of these
diagrams.

Your Task: Find all of the mistakes the students made in
setting up the graph your teacher assigns you. (There may be
more than one mistake in each graph!) Explain why this is an
incorrect way to set up a graph, or why this is not the best way
to set up the graph for this problem. Be ready to present your
team's ideas to the class.

i.

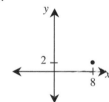

ii.

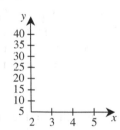

iii.

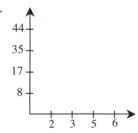

iv.

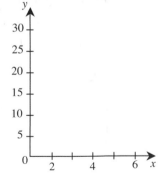

3-62. Sheila is in Ms. Cai's class. She noticed that the graph of the perimeter for the "dented square" in problem 3-60 was a line. "I wonder what the graph of its area looks like," she said to her teammates.

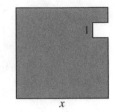

a. Write an equation for the area of the "dented square" if x represents the length of the large square and y represents the area of the square.

b. On graph paper, graph the rule you found for the area in part (a). Why does a 1ˢᵗ-quadrant graph make sense for this situation?

c. Explain to Sheila what the graph of the area looks like.

d. Use the graph to approximate x when the area of the shape is 20 square units.

3-63. Looking back at the mistakes Ms. Cai's students made, write a Learning Log entry that includes a checklist of errors you should make sure to avoid when setting up a graph. Title this entry "Graphing Errors" and label it with today's date.

3-64. The amount of money Theresa earns at her job varies directly with the number of hours she works. This means that her earnings are proportional with the time she works. She knows that when she works 2 hours, she earns $12. When she works 3 hours, she earns $18.

a. How much do you predict Theresa would earn after working 5 hours?

b. Explain how can you find Theresa's earnings (y) if she works for x hours.

c. Create a complete graph of Theresa's earnings over time. Should the graph be continuous or discrete? Explain your decision.

3-65.   ONE OF THESE POINTS IS NOT LIKE THE OTHERS, Part Two

a.   Plot and connect the points listed in the table below.

IN (x)	−2	4	1	−4	0	3	−3	2
OUT (y)	0	12	−3	12	−4	5	−2	0

b.   Identify the point that does not fit the pattern.

c.   What shape does the graph appear to make?

d.   Correct the point identified in part (b) so it fits the pattern. Write the points in (x, y) notation.

3-66.   For each rule below, make a table of x- and y-values and then graph the rule on graph paper. Label each graph with its equation.

a. $y = x^2$ b. $y = -x^2$

c.   Compare the graphs. What do you notice?

d.   For the graph of $y = x^2$, estimate the x-values corresponding to $y = 5$.

e.   For the graph of $y = -x^2$, estimate the x-values corresponding to $y = -10$.

3-67.   Paris is trying to solve the equation $3x^2 - (2x - 4) = 3 + 3x^2 + 1$. Her work is partially recorded below. Copy her table and fill in her missing work to solve for x.

Left Expression	Right Expression	Explanation
$3x^2 - (2x - 4)$	$3 + 3x^2 + 1$	Starting expressions.
$3x^2 - 2x + 4$	$3 + 3x^2 + 1$	
		Remove $3x^2$ from both sides.
$-2x$	0	
		Divide both sides by −2.

3-68.   Copy and complete each of the Diamond Problems below. The pattern used in the Diamond Problems is shown at right.

a.   b.   c.   d.

3.2.1 How can I check my answer?

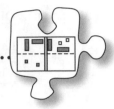

Solving Equations and Testing the Solution

In Section 2.2, you learned to solve equations on an equation mat. In this section, you will practice your equation-solving skills while adding a new element: You will check your answer to make sure it is correct.

While solving equations in this lesson, keep these focus questions in mind:

What is your goal?

How can you start?

How can you simplify?

Can you get *x* alone?

3-69.   For this activity, share algebra tiles and an equation mat with your partner.

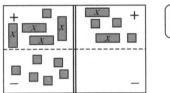

a.   Start by setting up your equation mat as shown at right. Write the equation on your paper.

b.   Next, solve the equation on your equation mat one step at a time. Every time you make a step, record your work in two ways:

- Record the step that was taken to get from the old equation to the new equation.

- Write a new equation that represents the tiles in the equation mat.

c.   With your partner, find a way to check if your solution is correct.

3-70.   WHAT IS A SOLUTION?

In this lesson you have found solutions to several algebraic equations. But what exactly is a solution? Answer each of these questions with your study team, but *do not use algebra tiles*. Be prepared to **justify** your answers!

a.   Preston solved the equation $3x - 2 = 8$ and got the solution $x = 100$. Is he correct? How do you know?

b.   Edwin solved the equation $2x + 3 - x = 3x - 5$ and got the solution $x = 4$. Is he correct? How do you know?

c.   With your partner, discuss what you think a solution to an equation is. Write down a description of what you and your partner agree on.

3-71.   Work with your partner to solve these equations, being careful to record your work. After solving each equation, be sure to check your solution, if possible.

a. $3x + 4 = x + 8$

b. $4 - 2y = y + 10$

c. $5x + 4 - 2x = -(x + 8)$

d. $-2 - 3k - 2 = -2k + 8 - k$

3-72.   IS THERE ANOTHER WAY?

Compare your solution to part (c) of problem 3-71 with the solution that another pair of students got. Did both solutions involve the same steps? Were the steps used in the same order? If not, copy the other pair's solution onto your paper. If both pairs used the same steps in the same order to solve the equation, come up with a different way to solve the problem and record it on your paper.

 METHODS AND MEANINGS

MATH NOTES

Complete Graph

A complete graph has the following components:

- x-axis and y-axis labeled, clearly showing the scale.
- Equation of the graph near the line or curve.
- Line or curve extended as far as possible on the graph.
- Coordinates of special points stated in (x, y) format.

x	–1	0	1	2	3
y	6	4	2	0	–2

Tables can be formatted horizontally, like the one above, or vertically, as shown below.

x	y
–1	6
0	4
1	2
2	0
3	–2
4	–4

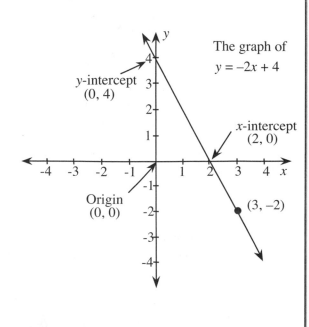

Throughout this course, you will continue to graph lines and other curves. Be sure to label your graphs appropriately.

3-73. For the following equations, solve for x. Be sure to check your answer, if possible. Show all work.

a. $3x + 7 = -x - 1$

b. $1 - 2x - 5 = 4x + 2$

c. $-3x = x - (6 - 2x)$

d. $2x + 3 = -2x + 5$

3-74. For the rule $y = -2x + 1$, calculate the y-values that complete the table below.

IN (x)	−4	−3	−2	−1	0	1	2	3	4
OUT (y)									

a. Graph your rule on a set of axes. Be sure to create a <u>complete</u> graph. If necessary, see the Math Notes box for this lesson to review what makes a graph complete.

b. Describe your resulting graph. What does your graph look like?

3-75. Simplify each expression below.

a. $4x + 7 + 3y - (1 + 3y + 2x)$

b. $16x^2 - 4x + 5 - (16x^2 - 8x) + 1$

c. $(32x - 7y) - (28x - 11y)$

d. $y + 2 + 2y + 2 + 2y - 2x + y$

3-76. Burgers-o-rama is the best hamburger place in town. The owner, Ms. Hamm, buys two 5-pound packages of meat for $27.50. Use proportional reasoning to determine the information below. Be sure to explain your answer and organize your reasoning.

a. What should Ms. Hamm pay for 25 pounds of meat?

b. How many pounds can Ms. Hamm buy for $55.00?

3-77. I'm thinking of a number. When I double my number, subtract five, and then add my original number, I get one. What's my number?

3.2.2 How many solutions are there?

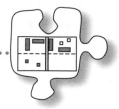

Determining the Number of Solutions

In Lesson 3.2.1, you reviewed your equation-solving skills to remember how to find a solution to an equation. But do all equations have a solution? And how can you tell if an equation does not have a solution?

Today you will continue to practice solving equations and will continue to investigate the meaning of a solution.

3-78.   GUESS MY NUMBER

Today you will play the "Guess My Number" game. You will need a pencil and a piece of paper. Your teacher will think of a number and tell you some information about that number. You will try to figure out what your teacher's number is. (You can use your paper if it helps.) When you think you know what the mystery number is, sit silently and do not tell anyone else. This will give others a chance to think about it.

3-79.   Use the process your teacher illustrated to analyze Game #3 of "Guess My Number" algebraically.

a.   Start by writing an equation that expresses the information in the game.

b.   Solve your equation, writing down each step as you go. When you reach a conclusion, discuss how it agrees with the answer for Game #3 you found as a class.

c.   Repeat this process to analyze Game #4 algebraically.

3-80.   How many solutions does each equation below have? To answer this question, solve these equations, recording all of your steps as you go along. Check your solution, if possible.

a. $4x - 5 = x - 5 + 3x$

b. $-x - 4x - 7 = -2x + 5$

c. $3 + 5x - 4 - 7x = 2x - 4x + 1$

d. $4x - (-3x + 2) = 7x - 2$

e. $x + 3 + x + 3 = -(x + 4) + (3x - 2)$

f. $x - 5 - (2 - x) = -3$

3-81.   Since the equation $x + 2 = x + 2$ is true for all values of x, it is **always true**. However, since the equation $x + 2 = 5$ is only true when $x = 3$, then it can be said that it is **sometimes true**. This means that it is not true for all cases, but there is at least one case for which it is true. Finally, the equation $x + 3 = x + 2$ is **never true**, regardless of the value of x.

For each equation in problem 3-80, determine if it is always true, sometimes true, or never true.

3-82.   Create your own "Guess My Number" game like the ones you worked with in class today. Start it with, "I'm thinking of a number that..." Make sure it is a game you know the answer to! Write the equation and solve it.

3-83.   Draw Figure 0 and Figure 4 for the pattern below on graph paper.

a.   Represent the number of tiles in each figure with:

- An $x \to y$ table.
- An algebraic rule.
- A graph.

Figure 1   Figure 2   Figure 3

b.   Without drawing Figure 5, predict where its point would lie on the graph. **Justify** your prediction.

3-84.   For the following equations, simplify and solve for the variable. Then state if the equation is always, sometimes, or never true. Show all work and check your solution, if possible.

a. $-2 + x = -x + 2$ b. $-(x - 1) = -x - 2$

c. $2 + 3x = 3x + 2$ d. $-(-x + 6) = -3x$

3-85.   For each equation, a possible solution is given. Check to see if the given solution is correct.

a.   If $3x + 7 = x - 1$, then does $x = -4$?

b.   If $-2x - 4 = -4x + 3$, then does $x = 3$?

c.   If $-3x + 5 + 5x - 1 = 0$, then does $x = 2$?

d.   If $-(x - 1) = 4x - 5 - 3x$, then does $x = 3$?

Algebra Connections

3-86.   Examine the graph at right.

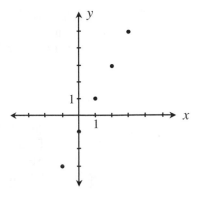

a.   Use the graph to complete the table:

IN (x)					
OUT (y)					

b.   Use the graph to find the rule:

$$y = \underline{\qquad}$$

3.2.3 How can I use my equation-solving skills?

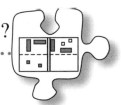

Solving Equations to Solve Problems

In the last two lessons you have practiced solving equations. In this lesson you will **apply** your equation-solving skills to the patterns you found at the beginning of this chapter. As you solve these problems, keep these questions in mind:

How can you simplify?

Is there more than one way to solve?

Can you get *x* alone?

How can you check your solution?

3-87.   In Lesson 3.1.3, you investigated the "Big Cs" pattern of tiles, shown at right. The rule you found for this pattern was $y = 6x + 3$, where *x* represented the figure number and *y* represented the number of tiles in the figure.

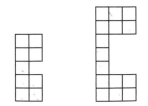
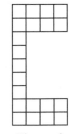

Figure 1   Figure 2   Figure 3

Penelope wants to know how many tiles will be in Figure 50. How can you determine this? Write out in words what you would need to do with your rule to answer her question. Then answer Penelope's question: How many tiles will be in Figure 50?

3-88. Lew wants to **reverse** the process: He says he has a "Big Cs" figure made up of 45 tiles. He wants to know which figure number this pattern is.

a. In the rule $y = 6x + 3$, which variable must equal 45 to solve Lew's problem?

b. Write an equation you could use to solve Lew's problem. Then solve your equation, recording all of your steps. Which "Big Cs" figure is made up of 45 tiles?

c. How can you check your answer to be sure it is correct? Check your solution.

3-89. Norm says he has a "Big Cs" pattern made up of 84 tiles. He wants to know which figure number this pattern is. Write and solve an equation as you did in problem 3-88. Does your solution make sense? Why or why not?

3-90. For the following equations, solve for x. Record your work and check your solution.

a. $\frac{1}{2}x - 2 = x - 4$

b. $8 - 0.25x = 0.5x + 2$

c. $x + 2 - 0.5x = 1 + 0.5x + 1$

d. $7x - 0.15 = 2x + 0.6$

3-91. Can an equation be solved using a graph? Consider this as you answer the questions below.

a. Solve the equation $5 = 1.6x + 1$. Check your solution.

b. Complete a table for the rule $y = 1.6x + 1$. Then, on graph paper, graph the line.

c. Use the graph from part (b) to find x when $y = 5$. Did you get the same result as in part (a)?

3-92.   Evaluate the expressions below for the given values.

a. $30 - 2x$ for $x = -6$

b. $x^2 + 2x$ for $x = -3$

c. $-\frac{1}{2}x + 9$ for $x = -6$

d. $\sqrt{k}$ for $k = 9$

3-93.   For the following equations, solve for x. Check your solution, if possible. Record your work.

a. $3x - 7 = 3x + 1$

b. $-2x - 5 = -4x + 2$

c. $2 + 3x = x + 2 + 2x$

d. $-(x - 2) = x + 2$

3-94.   The length of a rectangle is three centimeters more than twice the width. The perimeter is 78 centimeters. Use Guess and Check to find out how long and how wide the rectangle is.

3-95.   Use a diagram of the equation mat or some other method to explain why $-(x - 3) = -x + 3$.

3-96.   For the rule $y = 4 - x^2$, calculate the y-values that complete the table below. The first value is given for you.

IN (x)	−3	−2	−1	0	1	2	3
OUT (y)	−5						

a.   Create an x-axis and a y-axis and label your units. Plot and connect the points on your graph, and then label your graph with its rule.

b.   What does your graph look like?

3.2.4 How can I use my equation-solving skills?

More Solving Equations to Solve Problems

3-97.   JOHN'S GIANT REDWOOD, Part Two

In Lesson 3.1.2, you looked at how a tree increases in height as it gets older. Review the data below and, if possible, find your work from problem 3-10.

Number of Years after Planting	3	4	5
Height of Tree (in feet)	17	21	25

a.   Assuming the tree continues to grow at a constant rate, find a rule for the height of the tree using x and y.

b.   In your rule, what real-world quantity does x stand for? What real-world quantity does y stand for?

c.   John wants to know how tall the tree will be when it is 20 years after planting. Use your rule to answer his question.

d.   The tallest tree in the world, in Montgomery Woods State Reserve in California, is 367 feet high. John wants to know how long it would take for his tree to get that tall if it keeps growing at the same rate. Write and solve an equation you could use to answer John's question. Be sure to check your solution.

e.   Did you use algebra tiles to solve the equation in part (d)? Would it be easy to use algebra tiles to do so? Why or why not?

3-98.   For the following equations, solve for the given variable. Record your work and check the solution, if possible.

a. $75c - 300 = 25c + 200$ b. $26y - 4 - 11y = 15y + 6$

c. $-\frac{1}{2}x = 6$ d. $0.8 - 2t = 1 - 3t$

3-99.   MR. WALLIS IS BACK!

After much consideration, Mr. Wallis decided to use the tip table below to help him estimate what a 15% tip would be for various costs of dinner.

Cost of Dinner	$10	$20	$30	$35	$40	$45	$50	$100
Amount of Tip	$1.50	$3	$4.50	$5.25	$6	$6.75	$7.50	$15

a.   Find a rule for his table. That is, find a rule that calculates the amount of tip (y) based on the cost of the dinner (x). How did you find your rule?

b.   During the date, Mr. Wallis was so distracted that he forgot to write down the cost of the meal in his checkbook. All he remembers is that he left a $9 tip. What was the original cost of the meal before he paid the tip? Use your equation from part (a) to answer this question. Show all work.

c.   What was the total cost of the meal?

MᴇTHODS AND Mᴇᴀɴɪɴɢꜱ

MATH NOTES

Solutions to an Equation with One Variable

A **solution** to an equation gives a value of the variable that makes the equation true. For example, when 5 is substituted for x in the equation at right, both sides of the equation are equal. So $x = 5$ is a solution to this equation.

$$4x - 2 = 3x + 3$$
$$4(5) - 2 = 3(5) + 3$$
$$18 = 18$$

An equation can have more than one solution, or it may have no solution. Consider the examples at right.

Notice that no matter what the value of x is, the left side of the first equation will never equal the right side. Therefore, we say that $x + 2 = x + 6$ has **no solution**.

Equation with no solution:
$$x + 2 = x + 6$$

However, in the equation $x - 3 = x - 3$, no matter what value x has, the equation will always be true. So all numbers can make $x - 3 = x - 3$ true. Therefore, we say the solution for the equation $x - 3 = x - 3$ is **all numbers**.

Equation with infinite solutions:
$$x - 3 = x - 3$$

3-100. Copy and complete each of the Diamond Problems below. The pattern used in the Diamond Problems is shown at right.

a.

b.

c.

d.

3-101. The science club is selling homemade cookies to raise money for a field trip. They know that 12 dozen cookies uses 3 pounds of flour. Use proportional reasoning to determine the information below. Be sure to explain your answer and organize your reasoning.

a. How much flour is needed for 18 dozen cookies?

b. How many cookies can be made with 10 pounds of flour?

3-102. Simplify each of the following equations and solve for the variable. Show all work and check your solution, if possible.

a. $3x - 7 + 9 - 2x = x + 2$

b. $-2m + 8 + m + 1 = 0$

c. $2 = x + 6 - 2x$

d. $0.5p = p + 5$

3-103. Use your pattern-finding skills to copy and complete the table below.

IN (x)	1	2	3		5	6	8	12	24	x
OUT (y)	24	12		6	4.8	4		2		

a. Explain the pattern you found in your table. How are x and y related?

b. Write the rule you described in part (a) in algebraic symbols.

c. Use the points in your table to graph this rule on graph paper. Describe the resulting shape.

3-104. Translate each algebraic expression into ordinary words.

a. $5x - 3$

b. $2(x + y)$

c. $3 - (x + 5)$

Chapter 3 Closure What have I learned?

Reflection and Synthesis

The activities below offer you a chance to reflect on what you have learned during this chapter. As you work, look for concepts that you feel very comfortable with, ideas that you would like to learn more about, and topics you need more help with. Look for **connections** between ideas as well as **connections** with material you learned previously.

① TEAM BRAINSTORM

With your team, brainstorm a list for each of the following topics. Be as detailed as you can. How long can you make your list? Challenge yourselves. Be prepared to share your team's ideas with the class.

Topics: What have you studied in this chapter? What ideas and words were important in what you learned? Remember to be as detailed as you can.

Connections: What topics, ideas, and words that you learned *before* this chapter are **connected** to the new ideas in this chapter? Again, make your list as long as you can.

② MAKING CONNECTIONS

The following is a list of the vocabulary used in this chapter. The words that appear in bold are new to this chapter. Make sure that you are familiar with all of these words and know what they mean. Refer to the glossary or index for any words that you do not yet understand.

area	**continuous**	coordinates
dependent variable	**discrete**	equation
equation mat	evaluate	**figure number**
graph	**independent variable**	**input value** (*x*)
output value (*y*)	**parabola**	pattern
prediction	quadrant	**rule**
scale on axes	simplify	solution
variable	*x* →*y* **table**	*x*- and *y*-intercept

Make a concept map showing all of the **connections** you can find among the key words and ideas listed above. To show a **connection** between two words, draw a line between them and explain the **connection**, as shown in the example below. A word can be **connected** to any other word as long as there is a **justified connection**. For each key word or idea, provide a sketch that illustrates the idea (see the example below).

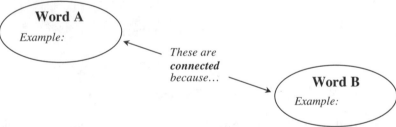

Your teacher may provide you with vocabulary cards to help you get started. If you use the cards to plan your concept map, be sure either to re-draw your concept map on your paper or to glue the vocabulary cards to a poster with all of the **connections** explained for others to see and understand.

While you are making your map, your team may think of related words or ideas that are not listed above. Be sure to include these ideas on your concept map.

③ SUMMARIZING MY UNDERSTANDING

This section gives you an opportunity to show what you know about certain math topics or ideas. Your teacher will give you directions for exactly how to do this. Your teacher may give you a "GO" page to work on. The "GO" stands for "Graphic Organizer," a tool you can use to organize your thoughts and communicate your ideas clearly.

④ **WHAT HAVE I LEARNED?**

This section will help you evaluate which types of problems you have seen with which you feel comfortable and those with which you need more help. This section appears at the end of every chapter to help you check your understanding. Even if your teacher does not assign this section, it is a good idea to try the problems and find out for yourself what you know and what you need to work on.

Solve each problem as completely as you can. The table at the end of the closure section has answers to these problems. It also tells you where you can find additional help and practice on problems like these.

CL 3-105. For the $x \rightarrow y$ table below, fill in the missing values and find the rule. Then find the zero of the rule (the input that makes the output zero).

IN (x)	−10	0	5	1	25	−6	8	−1.5	6	10
OUT (y)		3		5	53	−9				23

CL 3-106. One year ago, Josie moved into a new house and noticed a beautiful vine growing on the back fence. She recorded the data in the table below.

Weeks Since Josie Moved In	4	5	6
Height of Vine (in inches)	16	19	22

Assuming that the vine continues to grow at a constant rate:

a. How tall was the vine 7 weeks after Josie moved in?

b. How tall was the vine 3 weeks after Josie moved in?

c. How tall was the vine when Josie moved in? How do you know?

d. Predict how tall the vine was 19 weeks after Josie moved into her house. **Justify** your answer.

e. Predict when the vine reached the top of the garage (94 inches tall). How did you find your answer?

CL 3-107. Examine the tile pattern at right.

a. Draw Figure 1 and Figure 5.

b. Make an $x \rightarrow y$ table for the pattern.

c. Make a complete graph. Include points for Figures 0 through 5.

Figure 2   Figure 3   Figure 4

CL 3-108. Clifford is making a cake for his sister's birthday. The recipe calls for twice as much flour as sugar. It also calls for 20 ounces of ingredients other than flour and sugar. All the ingredients together total 80 ounces. How much flour does Clifford need?

CL 3-109. Simplify the expression $3x^2 - 5x - 4 + xy - (2xy + 2x^2)$. Then evaluate the result if $x = -1$ and $y = 6$.

CL 3-110. Follow the order of operations to simplify.

a. $6^2 - (5 - 4) + 2(8 - 2^2) \div 8$

b. $\frac{2(9-6)^2}{18}$

CL 3-111. Raphael had 5 hits in 7 at bats. If he continues this pattern, how many hits will he have in 210 at bats?

CL 3-112. Solve $6 - x - 3 = 4x - 12$ for x, recording your steps as you work.

CL 3-113. Make an $x \rightarrow y$ table from the points on the graph at right. Then write a rule for the table.

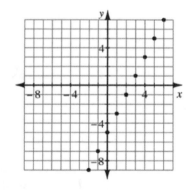

CL 3-114. Make an $x \rightarrow y$ table and complete graph for the equation $y = -2x + 5$.

CL 3-115. Jessica was solving an equation. After she finished simplifying, her result was $0 = 2$. This result confused her. Explain to Jessica what her result means. Explain your reasoning thoroughly.

CL 3-116. Check your answers using the table at the end of the closure section. Which problems do you feel confident about? Which problems were hard? Use the table to make a list of topics you need help on and a list of topics you need to practice more.

HOW AM I THINKING?

This course focuses on five different **Ways of Thinking**: reversing thinking, justifying, generalizing, making connections, and applying and extending understanding. These are some of the ways in which you think while trying to make sense of a concept or to solve a problem (even outside of math class). During this chapter, you have probably used each Way of Thinking multiple times without even realizing it!

This closure activity will focus on one of these Ways of Thinking: **generalizing**. Read the description of this Way of Thinking at right.

Think about the topics that you have learned during this chapter. When did you need to describe patterns? When did you draw a conclusion or make a **general** statement? You may want to flip through the chapter to refresh your memory about the problems that you have worked on. Discuss any ideas you have with the rest of the class.

Once your discussion is complete, examine some of the ways you have **generalized** as you answer the questions below.

a.   Examine the tile pattern below.

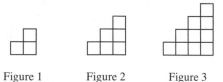

Figure 1   Figure 2   Figure 3

> **Generalizing**
>
> To generalize means to make a general statement or conclusion about something from partial evidence. You think this way when you describe patterns, because you are looking for a general statement that describes each term in the pattern. Often, a generalization is the answer to the question, "What is in common?" When you catch yourself thinking, "*I think this is always true…*", you are generalizing.
>
>

i.   Draw Figure 4 and Figure 5 on graph paper.

ii.   How do the figures appear to be growing? Make a **general** statement describing how all of the figures change to become the next figure in the pattern.

iii.   Sketch and describe Figure 100.

iv.   In **general**, what does each figure look like? That is, describe Figure *n*.

Continues on next page →

⑤   *Continued from previous page.*

b. During Section 3.2, you probably **generalized** about how to solve equations. For example, in Chapter 2, you solved equations with algebra tiles, such as those shown on the equation mat at right. However, during this chapter, you have solved some equations that cannot easily be expressed using algebra tiles. How? Because you **generalized** the process to include any type of linear equation, such as $8 - 0.25x = 0.5x + 2$ from problem 3-90. Consider this as you answer the questions below.

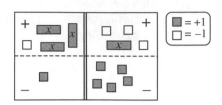

i. In **general**, what are some strategies you can use no matter how many x-tiles and unit tiles are placed on both sides of the equation?

ii. Use the general strategies you described in (*i*) above to solve the equation below. Show all work and check your solution.

$$\tfrac{1}{4}x - (3 - \tfrac{3}{4}x) = \tfrac{1}{2}x - 7$$

iii. Some equations have no solution. In **general**, describe how you know if an equation has no solution. Because you do not have a specific equation to solve, this description must help to describe all situations in which an equation has no solution. This is another example of a **generalization**.

c. Examine the data in the table below. Find a rule that describes how all of the x-values and y-values are related. Since this rule describes a **general** property that all of these points share, it is also an example of a **generalization**.

IN (x)	−10	0	5	1	25	−6	8	−1	6	10
OUT (y)	−26	4	19	7	79	−14	28	1	22	34

Answers and Support for Closure Activity #4
What Have I Learned?

Problem	Solution	Need Help?	More Practice
CL 3-105.	The missing y-values, in order, are: $-17, 13, 19, 1, 15$. The rule is $y = 2x + 3$.	Lesson 3.1.1	Problems 3-2, 3-3, 3-28, 3-37, 3-48, and 3-103
CL 3-106.	a. 25 inches b. 13 inches c. 4 inches d. 61 inches e. 30 weeks after Josie moved in	Lesson 3.1.2	Problems 3-10 and 3-97
CL 3-107.	a.	Section 3.1	Problems 3-1, 3-18, 3-47, 3-57, and 3-83

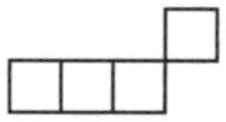

Figure 1

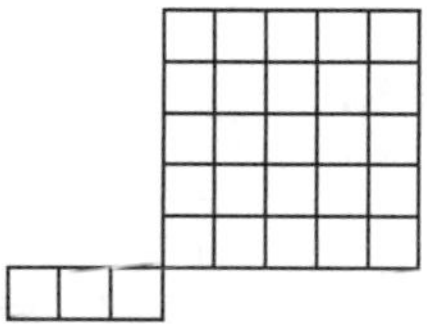

Figure 5

b.

x	1	2	3	4	5
y	4	7	12	19	28

c.

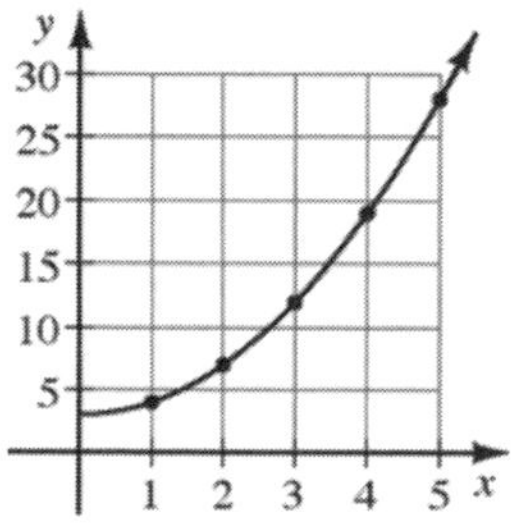

Note: In this course, tile patterns will represent elements of continuous relationships and will be graphed with a continuous line or curve.

Problem	Solution	Need Help?	More Practice
CL 3-108.	40 ounces	Lesson 2.1.7 Math Notes box	Problems 3-7, 3-26, 3-77, and 3-94
CL 3-109.	$x^2 - xy - 5x - 4$ $= (-1)^2 - (-1)(6) - 5(-1) - 4$ $= 8$	Lessons 2.1.1, 2.1.3, 2.1.5, and 2.1.6 Math Notes boxes	Problems 3-5, 3-14, 3-15, 3-31, 3-39, 3-75, and 3-92
CL 3-110.	a. 36 b. 1	Lesson 2.1.3 Math Notes box	Problems 3-16 and 3-27
CL 3-111.	150 hits	Lessons 2.2.1 and 2.2.3	Problems 3-17, 3-40, 3-64, 3-76, and 3-101
CL 3-112.	$x = 3$	Lesson 2.1.8 Math Notes box	Problems 3-24, 3-25, 3-30, 3-38, 3-49, 3-59, 3-73, 3-84, and 3-90
CL 3-113.	$\begin{array}{c\|c c c c c c c c c} x & -2 & -1 & 0 & 1 & 2 & 3 & 4 & 5 & 6 \\ \hline y & -9 & -7 & -5 & -3 & -1 & 1 & 3 & 5 & 7 \end{array}$ $y = 2x - 5$	Lesson 3.1.4	Problems 3-45 and 3-86
CL 3-114.	$\begin{array}{c\|c c c c c c c c} x & -3 & -2 & -1 & 0 & 1 & 2 & 3 & 4 \\ \hline y & 11 & 9 & 7 & 5 & 3 & 1 & -1 & -3 \end{array}$	Lesson 3.1.4, Lesson 3.2.1 Math Notes box	Problems 3-46, 3-55, 3-56, 3-66, 3-74, and 3-96
CL 3-115.	There is no solution for x in this equation.	Lesson 3.2.1, Lesson 3.2.4 Math Notes box	Problems 3-71, 3-80, and 3-93

CHAPTER 4　Multiple Representations

This chapter builds on the work you did in Chapters 2 and 3. The primary focus of Chapter 4 is to investigate the **connections** between the four representations of data: graphs, tables, patterns, and equations (also referred to as "rules"). You will also explore situations that can be represented by a line and study what it means when two lines intersect (cross each other). By the end of this chapter, you will know how to use graphs, tables, patterns, and rules to solve almost any problem involving lines.

In this chapter, you will learn:

> ➤ How to change any representation of data (such as a graph, pattern, rule, or table) to any of the other representations.

> ➤ How to write an equation from a word problem.

> ➤ How to find the point where two lines intersect.

> ➤ How to use the connections between graphs, tables, rules, and patterns to solve problems.

Guiding Questions

Think about these questions throughout this chapter:

What is the connection?

Is there a pattern?

How many different ways can it be represented?

How does the pattern show up in the rule, table, and graph?

How does the pattern grow?

Chapter Outline

Section 4.1　In this section, you will shift between different representations of linear patterns by using the web shown at left. By finding connections between each representation, you and your team will find ways to change from one representation to each of the other three representations.

Section 4.2　Section 4.2 will start by examining word problems in which two amounts are compared. You will use your knowledge of graphs and rules to write equations for word problems. Then, using the equation mat, you will solve a linear equation to determine where two lines cross. A final challenge will bring together word problems and the representations in the web.

4.1.1 What's the connection?

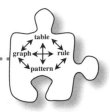

Finding Connections Between Representations

In Chapter 3 you studied different ways to represent patterns. You organized information into tables, graphed information about patterns, and learned how to find the rules that govern specific patterns.

Starting today and continuing throughout this chapter, you will find **connections** between different representations of the same pattern, explore each representation more deeply, and learn shorter ways to go from one representation to another. By the end of this chapter, you will have a deeper understanding of many of the most powerful tools of algebra.

4-1.   TILE PATTERN TEAM CHALLENGE

Your teacher will assign your team a tile pattern (one of the patterns labeled (a) through (e) on the next page). Your team's task is to create a poster showing every way you can represent your pattern and highlighting all of the connections between the representations that you can find. For this activity, **finding and showing the connections are the most important parts.** Clearly presenting the connections between representations on your poster will help you convince your classmates that your description of the pattern makes sense.

Pattern Analysis:

- **Extend** the pattern: Draw Figures 0, 4, and 5. Then describe Figure 100. Give as much information as you can. What will it look like? How will the tiles be arranged? How many tiles will it have?

- **Generalize** the pattern by writing a rule that will give the number of tiles in any figure in the pattern. Show how you got your answer.

- Find the number of tiles in each figure. Record your data in a table and on a graph.

- Demonstrate how the pattern grows using color, arrows, labels, and other math tools to help you show and explain. Show growth in each representation.

- What **connections** do you see between the different representations (graph, figures, and $x \rightarrow y$ table)? How can you show these **connections**?

Problem continues on next page →

4-1.   *Problem continued from previous page.*

Presenting the Connections:

As a team, organize your work into a large poster that clearly shows each representation of your pattern, as well as a description of Figure 100. When your team presents your poster to the class, you will need to support each statement with a reason from your observations. Each team member must explain something mathematical as part of your presentation.

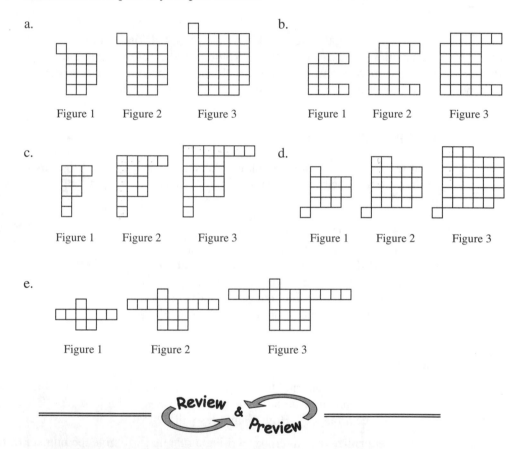

a.

Figure 1   Figure 2   Figure 3

b.

Figure 1   Figure 2   Figure 3

c.

Figure 1   Figure 2   Figure 3

d.

Figure 1   Figure 2   Figure 3

e.

Figure 1   Figure 2   Figure 3

Review & Preview

4-2.   For each tile pattern in problem 4-1, draw Figures 0, 4, and 5 on graph paper. If it helps, copy Figures 1, 2, and 3 onto your paper.

4-3.   Make an $x \rightarrow y$ table for the rule $y = x^2 - 2x$.

a.   Plot and connect the points on a complete graph.

b.   Does your graph look like a full parabola? If not, add more points to your table and graph to complete the picture.

4-4.   THE GAME SHOW

Susan had an incredible streak of good
fortune as a guest on the exciting game
show, "The Math Is Right." She
amassed winnings of $12,500, a sports
car, two round-trip airline tickets, and
five pieces of furniture.

In an amazing finish, Susan then
landed on a "Double Your Prize"
square and answered the
corresponding math question correctly!
She instantly became the show's
biggest winner ever, earning twice the
amounts of all her previous prizes.

A week later, $25,000, a sports car, four round-trip airline tickets, and five pieces of
furniture arrived at her house. Susan felt cheated. What was wrong?

4-5.   Write the equation represented by the
diagram at right.

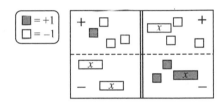

a.   Simplify as much as possible and
then solve for x.

b.   Check your solution.

4-6.   Copy and simplify the following expressions by combining like terms.

a. $y + 3x - 3 + 2x^2 + 8x - 5y$ b. $2x + 4x^2 - 6x^2 - 9 + 1 - x - 3x$

c. $2y^2 + 30y - 3y^2 + 4y - 14 - y$ d. $-10 + 3xy - 3xy + y^2 + 10 - y^2$

4-7.   Use your pattern-finding techniques to fill in the missing entries for the table below.
Then find a rule for the pattern.

IN (x)	4	8	3	–2	–6	0	5	7
OUT (y)	17	65	10	5		1	26	

4.1.2 How does it grow?

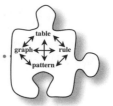

Seeing Growth in Different Representations

In Lesson 4.1.1, you looked at four different ways of representing patterns and began to find **connections** between them.

Throughout this chapter you will explore **connections** and find shortcuts between the representations. Today, you will look for specific connections between geometric patterns and equations. As you work today, keep these questions in mind:

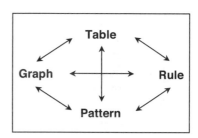

How can you see growth in the rule?

How do you know your rule is correct?

What does the representation tell you?

What are the connections between the representations?

At the end of this lesson, put your work from today in a safe place, because you will need to use it during Lesson 4.1.3!

4-8.   **Tile Pattern #1:**

Examine the tile pattern at right.

a.   What do you notice? After everyone has had a moment on his or her own to examine the figures, discuss what you see with your team.

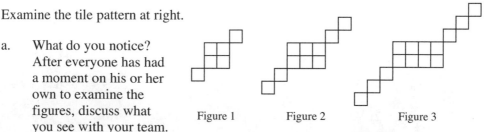

Figure 1   Figure 2   Figure 3

b.   Sketch the next figure in the sequence (Figure 4) on your resource page. Sketch the figure that comes before Figure 1 (Figure 0).

c.   How is the tile pattern growing? Where are the tiles being added with each new figure? Color in the new tiles in each figure with a marker or colored pencil on your resource page.

d.   What would Figure 100 look like? Describe it in words. How many tiles would be in the 100th figure? Find as many ways as you can to **justify** your conclusion. Be prepared to report back to the class with your team's findings and methods.

4-9.   Answer questions (a) through (d) from problem 4-8 for each of the patterns below. Use color to shade in the new tiles on each pattern on your resource page. Choose one color for the new tiles in part (a) and a different color for the new tiles in part (b).

a.   **Tile Pattern #2:**

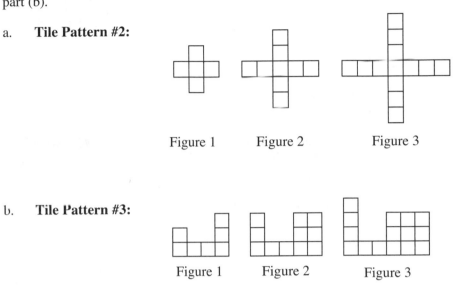

Figure 1   Figure 2   Figure 3

b.   **Tile Pattern #3:**

Figure 1   Figure 2   Figure 3

4-10.   PUTTING IT TOGETHER

Look back at the three different tile patterns in problems 4-8 and 4-9 to answer these questions.

a.   What is the same and what is different between these three patterns? Explain in a few sentences.

b.   Write an equation (rule) for the number of tiles in each pattern.

c.   What connections do you see between your equations and the tile pattern? Show and explain these connections.

d.   Imagine that the team next to you created a new tile pattern that grows in the same way as the ones you have just worked with, but they refused to show it to you. What other information would you need in order to predict the number of tiles in Figure 100? Explain your reasoning.

4-11.   Consider **Tile Pattern #4**, shown below.

a.   Draw Figures 0 and 4 on the resource page.

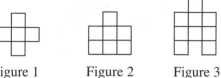

Figure 1   Figure 2   Figure 3

b.   Write an equation (rule) for the number of tiles in this pattern. Use a new color to show where the numbers in your rule appear in the tile pattern.

c.   What is the same about this pattern and Tile Pattern #3? What is different? What do those similarities and differences look like in the tile pattern? In the equation?

d.   How is the growth represented in each equation?

Don't forget to put your work from today in a safe place, because you will need to use it during the next lesson.

4-12.   For today's Learning Log entry, draw a web of the different representations, starting with the diagram below. Draw lines and/or arrows to show which representations you have connected so far. Explain the connections you learned today. Be sure to include anything you figured out about how the numbers in equations (rules) relate to tile patterns. Title this entry "Starting the Web" and label it with today's date.

```
              Table


    Graph              Rule


              Pattern
```

4-13. Write the equation represented in the equation mat at right.

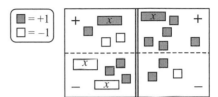

a. Simplify as much as possible and then solve for x.

b. Check your solution.

4-14. Simplify each of the following equations and solve for x. Show all work and check your solution.

a. $7 - 3x = -x + 1$

b. $-2 + 3x = -(x + 6)$

4-15. Leala can write a 500-word essay in an hour. If she writes an essay in 10 minutes, approximately how many words do you think the essay contains?

4-16. Copy and complete the table below.

IN (x)	2	10	6	7	–3		–10	1000	x
OUT (y)	9	25	17			15			

a. Explain in words what is done to the input value (x) to produce the output value (y).

b. Write the rule you described in part (a) with algebraic symbols.

4-17. When Susan's brother went to college, she and her two sisters evenly divided his belongings. Among his possessions were 3 posters, 216 books, and 24 CDs. How were these items divided?

4.1.3 How does it grow?

Connecting Linear Rules and Graphs

You have been looking at geometric patterns and ways that those patterns can be represented with equations, graphs, and $x \rightarrow y$ tables. In Lesson 4.1.2 you worked with four different tile patterns and looked for **connections** between the geometric shapes and the numbers in the equations. Today you will go back to those four equations and look for **connections** to other representations.

By the end of this lesson, you should be able to answer the following target questions:

How is growth shown in a rule?

How is growth shown in a graph?

How can you determine the number of tiles in Figure 0 from a graph?

How can you determine which tile pattern grows faster from a graph?

4-18.   Examine your Lesson 4.1.2 Resource Page ("Pattern Analysis").

a.   Make sure you have a rule for each tile pattern.

b.   Draw a graph. Put all patterns on the same set of axes. Use different colors for each, matching the color you used on the resource page.

c.   Explain how the growth appears in the pattern, in the rule, and in the graph.

d.   What **connections** do you see between these representations? Describe any **connections** you see.

4-19. The graph at right is also on the Lesson 4.1.3 Resource Page provided by your teacher. It gives information about three new tile patterns. **Note:** In this course, tile patterns will be considered to be elements of continuous relationships and thus will be graphed with a continuous line or curve.

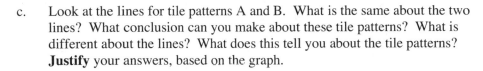

Figure Number

Answer the following questions as a team.

a. What information does the circled point (O) on the graph tell you about tile pattern A?

b. Find the growth of each tile pattern. For example, how much does tile pattern A increase from one figure to the next? Explain how you know.

c. Look at the lines for tile patterns A and B. What is the same about the two lines? What conclusion can you make about these tile patterns? What is different about the lines? What does this tell you about the tile patterns? **Justify** your answers, based on the graph.

d. Look at lines A and C on the graph. What do these two lines have in common? In what ways are the lines different? What does this tell you about the tile patterns? Explain completely.

4-20. In your Learning Log, answer the target questions for this lesson, reprinted below:

How is growth shown in a rule?

How is growth shown in a graph?

How can you determine the number of tiles in Figure 0 from a graph?

How can you determine which tile pattern grows faster from a graph?

Be sure to include at least one example. Title this entry "Connecting Linear Rules and Graphs" and label it with today's date.

4-21.   Two of the connections in your representations web are pattern → table and pattern → rule. Practice these connections as you answer the questions below.

   a.   On graph paper, draw Figure 0 and Figure 4 for the pattern at right.

         Figure 1   Figure 2   Figure 3

   b.   Represent the number of tiles in each figure with a table.

   c.   Represent the number of tiles in each figure with an algebraic rule.

4-22.   For the rule $y = x^2 - 4$, calculate the y-values that complete the table below. Plot the points and connect them on a complete graph on graph paper. What does your graph look like?

IN (x)	−3	−2	−1	0	1	2	3
OUT (y)							

4-23.   For each of the equations below, solve for x. Show all work and check your solution.

   a. $-2 + 2x = -x + 2 + x$ b. $2 - 3x = x + 2$

4-24.   The length of a rectangle is five centimeters more than twice its width. The perimeter is 100 centimeters. Use Guess and Check to find out how long and how wide the rectangle is.

4-25.   Another one of the connections in your representations web is graph → table. In Chapters 1 through 3, you developed tools to find a table from a graph. Consider this connection as you complete the table below based on the graph at right.

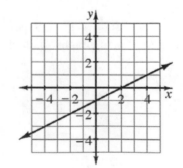

IN (x)	−3	−2	−1	0	1	2	3
OUT (y)							

4.1.4 What's the rule? How can I use it?

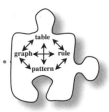

$y = mx + b$

In Lessons 4.1.2 and 4.1.3, you investigated connections between tile patterns, $x \rightarrow y$ tables, graphs, and rules (equations). Today you will use your observations about growth and Figure 0 to write rules for linear patterns and to create new tile patterns for given rules.

4-26.   UNDERSTANDING $y = mx + b$

With your team, list some of the equations you have been working with in the past two lessons.

a.   What do all of these rules have in common?

Rules for linear patterns can all be written in the form $y = mx + b$, where x and y represent variables, but m and b represent **constants** (numbers that stay the same in the equation after they are chosen). Discuss these questions with your team:

b.   What does m tell you about the pattern?

c.   What does b tell you about the pattern?

4-27.   GRAPH → RULE

Allysha claims she can find the equation of a line by its graph without a table. How is that possible? Discuss this idea with your team and then try to find the equation of the line at right without first making a table. Be ready to share with the class how you found the rule.

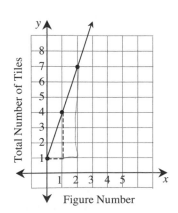

4-28.   TABLE → RULE

Allysha wonders if she can use the idea of m and b to find the equation of a line from its table.

a.   For example, if she knows the information about a linear pattern given in the table below, how can she find the equation of the line? Work with your team to complete the table and find the rule.

IN (x)	0	1	2	3	4	5	6
OUT (y)	−2						

+5   +5   +5   +5   +5   +5

b.   Use this same idea to find the rule of the linear tile patterns represented by the tables below.

i.

IN (x)	−1	0	1	2	3	4	5
OUT (y)	3	5	7	9	11	13	15

ii.

IN (x)	0	1	2	3	4	5	6
OUT (y)	7	4	1	−2	−5	−8	−11

c.   Write a summary statement explaining how you used your knowledge about m and b to quickly write a rule.

4-29.   RULE → PATTERN

In each problem below, invent your own pattern that meets the stated conditions. Draw Figures 0, 1, 2, and 3 and write the rule (equation) for your pattern.

a.   A tile pattern that has $y = 4x + 3$ as a rule.

b.   A tile pattern that decreases by 2 tiles and Figure 2 has 8 tiles.

4-30.   Invent two different tile patterns that grow by 4 every time but have different $x \rightarrow y$ tables. Draw Figures 0, 1, 2, and 3 and find rules for each of your patterns. What is different about your rules? What is the same?

4-31.   The linear equations you have been working with can be written in the general form:

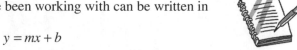

$$y = mx + b$$

In your Learning Log, summarize what you know about m and b so far. What does the m tell you about a pattern? What does the b tell you about a pattern? Where can you see m and b in each representation? Sketch examples if it helps. Title this entry "$y = mx + b$" and label it with today's date.

4-32.   For each equation below, solve for x. Check your solution, if possible, and show all work.

a. $3x\ 6+1--2x-5+5x$

b. $-2x-5=2-4x-(x-1)$

4-33.   I am thinking of a number. When I double my number and then subtract the result from five, I get negative one. What is my number? Write and solve an equation.

4-34.   Copy this table and use your pattern skills to complete it.

IN (x)	2	10				−3			x
OUT (y)	4	28	13	−17	10		2.5	148	$3x - 2$

a.   Explain in words what is done to the input value, x, to produce the output value, y.

b.   Explain the process you used to find the missing input values.

4-35.   Examine the $x \rightarrow y$ table at right.

a.   Invent a tile pattern that fits this data.

b.   What is the pattern's growth factor? Show where the growth factor appears in the $x \rightarrow y$ table and the tile pattern.

Figure Number	Number of Tiles
0	5
1	9
2	13
3	17

4-36.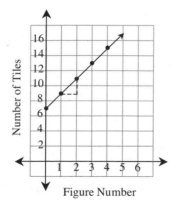

Look at the graph at left. What statements can you make about the tile pattern the graph represents? How many tiles are in Figure 0? Figure 1? What is the growth factor?

4.1.5 What are the connections?

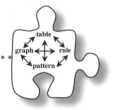

Checking the Connections

In the last several lessons you have been finding **connections** and relationships between different representations of patterns. You have worked backward and forward and have used information about Figure 0 (or the starting point) and the growth factor in order to write rules. In today's activity, you will check your **connections** by using pieces of information from different parts of the web to generate a complete pattern.

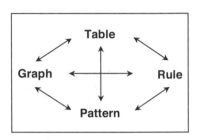

4-37. CHECKING THE CONNECTIONS: TEAM CHALLENGE

Today you are going to **apply** what you know about the starting point (Figure 0), growth factor, and the **connections** between representations to answer some challenging questions. The information in each question, parts (a) through (d), describes a different pattern. The graph of each pattern is a line. From this information, generate the rule, $x \rightarrow y$ table, graph, and tile pattern (Figures 0 through 3) that follow the pattern. You may answer these questions in any order, but make sure you answer each one completely before starting another problem.

Work together as a team. The more you listen to how other people see the **connections** and the more you share your own ideas, the more you will know at the end of the lesson. Stick together and be sure to talk through every idea.

Each person will turn in his or her own paper at the end of this activity, showing four complete representations for each pattern. Your work does not need to be identical to your teammates' work, but you should have talked and agreed that all explanations are correct.

a.

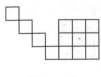

Figure 3

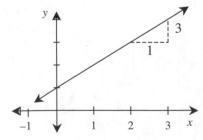

Problem continues on next page →

4-37.   *Problem continued from previous page.*

b.

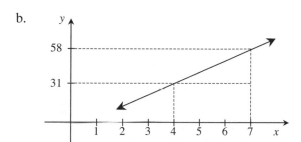

c.

Figure Number	Number of Tiles
0	
1	
2	
3	12

Figure 8

d. $y = -3x + 7$

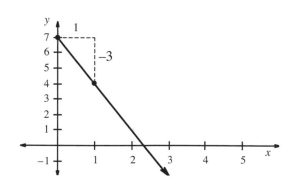

4-38.   REPRESENTATIONS WEB

Update your representations web from problem 4-12 with any new **connections** you have found. Pay attention to which direction(s) the arrow points.

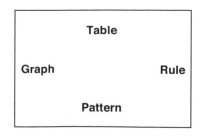

4-39.   For each equation below, solve for the variable. Check your solutions, if possible, and show all work.

a. $-3 + x = -x + 5$

b. $-(x - 3) = 2x - 4 - 3x$

c. $2 + 4k = 2k + 9$

d. $-(-t + 4) = -3t$

4-40.   Copy and complete each of the Diamond Problems below. The pattern used in the Diamond Problems is shown at right.

a.

b.

c.

d.

4-41.   Complete a table for the rule $y = 3x - 2$.

a.   Draw a complete graph for this rule.

b.   Is $(-50, -152)$ a point on the graph? Explain how you know.

4-42.   Write down everything you know about the tile pattern represented by the $x \rightarrow y$ table at right. Be as specific as possible.

x	y
3	25
5	39
6	46
1	11

4-43.   Simplify each of the expressions below. You may use an equation mat and tiles.

a. $-(5x + 1)$

b. $6x - (-5x + 1)$

c. $-(1 - 5x)$

d. $-5x + (x - 1)$

4-44.   Invent a tile pattern that grows by 4 each time. Draw Figures 0, 1, 2, and 3. Use color or shading to show the growth.

4-45. For each equation below, solve for the variable. Check your solutions, if possible, and show all work.

    a. $3p - 7 + 9 - 2p = p + 2$

    b. $-2x + 5 + (-x) - 5 = 0$

    c. $12 = r + 6 - 2r$

    d. $-(y^2 - 2) = y^2 - 5 - 2y^2$

4-46. Sketch a graph to match each story below using axes labeled as shown at right.

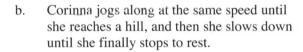

    a.   Luis rides his skateboard at the same speed all the way home. It takes him ten minutes to get there.

    b.   Corinna jogs along at the same speed until she reaches a hill, and then she slows down until she finally stops to rest.

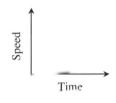

    c.   Sergei is talking with his friends at the donut shop when he realizes that it's almost time for math class! He runs toward school, but slows to a walk when he hears the bell ring and realizes that he is already late. He sits down in class four minutes after he left the donut shop.

4-47. Complete a table for the rule $y = 3 - x$.

    a.   Draw a complete graph for this rule.

    b.   Is (32, –29) a point on this graph? Explain why or why not.

4-48. Mr. Wallis decided to create another table to figure out how much it costs to send a certain number of regular letters through the mail. Use proportional reasoning to complete his table at right.

Number of Letters	Cost of Stamps
10	$3.40
2	$0.68
	$5.10
7	
1	
500	
	$14.28

4.1.6 How can I use growth?

Graphing a Line Without an $x \rightarrow y$ Table

You have now used your knowledge of growth factors and Figure 0 to create tile patterns and $x \rightarrow y$ tables directly from rules. You have also looked at graphs to determine the equation or rule for the pattern. Today you will reverse that process and use an equation to create a graph without the intermediate step of creating an $x \rightarrow y$ table.

4-49.　　For each of the graphs below:

- Write a rule.

- Describe how the pattern changes and how many tiles are in Figure 0.

a.
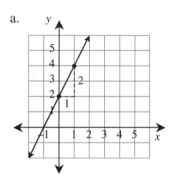

b.
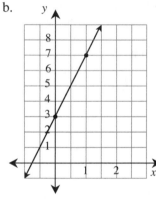

c.
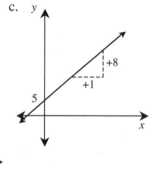

d.
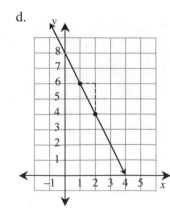

e.
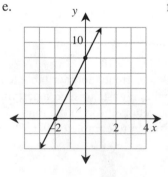

f.
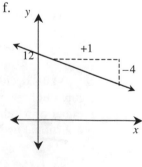

Algebra Connections

4-50.   Now **reverse** the process. Graph the following rules without first making a table. Parts (a) and (b) can go on the same set of axes, as can parts (c) and (d). Label each line with its equation, **y-intercept** (where it crosses the y-axis), and a growth triangle.

a. $y = 4x + 3$ b. $y = 3x$

c. $y = -3x + 8$ d. $y = x - 1$

4-51.   Sketch a graph that fits each description below and then label each line with its equation. You can put all of the graphs on one set of axes if you label the lines clearly. Use what you know about growth factor and Figure 0 to help you.

a.   A pattern that has three tiles in Figure 0 and adds four tiles in each new figure.

b.   A pattern that shrinks by three tiles between figures and starts with five tiles in Figure 0.

c.   A pattern that has two tiles in all figures.

4-52.   Now **reverse** your process to describe the pattern represented by the rule $y = -2x + 13$. Be as detailed as you can.

4-53.   CONSOLIDATING YOUR LEARNING

a.   Find the web that you updated at the end of Lesson 4.1.5. On it, add arrows for any new connections that you have made.

b.   In your Learning Log, write a step-by-step process for **graphing directly from a rule**. A student who has not taken algebra yet should be able to read your process and understand how to create a graph. It may help you to think about these questions as you write:

What information do you get from your rule?

How does that information show up on the graph?

Where does your graph start?

How do you figure out the next point?

What should you label to make it a complete graph?

Title this entry "Graphing Without an $x \to y$ Table," and label it with today's date.

4-54.   Use what you know about *m* and *b* to graph each rule below without making a table. Draw a growth triangle for each line.

a. $y = 2x - 3$ b. $y = -2x + 5$

c. $y = 3x$ d. $y = \frac{1}{2}x + 1$

4-55.   Examine the graph at right showing three tile patterns.

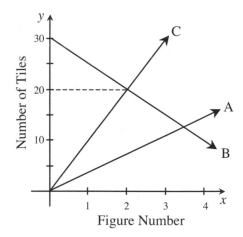

a.   What do you know about Figure 0 for each of the three patterns?

b.   Which pattern changes most quickly? How quickly does it change? Show how you know.

c.   Which figure number has the same number of tiles in patterns B and C? Explain how you know.

d.   Write a rule for pattern B.

4-56.   Translate these algebraic statements into words: $y = 2x + 5$ and $y = 6x + 5$.

a.   What do you know about Figure 0 for each pattern?

b.   Which pattern grows most quickly? How do you know?

4-57.   Evaluate each expression below when $x = -3$.

a. $4x + 16$ b. $3x^2 - 2x + 1$

4-58.   Ms. B is making snickerdoodle cookies. Her recipe uses one-and-a-half teaspoons of cinnamon to make two-dozen cookies. If she needs to make thirteen-dozen cookies in order to give one cookie to each of her students, how much cinnamon will she need?

4.1.7 What are the connections?

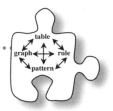

Completing the Web

After all of the work you have done with equations in $y = mx + b$ form, you know a lot about starting with one representation of a pattern and moving to different representations. Today you will work with your team to make sure you are confident moving around the representations web.

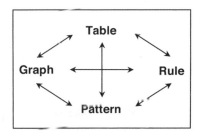

Answer problems 4-59 and 4-60 on graph paper. Discuss each problem with your team to get as much as you can out of these problems.

4-59.   GRAPH → PATTERN and TABLE → PATTERN

On graph paper, draw tile patterns (Figures 0, 1, and 2) that could represent the data shown below. Be creative, but make sure that the growth of each pattern makes sense to your teammates.

a.

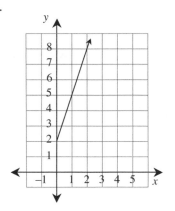

b.

x	y
0	14
1	11
2	8
3	5
4	2

4-60.   REVISITING "GROWING, GROWING, GROWING"

Problem 1-32 from Chapter 1 asked you to determine which figure in the pattern shown below would have 79 tiles. Now that you know more about graphs, $x \rightarrow y$ tables, rules, and tile patterns themselves, you can show the answer to this question in multiple ways.

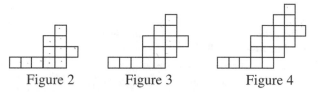

   Figure 2   Figure 3   Figure 4

Your Task: Solve this problem by completing the following tasks. Use a graphing calculator or other graphing technology to help you find a graph and a table. Be sure to record your work and **justify** your thinking.

- Copy the three figures above onto a piece of graph paper. Extend the pattern on graph paper to include Figures 1 and 5.

- Find a rule, table, and graph for this pattern.

- Which figure will have 79 tiles? Use as many representations as you can to justify your answer.

4-61.   EXTENSION

Invent an equation to fit these clues: The *x*-intercept is 2, and the pattern grows by 4. Show and explain your reasoning.

METHODS AND **M**EANINGS

MATH NOTES

Multiple Representations

Consider the areas of the figures in the **tile pattern** below. The number of tiles in each figure can also be represented in an $x \rightarrow y$ **table**, on a **graph**, or with a **rule** (equation).

Remember that in this course, tile patterns will be considered to be elements of continuous relationships and thus will be graphed with a continuous line or curve.

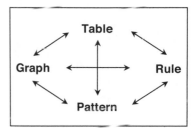

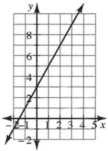

Graph

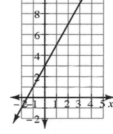

Figure 0   Figure 1   Figure 2

Tile Pattern

$$y = 2x + 3$$

Rule (Equation)

Figure Number (x)	0	1	2
Number of Tiles (y)	3	5	7

$x \rightarrow y$ **Table**

Review & Preview

4-62.   Use what you know about m and b to graph each equation below without making a table. Show a growth triangle on each graph and label the x- and y-intercepts.

a. $y = 3 - 2x$

b. $y = 2x$

c. $y = 3$

d. $y = -\frac{1}{2}x + 3$

4-63. Copy and complete each $x \rightarrow y$ table below on your paper. Using what you know about m and b, write an equation that represents the data in the table.

a.

x	y
0	5
1	7
2	9
3	11
4	13
30	
200	
	505
x	

b.

x	y
0	4
1	2
2	0
3	-2
4	-4
30	
150	
300	
x	

c.

x	y
-2	7
-1	4
0	1
1	-2
2	-5
3	
100	
	70
x	

4-64. Solve each of the following equations and check your answers.

a. $2x - 3 = 7$

b. $3x + 5 - x = x - 3$

c. $5x - (x + 1) = 6 - 2x$

d. $0.5x - 5 = x + 4$

4-65. For a tile pattern with the rule $y = 6x + 4$ (where x represents the figure number and y represents the number of tiles), which figure number has 40 tiles in it? How do you know?

4-66. Josie and Jules are building a model car. They find that the real car is 54 inches tall and 180 inches long. They decide to make their model 3 inches tall, but now they are having a disagreement. Josie thinks that their model should be 10 inches long and Jules thinks it should be 129 inches long. Help them settle their argument by deciding if either of them is correct. Explain how you know exactly how long their model should be.

4.2.1 When are they the same?

Introduction to Systems of Equations

In Section 4.1, you graphed lines and curves that represented tile patterns. But what happens when you graph two lines at the same time? What can you learn? Today you will use data, graphs, and rules to examine what happens when two lines (or curves) intersect.

4-67. The Iditarod Trail Sled Dog Race is famous for its incredible length and its use of dogs. In 2003, the sled drivers, known as mushers, started their dog sleds at Fairbanks, Alaska and rode through the snow for many days until they reached Nome, Alaska. Along the route there were stations where the competitors checked in, so data was kept on the progress of each team.

Joyla and her team of dogs made it through the first five checkpoints. At the same time, her buddy Evie left Nome (the finish line) on the day the race started in an effort to meet Joyla and offer encouragement. Evie traveled along the route toward the racers on her snowmobile. The progress of each person is shown on the graph below.

Your Task: With your team, analyze the data in the graph. Consider the questions below as you work. Be prepared to defend your results.

- Which data represents Evie? Which represents Joyla? How can you tell?

- When did Evie meet Joyla?

- How long was the race? How can you tell?

- Who traveled faster? Explain how you know.

- Approximately how long did it take Joyla to finish the race? How did you find your answer?

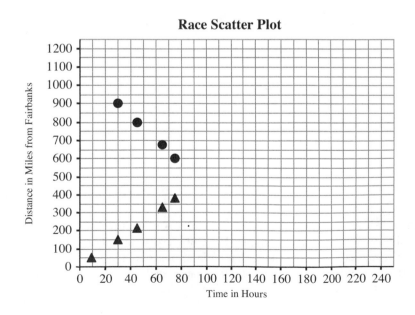

Race Scatter Plot

4-68.   The point where two lines (or curves) cross is called a **point of intersection**. Two or more lines (or curves) are called a **system of equations**. When you work with data, points of intersection can be meaningful, as you saw in the last problem.

a.   On graph paper, graph $y = 3x - 4$ and $y = -2x + 6$ on the same set of axes.

b.   Find the point of intersection of these two lines and label the point with its coordinates; that is, write it in the form (x, y).

4-69.   The meaning of a point of intersection depends on what the graph is describing. For example, in problem 4-67, the point where Joyla's and Evie's lines cross represents when they met during the race.

Examine each of the graphs below and write a brief story that describes the information in the graph. Include a sentence explaining what the point of intersection represents.

a.

Temperature

Rio de Janeiro

San Francisco

Time of Year in Spring

b.

Cost to Produce

Handmade

Machine-made

Number of Tortillas Manufactured

c.

Pollution

Boston

Denver

Population

d.

Distance from Starting Line

Tortoise

Hare

Time

4-70.   In your Learning Log, write your own situation like the ones in problem 4-69 and make a graph. Have at least two lines or curves intersect. Explain what the intersection represents in your situation. Title this entry "Points of Intersection" and label it with today's date.

Algebra Connections

METHODS AND **M**EANINGS

Systems of Equations Vocabulary

The point where two lines (or curves) intersect is called a **point of intersection**. This point's significance depends on the context of the problem.

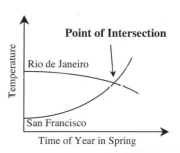

Two or more lines or curves used to find a point of intersection are called a **system of equations**. A system of equations can represent a variety of contexts and can be used to compare how two or more things are related. For example, the system of equations graphed at right compares the temperature in two different cities over time.

4-71. To ride to school, Elaine takes 15 minutes to ride 8 blocks. Assuming she rides at a constant speed, how long should it take her to go 20 blocks? Justify your answer.

4-72. Find the area of the entire rectangle in each diagram below. Show all work.

a.
48
102

b.
13
x 7

c.
20
32   13

d.
15
9
11   3

4-73.   Gale and Leslie are engaged in a friendly 60-mile bike race that started at noon. The graph at right represents their progress so far.

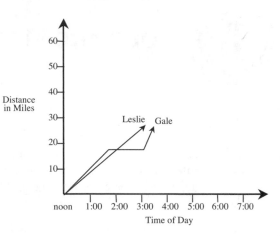

a.   What does the intersection of the two lines represent?

b.   At what time (approximately) did Leslie pass Gale?

c.   About how far had Leslie traveled when she passed Gale?

d.   What do you think happened to Gale between 1:30 and 3:00?

e.   If Leslie continues at a steady pace, when will she complete the race?

4-74.   Write an equation (rule) for each of the $x \rightarrow y$ tables below. Then, on one set of axes, use each rule to graph.

a.

x	y
8	23
2	5
−3	−10
9	26
x	

b.

x	y
6	32
−2	−8
0	2
10	52
x	

4-75.   Translate each part below from symbols into words or from words into symbols.

a. $-y + 8$

b. $2x - 48$

c. $(x + 3)^2$

d.   The opposite of six times the square of a number.

e.   A number multiplied by itself, then added to five.

4.2.2 When are they the same?

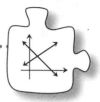

Writing Rules from Word Problems

In Lesson 4.2.1, you discovered that the point of intersection of two lines or curves can have an important meaning. Finding points of intersection is another strategy you can use to solve problems, especially those with two quantities being compared.

Analyze the following situations using the multiple tools you have studied so far.

4-76.   BUYING BICYCLES

Latanya and George are saving up money because they both want to buy new bicycles. Latanya opened a savings account with $50. She just got a job and is determined to save an additional $30 a week. George started a savings account with $75. He is able to save $25 a week.

Your Task: Use at least **two different ways** to find the time (in weeks) when Latanya and George will have the same amount of money in their savings accounts. Be prepared to share your methods with the class.

4-77.   Did you graph the scenario in problem 4-76? If not, graph a line for Latanya and another line for George on the same set of axes. Confirm your answer to problem 4-76 on the graph. Consider the questions below to help you decide how to set up the graph.

  - What should the *x*-axis represent? What should the *y*-axis represent?

  - How should the axes be scaled?

  - Should the amounts in the savings accounts be graphed on the same set of axes or graphed separately? Why?

4-78.   If you have not done so already, consider how to use rules to confirm the point of intersection for Latanya's and George's lines.

    a.   Write a rule for Latanya's savings account.

    b.   Write a rule for George's savings account.

    c.   Use the rules to check your solution to problem 4-76.

4-79.   Gerardo decided to use tables to find the point of intersection of the lines $y = 4x - 6$
         and $y = -2x + 3$. His tables are shown below.

$y = 4x - 6$

IN (x)	−3	−2	−1	0	1	2	3
OUT (y)	−18	−14	−10	−6	−2	2	6

$y = -2x + 3$

IN (x)	−3	−2	−1	0	1	2	3
OUT (y)	9	7	5	3	1	−1	−3

   a.   Examine his tables. Is there a common point that makes both rules true? If
         not, can you describe where the point of intersection is?

   b.   Now graph the rules on the same set of axes. Where do the lines intersect?

   c.   Use the rules to confirm your answer to part (b).

Review & Preview

4-80.   It's the end of the semester, and the clubs at school are
         recording their profits. The Science Club started out
         with $20 and has increased its balance by an average of
         $10 per week. The Math Club saved $5 per week and
         started out with $50 at the beginning of the semester.

   a.   Create an equation for each club. Let x represent
         the number of weeks and y represent the balance of
         the club's account.

   b.   Graph both lines on one set of axes. When do the clubs have the same
         balance?

   c.   What is the balance at that point?

4-81.   Examine the rectangle formed with algebra tiles at right.

   a.   Find the area of the entire rectangle. That is, what is the sum
         of the areas of the algebra tiles?

   b.   Find the perimeter of the entire rectangle. Show all work.

4-82.   On graph paper, plot the points (−3, 7) and (2, −3) and draw a line through them.
         Then name the x- and y-intercepts of the line.

4-83.   Use the rectangle at right to answer the following questions.

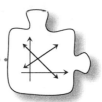

       a.   Find the area of the entire rectangle. Explain how you found your solution.

       b.   Calculate the perimeter of the figure.

4-84.   In Spring, the daily high temperature in Boulder, Colorado rises about $\frac{1}{3}$ degree per day. On Friday, May 2, the temperature reached 74°. Predict when the temperature will reach 90°.

4.2.3 When are they the same?

Solving Systems Algebraically

So far in Section 4.2, you have solved systems of equations by graphing two lines and finding where they intersect. However, it is not always convenient (nor accurate) to solve by graphing.

Today you will explore a new way to approach solving a system of equations. Questions to ask your teammates today include:

How can you find a rule?

How can you compare two rules?

How can you use what you know about solving?

4-85.   CHUBBY BUNNY

Use tables, rules, and a graph to find and check the solution for the problem below.

Barbara has a bunny that weighs 5 pounds and gains 3 pounds per year. Her cat weighs 19 pounds and gains 1 pound per year. When will the bunny and the cat weigh the same amount?

4-86. SOLVING SYSTEMS OF EQUATIONS ALGEBRAICALLY

In problem 4-85, you found rules like those shown below to represent the weights of Barbara's cat and bunny. For these rules, x represents the number of years and y represents the weight of the animal.

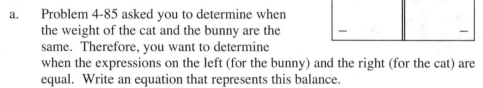

$$y = \underbrace{5 + 3x}_{\substack{\text{weight of} \\ \text{bunny}}} \quad \text{and} \quad y = \underbrace{19 + x}_{\substack{\text{weight of} \\ \text{cat}}}$$

Since you want to know when the weights of the cat and bunny are the same, you can use an equation mat to represent this relationship, as shown at right.

a. Problem 4-85 asked you to determine when the weight of the cat and the bunny are the same. Therefore, you want to determine when the expressions on the left (for the bunny) and the right (for the cat) are equal. Write an equation that represents this balance.

b. Solve your equation for x, which represents years. According to your solution, how many years will it take for the bunny and the cat to weigh the same number of pounds? Does this answer match your answer from the graph of problem 4-85?

c. How much do the cat and bunny weigh at this time?

4-87. CHANGING POPULATIONS

Post Falls High School in Idaho has 1160 students and is growing by 22 students per year. Richmond High School in Indiana has 1900 students and is shrinking by 15 students per year.

a. Without graphing, write a rule that represents the population at Richmond High School and another rule that represents the population at Post Falls High School. Let x represent years and y represent population.

b. Graphing the rules for part (a) is challenging because of the large numbers involved. Using a table could take a long time. Therefore, this problem is a good one to solve algebraically, the way you solved problem 4-86.

   Use the rules together to write an equation that represents when these high schools will have the same population. Then solve your equation to find out when the schools' populations will be the same.

c. What will the population be at that time?

4-88.   PUTTING IT ALL TOGETHER

Find the solution to the problem below by **graphing** and also by **solving an equation**. The solutions using both methods should match, so be sure to review your work carefully if the results disagree.

Your school planted two trees when it was first opened. One tree, a ficus, was 6 feet tall when it was planted and has grown 1.5 feet per year. The other tree, an oak, was grown from an acorn (on the ground) and has grown 2 feet per year. When will the trees be the same height? How tall will the trees be when they are the same height?

4-89.   Ms. Harlow calls the method you have been using today to solve equations the **Equal Values Method**. Explain why this name makes sense.

METHODS AND **M**EANINGS

Solving a Linear Equation

When solving an equation like the one shown below, several important strategies are involved.

- **Simplify.** Combine like terms and "make zeros" on each side of the equation whenever possible.

- **Keep equations balanced.** The "equals" sign in an equation indicates that the expressions on the left and right are balanced. Anything done to the equation must keep that balance.

$$3x - 2 + 4 = x - 6 \quad \text{combine like terms}$$
$$3x + 2 = x - 6$$
$$\underline{-x \qquad = -x} \quad \text{subtract } x \text{ on both sides}$$
$$2x + 2 = -6$$
$$\underline{-2 = -2} \quad \text{subtract 2 on both sides}$$
$$\frac{2x}{2} = \frac{-8}{2} \quad \text{divide both sides by 2}$$
$$x = -4$$

- **Get *x* alone.** Isolate the variable on one side of the equation and the constants on the other.

- **Undo operations.** Use the fact that addition is the opposite of subtraction and that multiplication is the opposite of division to solve for *x*. For example, in the equation $2x = -8$, since the 2 and *x* are multiplied, dividing both sides by 2 will get *x* alone.

4-90.   A local restaurant offers a Dim Sum lunch
         special that includes two dumplings, three egg
         rolls, a sweet bun, and a drink. Susan and her
         friends ordered four Dim Sum lunch specials.

         How many of each item should they receive?

4-91.   Kenneth claims that (2, 0) is the point of intersection of the lines $y = -2x + 4$ and
         $y = x - 2$. Is he correct? How do you know?

4-92.   Graph the lines $y = 2x - 3$ and $y = -x + 3$.

         a.   Where do they intersect? Label the point on the graph.

         b.   Find the point of intersection using the Equal Values Method. That is, start by
               combining both equations into one equation that you can solve for x.

         c.   Which method is easier, graphing or using algebra to solve?

4-93.   Determine the coordinates of each point of intersection without graphing.

         a. $y = 2x - 3$ b. $y = 2x - 5$
               $y = 4x + 1$ $y = -4x - 2$

4-94.   MORE OR LESS

         Judy has $20 and is saving at a rate of $6 per week. Ida has $172 and is spending at
         a rate of $4 per week. After how many weeks will each have the same amount of
         money?

         a.   Write an equation using x and y for Judy and Ida. What does x represent?
               What does y represent?

         b.   Solve this problem using any method you choose.

4.2.4 How can I use $y = mx + b$?

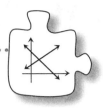

Extending the Web to Other Linear Situations

Today you will take what you have learned in this chapter and **apply** it to linear situations that are not tile patterns.

4-95.   EXTENDING THE WEB TO NEW
         SITUATIONS: TEAM CHALLENGE

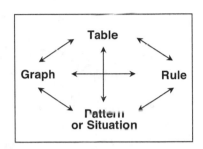

Today you are going to **apply** what you know about the starting point (Figure 0), growth factor, and the **connections** between representations to answer some challenging questions in real-life situations. The information in each question, parts (a) through (e) below, describes a different situation. All of the situations are **linear** (when graphed, they are lines).

Based on the given information, answer the questions in each problem. Show your answers completely and explain your strategies for answering the questions. You may answer these problems in any order, but make sure you answer each one completely before moving to another problem.

Work together as a team. The more you listen to how other people see the **connections** and share your own ideas, the more you will know at the end of this challenge. Stick together and be sure to talk through every idea.

Each person will turn in his or her own paper at the end of activity, showing solutions and explanations to each problem. Your work does *not* need to be identical to your teammates' work, but you should have talked and agreed that all explanations are correct.

a.   SAVING MONEY

Julia has $325 in her savings account. She just got a new job and will be saving money every month. If she always deposits the same amount, how much money will be in her account after she has been saving for a year? (Assume she never spends money from this account.)

Number of Months	Money in Account
...	...
7	$780
8	$845
9	$910
...	...

Problem continues on next page →

4-95.   *Problem continued from previous page.*

b.   POPULATION GROWTH

The $x \rightarrow y$ table, graph, rule, and words below each describe a different town. Based on the information you are given about each town's population, decide which town is growing the fastest. Explain how you know.

Population of Town A

Year	Number of People
1975	32,000
1979	50,000
1980	54,500

Population of Town B

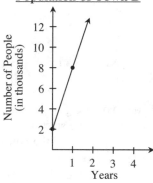

Population of Town C

If x = year and y = number of people, then:

$$y = 46000 - 5200x$$

Population of Town D

Town D is growing. Oddly, the same number of people moves to the town each year. Two years ago, the town had 9100 people. Now the town has 15,500 people.

c.   FUNDRAISING

The graph at right describes the money two clubs are earning from fundraising. In how many weeks will the two clubs have the same amount of money? Explain your thinking completely.

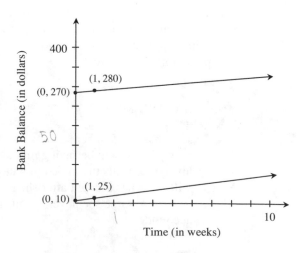

Problem continues on next page →

Algebra Connections

4-95. *Problem continued from previous page.*

d. **STORY TIME**

The graph and $x \rightarrow y$ tables below describe a situation. Write a story that fits the given information. Show the **connections** between the information you are given and the information in your story. Your story must give meaning to the point of intersection.

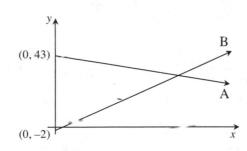

Line A			Line B	
x	y		x	y
⋮	⋮		⋮	⋮
8	11		4	22
9	7		5	28
10	3		⋮	⋮
⋮	⋮			

e. **VIDEO RENTAL**

Gina has a prepaid video rental card. She currently has a credit of $84 on the card.

The graph at right describes the amount of money there was on the card recently. Use this information to determine:

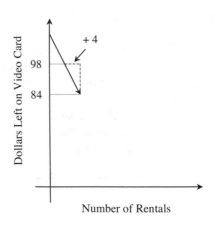

- How much one video rental costs.

- How many more videos can Gina rent before the card is used up.

METHODS AND MEANINGS

The Equal Values Method

The **Equal Values Method** is a non-graphing method to find the point of intersection or solution to a system of equations.

Start with two equations in $y = mx + b$ form, such as $y = -2x + 5$ and $y = x - 1$. Take the two expressions that equal y and set them equal to each other. Then solve this new equation to find x. See the example at right.

$$-2x + 5 = x - 1$$
$$-3x = -6$$
$$x = 2$$

Once you know the x-coordinate of the point of intersection, substitute your solution for x into *either* original equation to find y. In this example, the first equation is used.

$$y = -2x + 5$$
$$y = -2(2) + 5$$
$$y = 1$$

A good way to check your solution is to substitute your solution for x into *both* equations to verify that you get equal y-values.

$$y = x - 1$$
$$y = (2) - 1$$
$$y = 1$$

Write the solution as an ordered pair to represent the point on the graph where the equations intersect.

$$(2, 1)$$

Review & Preview

4-96.   Ariyonne claims that (3, 6) is the point of intersection of the lines $y = 4x - 2$ and $y = \frac{1}{2}x + 5$. Is she correct? How do you know?

4-97.   Determine the coordinates of each point of intersection without graphing.

a. $y = -x + 8$
      $y = x - 2$

b. $y = -3x$
      $y = -4x + 2$

Algebra Connections

4-98.   Graph the lines $y = 2x - 3$ and $y = 2x + 1$.

   a.   Where do they intersect?

   b.   Solve this system using the Equal Values Method.

   c.   Explain how your graph and algebraic solution relate to each other.

4-99.   CHANGING POPULATIONS

   Highland has a population of 12,200. Its population has been increasing at a rate of 300 people per year. Lowville has a population of 21,000 but is declining by 250 people per year. Assuming these rates do not change, in how many years will the populations be equal?

   a.   Write an equation that represents each city's population over time. What do your variables represent?

   b.   Solve the problem. Show your work.

4-100.   The table below shows the amount of money Francis had in his bank account each day since he started his new job.

Days at New Job	Money in Account
0	$27
1	$70
2	$113
3	$156

   a.   Write a rule for the amount of money in Francis's account. Let x represent the number of days and y represent the number of dollars in the account.

   b.   When will Francis have more than $1000 in his account?

4-101.   Kathy is thinking of a number. When she triples her number, adds eighteen, and then subtracts her original number from the sum, she gets four. What is Kathy's original number?

4-102.   Graph the equation $y = -2x^2 - 4x$. Start by making an $x \rightarrow y$ table. Be sure to include negative values for x.

4-103.   Solve this problem using Guess and Check. Write your solution in a sentence.

The number of students attending the Fall play was 150 fewer than three times the number of adults. Together, students and adults purchased 1778 tickets. How many students attended the Fall play?

4-104.   Predict where each rule will cross the y-axis.

a. $y = 17x + 3$ b. $y = \frac{16}{3}x - \frac{5}{12}$ c. $y = 12 - 4x$

4-105.   When Ellen started with Regina's favorite number and tripled it, the result was twelve more than twice the favorite number. Define a variable, write an equation, and then use the equation to find Regina's favorite number.

4-106.   Graph the lines $y = -4x - 3$ and $y = -4x + 1$ on graph paper.

a.   Where do they intersect?

b.   Solve this system using the Equal Values Method.

c.   Explain how your graph and algebraic solution relate to each other.

Chapter 4 Closure   What have I learned?

Reflection and Synthesis

The activities below offer you a chance to reflect on what you have learned during this chapter. As you work, look for concepts that you feel very comfortable with, ideas that you would like to learn more about, and topics you need more help with. Look for **connections** between ideas as well as **connections** with material you learned previously.

①   TEAM BRAINSTORM

      With your team, brainstorm a list for each of the following topics. Be as detailed as you can. How long can you make your list? Challenge yourselves. Be prepared to share your team's ideas with the class.

      Topics: What have you studied in this chapter? What ideas and words were important in what you learned? Remember to be as detailed as you can.

      Connections: What topics, ideas, and words that you learned *before* this chapter are **connected** to the new ideas in this chapter? Again, make your list as long as you can.

② MAKING CONNECTIONS

The following is a list of the vocabulary used in this chapter. The words that appear in bold are new to this chapter. Make sure that you are familiar with all of these words and know what they mean. Refer to the glossary or index for any words that you do not yet understand.

b	continuous	coordinates
dependent variable	discrete	**Equal Values Method**
equation	**Figure 0**	graph
growth	independent variable	*m*
pattern	**point of intersection**	**representation**
rule	solution	starting value
system of equations	**web**	$x \rightarrow y$ table
x- and *y*-intercepts	$y = mx + b$	

Make a concept map showing all of the **connections** you can find among the key words and ideas listed above. To show a **connection** between two words, draw a line between them and explain the **connection**, as shown in the example below. A word can be **connected** to any other word as long as there is a **justified connection**. For each key word or idea, provide a sketch that illustrates the idea (see the example below).

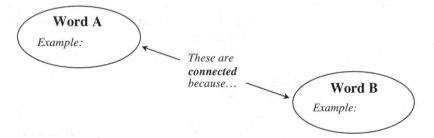

Your teacher may provide you with vocabulary cards to help you get started. If you use the cards to plan your concept map, be sure either to re-draw your concept map on your paper or to glue the vocabulary cards to a poster with all of the **connections** explained for others to see and understand.

While you are making your map, your team may think of related words or ideas that are not listed above. Be sure to include these ideas on your concept map.

③   SUMMARIZING MY UNDERSTANDING

This section gives you an opportunity to show what you know about certain math topics or ideas. Your teacher will give you directions for exactly how to do this.

④   WHAT HAVE I LEARNED?

This section will help you evaluate which types of problems you have seen with which you feel comfortable and those with which you need more help. This section appears at the end of every chapter to help you check your understanding. Even if your teacher does not assign this section, it is a good idea to try the problems and find out for yourself what you know and what you need to work on.

Solve each problem as completely as you can. The table at the end of the closure section has answers to these problems. It also tells you where you can find additional help and practice on problems like these.

CL 4-107. Examine the pattern below.

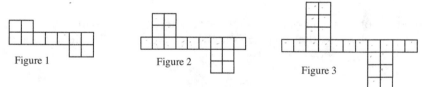

Figure 1   Figure 2   Figure 3

a.   On graph paper, sketch Figure 0 and Figure 4.

b.   Make a table showing Figure 0 through Figure 4.

c.   Write a rule to represent the pattern.

d.   On graph paper, create a graph of the number of tiles in each figure.

e.   What is the growth for the pattern?

f.   Predict how many tiles Figure 100 will have.

CL 4-108. Are the two expressions below equal? Show how you know.

$$4x^2 + 2x - 5 - 3x \quad \text{and} \quad 6x^2 - x + 3 - 2x^2 - 8$$

CL 4-109. Priscilla and Ursula went fishing. Priscilla brought a full box of 32 worms and used one worm every minute. Ursula brought a box with five worms and decided to dig for more before she began fishing. Ursula dug up two worms per minute. When did Priscilla and Ursula have the same number of worms? Show how you know.

CL 4-110. Examine the graph at right.

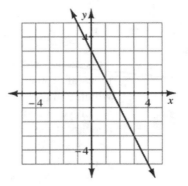

    a.   Give two ways you can tell that the rule $y = 2x - 3$ does not match the graph.

    b.   Make a graph that matches the rule $y = 2x - 3$.

    c.   Find a rule that represents the graph at right.

CL 4-111. Consider the rule $y = 5x + 7$.

    a.   How many tiles are in Figure 0?

    b.   Which figure has 37 tiles?

    c.   In the equation $y = mx + b$, what do the letters m and b represent?

CL 4-112. For each pair of lines below, solve the system by **graphing** and solve it **algebraically** using the Equal Values Method. Explain how the graph confirms the algebraic result.

    a. $y = 7x - 5$ and $y = -2x + 13$

    b. $y = 3x - 1$ and $y = 3x + 2$

CL 4-113. To rent a jet ski at Sam's costs $25 plus $3 per hour. At Claire's, it costs $5 plus $8 per hour. At how many hours will the rental cost at both shops be equal?

    a.   Write an equation that represents each shop's charges. What do your variables represent?

    b.   Solve the problem. Show your work.

CL 4-114. Simplify the following expressions, if possible.

    a. $x + 4x - 3 + 3x^2 - 2x$

    b. $2x + 4y^2 - 6y^2 - 9 - x + 3x$

    c. $3x^2 + 10y - 2y^2 + 4x - 14$

    d. $20 + 3xy - 4xy + y^2 + 10 - y^2$

    e.   Evaluate the expressions in parts (a) and (b) above when $x = 5$ and $y = -2$.

CL 4-115. Copy and complete the table for the linear pattern below.

IN (x)	−4	−3	−2	−1	0	1	2	3	4
OUT (y)					−2	3	8		

    a.   What is the y-intercept? What is the growth factor?

    b.   Find the rule for this line.

    c.   If the output number (y) is −52, what was the input number (x)?

CL 4-116. Use Guess and Check to solve the problem below.

For the school play, the advance tickets cost $3 and tickets at the door cost $5. Thirty more tickets were sold at door than in advance, and $2630 was collected. How many tickets were sold at the door? Write your answer in a sentence.

CL 4-117. Check your answers using the table at the end of the closure section. Which problems do you feel confident about? Which problems were hard? Use the table to make a list of topics you need help on and a list of topics you need to practice more.

⑤   HOW AM I THINKING?

This course focuses on five different **Ways of Thinking**: reversing thinking, justifying, generalizing, making connections, and applying and extending understanding. These are some of the ways in which you think while trying to make sense of a concept or to solve a problem (even outside of math class). During this chapter, you have probably used each Way of Thinking multiple times without even realizing it!

This closure activity will focus on one of these Ways of Thinking: **reversing thinking**. Read the description of this Way of Thinking at right.

Think about the topics that you have learned during this chapter. When did you undo a process? When did you try to go backward in your problem-solving process? You may want to

Reversing Thinking

To reverse your thinking can be described as "thinking backward." You think this way when you want to understand a concept in a new direction. Often, it requires you to try to undo a process. When you catch yourself thinking, "*What if I try to go backwards?*", you are reversing your thinking.

flip through the chapter to refresh your memory about the problems that you have worked on. Discuss any ideas you have with the rest of the class. Once your discussion is complete, examine some of the ways you have **reversed your thinking** as you answer the questions below.

a.   If you know how to go from one representation to another, then there is a way to **reverse the process**. Consider the web connection graph ↔ rule.

   i.   Find the equation of the line graphed at right.

   ii.   Now **reverse the process**. On graph paper, graph the rule $y = 2x - 3$.

   iii. Explore another connection on the web where you **reversed your thinking**. Find or create a problem that represents one direction of solving. Then write and solve another problem that requires you to reverse the process.

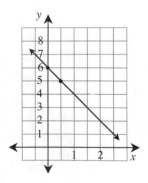

Continues on next page →

Algebra Connections

⑤   *Continued from previous page.*

b.   Usually, if you change an expression into an equivalent expression, there is a
       way to **reverse the process** to return to the original expression. Consider this
       as you answer the questions below.

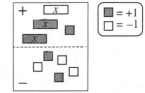

       i.   On your paper, write and simplify the
                expression represented on the expression
                mat at right.

       ii.   Draw an expression mat on your paper that
                uses 8 tiles and has a value of $x + 3$.

       iii.   Explain how you **reversed your thinking** from part (*i*) to solve part (*ii*)
                above.

c.   Now consider how you can **reverse your thinking** when solving a problem
       with proportional relationships.

       i.   For example, if Mr. Wallis pays $25 for 10 gallons of gasoline, how much
                would he pay to fill his scooter (which uses 3 gallons of gasoline)?

       ii.   Now write a question about Mr. Wallis's gasoline use that would require
                you to **reverse your thinking** from part (a) to solve. Explain why and
                how it requires you to **reverse your thinking**.

Answers and Support for Closure Activity #4
What Have I Learned?

Problem	Solution	Need Help?	More Practice

CL 4-107. a.

Figure 0   Figure 4

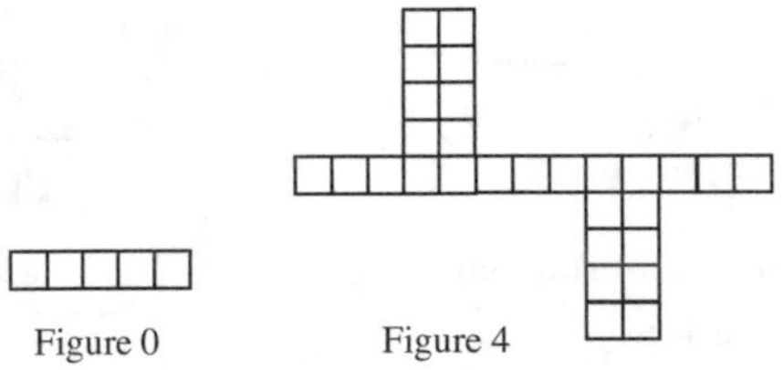

b.

Figure Number	0	1	2	3	4
Number of Tiles	5	11	17	23	29

c. $y = 6x + 5$

d.

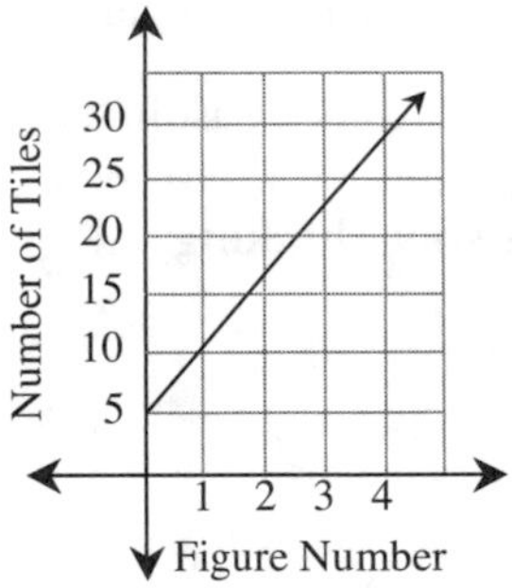

e. Each figure has 6 more tiles than the previous figure.

f. Figure 100 will have 605 tiles.

Need Help? Sections 3.1 and 4.1, Lesson 4.1.7 Math Notes box

More Practice Problems 4-8, 4-9, 4-11, 4-21, 4-35, 4-36, 4-37, 4-49, 4-59, and 4-60

CL 4-108. yes; $4x^2 - x - 5 = 4x^2 - x - 5$

Need Help? Lesson 2.1.5 Math Notes box

More Practice Problem 4-6

CL 4-109. They will have the same number of worms after 9 minutes.

Need Help? Lesson 4.2.1 Math Notes box, Lesson 4.2.2

More Practice Problems 4-80, 4-85, 4-87, 4-88, 4-94, and 4-99

Problem	Solution	Need Help?	More Practice

CL 4-110. a. The line goes down as x increases. The y-intercept is at +3.

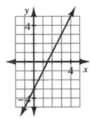

b. See graph at right.

c. $y = -2x + 3$

Lessons 4.1.3, 4.1.4, and 4.1.6; Lesson 4.1.7 Math Notes box

Problems 4-19, 4-27, 4-36, 4-49, 4-50, 4-51, 4-54, and 4-55

CL 4-111. a. There are 7 tiles in figure 0.

b. Figure 6 has 37 tiles.

c. m represents the growth factor, and b represents the number of tiles in Figure 0.

Lessons 4.1.2 and 4.1.4, Lesson 4.1.7 Math Notes box

Problems 4-10, 4-11, 4-26, 4-29, 4-52, 4-54, 4-56, and 4-62

CL 4-112. a. The two lines intersect at the point (2, 9).

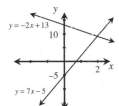

b. There is no solution to the system of equations, because the lines are parallel.

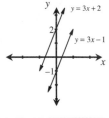

Lesson 4.2.1 Math Notes box, Lesson 4.2.3, problem 4-86, Lesson 4.2.4 Math Notes box

Problems 4-68, 4-88, 4-92, 4-96, 4-97, 4-98, and 4-106

CL 4-113. a. $y = 25 + 3x$ and $y = 5 + 8x$; x represents the number of hours rental, and y represents the cost.

b. After 4 hours of ski rental, the cost at both shops will be equal.

Lesson 4.2.1 Math Notes box, Lesson 4.2.2

Problems 4-80, 4-85, 4-87, 4-88, 4-94, and 4-99

Problem	Solution	Need Help?	More Practice
CL 4-114.	a. $3x^2 + 3x - 3$ b. $-2y^2 + 4x - 9$ c. It cannot be simplified any further. d. $-xy + 30$ e. (a) 87; (b) 3	Lesson 2.1.3 Math Notes box, Lesson 2.1.5 Math Notes box	Problems 4-6 and 4-57

CL 4-115.

IN (x)	−4	−3	−2	−1	0
OUT (y)	−22	−17	−12	−7	−2

table continued:

1	2	3	4
3	8	13	18

a. The starting value is −2. The growth factor is 5.

b. $y = 5x - 2$

c. −10

Lesson 4.1.4, Lesson 4.1.7 Math Notes box

Problems 4-7, 4-28, 4-34, 4-35, 4-63, 4-74, and 4-100

CL 4-116.   340 tickets were sold at the door.

Problems 1-41 and 1-42, Lesson 2.1.7 Math Notes box

Problems 4-24 and 4-103

CHAPTER 5   Multiplication and Proportions

In Chapter 2, you focused on simplifying expressions by adding and subtracting like terms. In Section 5.1, you will focus on multiplying expressions. You will also solve equations that contain products. While these new ideas will be introduced using algebra tiles, you will also develop a method to multiply expressions without using tiles.

Then in Section 5.2, you will continue your study of proportional situations started in Section 2.2. By the end of this chapter, you will develop an algebraic method to solve problems involving proportional relationships.

In this chapter, you will learn:

➢ How to distribute an expression with and without algebra tiles.

➢ How to multiply binomials and trinomials using algebra tiles and a generic rectangle.

➢ How to use the Distributive Property to rewrite expressions and solve equations.

➢ How to solve multi-variable equations for one of the variables.

➢ How to write and solve equations with equivalent ratios to solve problems involving proportional relationships.

Guiding Questions

Think about these questions throughout this chapter:

What is the area?

How can I write it?

What's the relationship?

How can I solve it?

Is there another way?

Chapter Outline

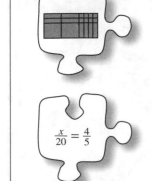

Section 5.1 Using algebra tiles and generic rectangles, you will develop a method to rewrite products, such as $(3x - 2)(4 + x)$. Then, continuing the solving focus of Chapter 3, you will study how to solve one-variable equations containing products and how to solve multi-variable equations for one of the variables.

Section 5.2 Here you will continue your study of proportional situations started in Section 2.2. You will develop algebraic techniques to solve proportions and continue to build intuition about what makes a relationship proportional.

5.1.1 What can I do with rectangles?

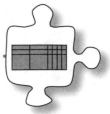

Exploring an Area Model

In Chapter 2, you used tiles to rewrite algebraic expressions involving addition and subtraction. In this chapter, you will use algebra tiles again, but this time you will rewrite expressions using multiplication.

5-1.   Your teacher will put this group of tiles on the overhead:

     a.   Using your own tiles, arrange the same group of tiles into one large rectangle. On your paper, sketch what your rectangle looks like.

     b.   What are the dimensions (length and width) of the rectangle you made? Label your sketch with its dimensions.

     c.   Write a *length · width = area* statement showing the equivalence of the area as the **product** of its length and width and as the **sum** of its parts.

5-2.   Your teacher will assign several of the expressions below. For each expression, build a rectangle using all of the tiles, if possible. Sketch each rectangle, find its dimensions, and write an expression showing the equivalence of the area as a **sum** (like $x^2 + 5x + 6$) and as a **product** (like $(x + 3)(x + 2)$). If it is not possible to build a rectangle, explain why not.

     a. $x^2 + 3x + 2$ b. $6x + 15$

     c. $2x^2 + 7x + 6$ d. $xy + x + y + 1$

     e. $2x^2 + 10x + 12$ f. $2y^2 + 6y$

     g. $y^2 + xy + 2x + 2y$ h. $3x^2 + 4x + 1$

     i. $x^2 + 2xy + y^2 + 3x + 3y + 2$ j. $2xy + 4y + x + 2$

5-3.   Make a rectangle from any number of tiles. Your rectangle must contain at least one of each of the following tiles: x^2, y^2, xy, x, y, and 1. Sketch your rectangle in your Learning Log and write its area as a **product** and as a **sum**. Explain how you know that the product and sum are equivalent. Title this entry "Area as a Product and as a Sum" and label it with today's date.

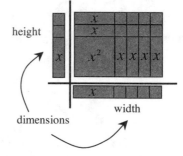

METHODS AND MEANINGS

Multiplying Algebraic Expressions with Tiles

MATH NOTES

The area of a rectangle can be written two different ways. It can be written as a **product** of its base and height or as a **sum** of its parts. For example, the area of the shaded rectangle at right can be written two ways:

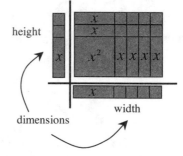

height

width

dimensions

area as a product   **area as a sum**

$$\underbrace{(x+4)}_{base}\underbrace{(x+2)}_{height} = \underbrace{x^2+6x+8}_{area}$$

Review & Preview

5-4.   For the entire rectangle at right, find the area of each part and then find the area of the whole.

	11	8
7		
3		

5-5.   A tile pattern has 5 tiles in Figure 0 and adds 7 tiles in each new figure. Write the equation of the line that represents the growth of this pattern.

5-6.   Write the area of the rectangle at right as a **product** and as a **sum**. Refer to the Math Notes box for this lesson if you need help.

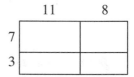

5-7.   Draw Figures 1, 2, and 3 for a tile pattern that could be described by $y = -3x + 10$.

5-8.   Fisher thinks that any two lines must have a point of intersection. Is he correct? If so, explain how you know. If not, produce a **counterexample**. That is, find two lines that do not have a point of intersection and explain how you know.

5-9.   In the last election, candidate A received twice as many votes as candidate B. Candidate C received 15,000 fewer votes than candidate B. If a total of 109,000 votes were cast, how many votes did candidate A receive?

5.1.2 How can I rewrite a product?

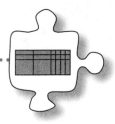

Multiplying Binomials and the Distributive Property

In Lesson 5.1.1, you made rectangles with algebra tiles and found the dimensions of the rectangles. You wrote the area both as a sum and as a product. Today you will **reverse** the process, starting with the product of the dimensions of a rectangle and finding its area as a sum.

5-10.   For each of the following rectangles, find the dimensions (length and width) and write the area as the **product** of the dimensions and as the **sum** of the tiles. Remember to combine like terms whenever possible.

a.

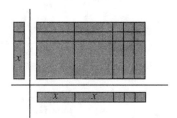

b.

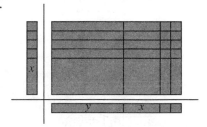

5-11.   Your teacher will assign your team four of the expressions below. Use your cornerpiece to build rectangles with the given dimensions. Sketch each rectangle on your paper, label its dimensions, and write an equivalence statement for its area as a **product** and as a **sum**. Be prepared to share your solutions with the class.

a. $(2x)(4x)$

b. $(x+3)(2x+1)$

c. $2x(x+5)$

d. $(2x+1)(2x+1)$

e. $x(2x+y)$

f. $(2x+5)(x+y+2)$

g. $2(3x+5)$

h. $y(2x+y+3)$

5-12.   With the class, examine the solutions you found
        for parts (c), (e), (g), and (h) of problem 5-11.
        As you discuss your observations, you may
        want to focus on these questions:

                Do you see a pattern?

        What happens to the term outside the parentheses?

        What happens to the terms inside the parentheses?

                Does this pattern make sense?

5-13.   Using the patterns your team identified, multiply the following expressions *without*
        using your tiles. Be ready to share your process with the class.

        a. $2x(6x + 5)$ b. $6(4x + 1)$

        c. $3y(4x + 3)$ d. $7y(10x + 11y)$

5-14.   The pattern you used to multiply a one-term expression (like x) by
        a multiple-term expression (like $x + 2$) is called the **Distributive
        Property**. In your Learning Log, describe this pattern. Make up
        your own example and show the pattern in as many ways as you
        can. Title this entry "The Distributive Property" and label it with
        today's date.

5-15.   Examine the rectangles formed with tiles below. For each figure, write its area as a
        product of the base and height and as a **sum** of its parts.

        a.   b.

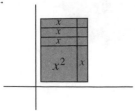   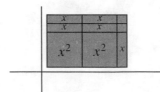

5-16.   Find the total area of each rectangle below. Each number inside the rectangle
          represents the area of that smaller rectangle, while each number along the side
          represents the length of that portion of the side.

a.
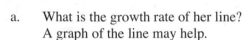

b.

5-17.   When solving $\frac{x}{6} = \frac{5}{2}$ for x, Nathan noticed that x is divided by 6.

a.   What can he do to both sides of the equation to get x alone?

b.   Solve for x. Then check your solution in the original equation.

c.   Use the same process to solve this equation for x: $\frac{x}{10} = \frac{2}{5}$.

5-18.   Jamila wants to play a game called "Guess My
          Line." She gives you the following hints:
          "Two points on my line are (1, 1) and (2, 4)."

a.   What is the growth rate of her line?
       A graph of the line may help.

b.   What is the y-intercept of her line?

c.   What is the equation of her line?

5-19.   A calculator manufacturer offers two different models for students. The company
          has sold 10,000 scientific calculators so far and continues to sell 1500 per month.
          It has sold 18,000 graphical models and continues to sell 1300 of this model each
          month. When will the sales of scientific calculators equal the sales of graphical
          calculators?

5-20.   On graph paper, make an $x \rightarrow y$ table and graph $y = 2x^2 - x - 3$. Find its x- and
          y-intercepts.

5.1.3 How can I generalize the process?

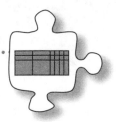

Using Generic Rectangles to Multiply

You have been using algebra tiles and the concept of area to multiply algebraic expressions. Today you will be introduced to a tool that will help you find the product of the dimensions of a rectangle. This will allow you to multiply expressions without tiles.

5-21.   Use the Distributive Property to find each product below.

   a. $6(-3x + 2)$

   b. $x(4x - 2)$

   c. $5t(10 - 3t)$

   d. $-4(8 - 6k + y)$

5-22.   Write the area as a **product** and as a **sum** for the composite rectangle shown at right.

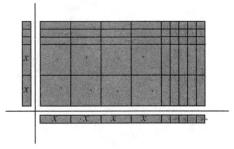

5-23.   Now examine the following diagram. How is it similar to the set of tiles in problem 5-22? How is it different? Talk with your teammates and write down all of your observations.

	$4x$	5
3	$12x$	15
$2x$	$8x^2$	$10x$

Algebra Connections

5-24.   Diagrams like the one in problem 5-23 are referred to as **generic rectangles**.
Generic rectangles allow you to use an area model to multiply expressions without
using the algebra tiles. Using this model, you can multiply with values that are
difficult to represent with tiles.

Draw each of the following generic rectangles on your paper. Then find the area of
each part and write the area of the whole rectangle as a **product** and as a **sum**.

a.

b.

c.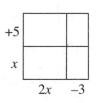

d.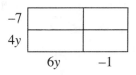

e.   How did you find the area of the individual parts of each generic rectangle?

5-25.   Multiply and simplify the following expressions using either a generic rectangle or
the Distributive Property. For part (a), verify that your solution is correct by
building a rectangle with algebra tiles.

a. $(x+5)(3x+2)$

b. $(2y-5)(5y+7)$

c. $3x(6y-11)$

d. $(5w-2p)(3w+p-4)$

5-26.   THE GENERIC RECTANGLE CHALLENGE

Copy each of the generic rectangles below and fill in the missing dimensions and
areas. Then write the entire area as a product and as a sum. Be prepared to share your
reasoning with the class.

a.

b.

5

c.

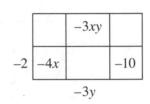

−3y

d.

Ⓜ ETHODS AND MEANINGS

The Distributive Property

The **Distributive Property** states that for any three terms a, b, and c:

$$a(b + c) = ab + ac$$

That is, when a multiplies a group of terms, such as $(b + c)$, then it
multiplies *each* term of the group. For example, when multiplying $2(x + 4)$,
the 2 multiplies both the x and the 4. This can be shown with **algebra tiles**
or in a **generic rectangle** (see below).

	$2 \cdot x$	$2 \cdot 4$

2 | |

x $+4$

$$2(x + 4) = 2 \cdot x + 2 \cdot 4 = 2x + 8$$

The 2 multiplies each term.

5-27. Use a generic rectangle to multiply the following expressions. Write each solution both as a sum and as a product.

   a. $(2x+5)(x+6)$

   b. $(m-3)(3m+5)$

   c. $(12x+1)(x-5)$

   d. $(3-5y)(2+y)$

5-28. Solve each equation below for x. Then check your solutions.

   a. $\frac{x}{8} = \frac{3}{4}$

   b. $\frac{2}{5} = \frac{x}{40}$

   c. $\frac{1}{8} = \frac{x}{12}$

   d. $\frac{x}{10} = \frac{12}{15}$

5-29. Copy and complete each of the Diamond Problems below. The pattern used in the Diamond Problems is shown at right.

   a.

   b.

   c.

   d.

5-30. Review what you know about graphs by answering the following questions.

   a. Find the equation of the line graphed at right.

   b. What are its x- and y-intercepts?

   c. On your own graph paper, graph the line.

   d. On the same set of axes, graph a line *parallel* to the line graphed at right, but through the *origin* $(0, 0)$. Find the equation of this new line.

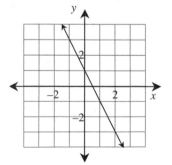

5-31. Mailboxes Plus sends packages overnight for $5 plus $0.25 per ounce. United Packages charges $2 plus $0.35 per ounce. Mr. Molinari noticed that his package would cost the same to mail using either service. How much does his package weigh?

5-32. Decide if the statement below is true or false. **Justify** your response.

"The expression $(x+3)(x-1)$ is equivalent to $(x-1)(3+x)$."

5.1.4 What if an equation has a product?

Solving Equations With Multiplication

Now that you know how to multiply algebraic expressions, you can solve equations that involve multiplication.

5-33.   Review what you learned in Lesson 5.1.3 by multiplying each expression below. First decide if you will multiply each expression using the Distributive Property or using a generic rectangle. Remember to simplify your result.

   a. $(6x - 11)(2x + 5)$

   b. $-2x(15x - 3)$

   c. $(6 - y)(y + 2)$

   d. $16(3 - m^2)$

5-34.   How can you represent $3(2x + 1)$ with algebra tiles? Work with your team to build this expression.

   a.   Build an equation mat to represent the equation $3(2x + 1) = 8x - 5$. Solve this equation and record your steps algebraically.

   b.   Check that your solution is correct by substituting your answer into the original equation.

5-35.   **Multiple Choice:** Which equations below are represented by the diagram at right? Be prepared to defend your answer.

   a. $3(x + 1) - 3 - 2(x + 3) = -2(x + 6)$

   b. $3x - 1 - 3 - 2x + 6 = -2x + 12$

   c. $3x + 3 - 3 - 2x - 6 = -2x - 12$

5-36.   Copy one of the correct equations from problem 5-35 and solve for x. Be sure to record all of your steps. Check your solution by substituting your answer into your equation.

Algebra Connections

5-37.   Your teacher will assign you several of the equations below. Work with a partner to solve the equations using algebra tiles and an equation mat. Check your solution by substituting your answer into the original equation.

   a. $3(x-4)=15$

   b. $1-2(3x-5)=11$

   c. $5(y-4)=10$

   d. $-2(x-2)=11$

   e. $6(x+4)=3(5x+2)$

   f. $5-x(x+3)=-(x+5)(x+1)$

5-38.   Now work with your team to solve each of these equations without using tiles. You may want to draw generic rectangles to help you rewrite the products.

   a. $2(y-2)=-6$

   b. $43=4(x+6)-1$

   c. $(x+3)(x+4)=(x+1)(x+2)$

   d. $2(x+1)+3=3(x-1)$

METHODS AND MEANINGS

Checking a Solution

To check a solution to an equation, substitute the solution into the equation and verify that it makes the two sides of the equation equal.

For example, to verify that $x=10$ is a solution to the equation $3(x-5)=15$, substitute 10 into the equation for x and then verify that the two sides of the equation are equal.

As shown at right, $x=10$ is a solution to the equation $3(x-5)=15$.

$$3(10-5)\overset{?}{=}15$$
$$3(5)\overset{?}{=}15$$
$$15=15 \quad \checkmark \quad Correct!$$

What happens if your answer is incorrect? To investigate this, test any solution that is not correct. For example, try substituting $x=2$ into the same equation. The result shows that $x=2$ is not a solution to this equation.

$$3(2-5)\overset{?}{=}15$$
$$3(-3)\overset{?}{=}15$$
$$-9\neq15 \quad ✗ \quad Not\ true,\ so\ x=2\ is\ not\ a\ solution.$$

5-39. Which equation below has *no* solution? Explain how you know.

    a. $4(x+1) = 2x + 4$ b. $9 - 5x + 2 = 4 - 5x$

5-40. Rena says that if $x = -5$, the equation below is true. Her friend, Dean, says the answer is $x = 3$. Who is correct? **Justify** your conclusion.

$$9(x + 4) = 1 + 2x$$

5-41. Find the rule for the pattern represented at right.

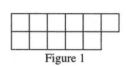

Figure 1

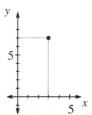

5-42. Harry the Hungry Hippo is munching on the lily pads in his pond. When he got to the pond, there were 20 lily pads, but he is eating 4 lily pads an hour. Heinrick the Hungrier Hippo found a better pond with 29 lily pads! He eats 7 lily pads every hour.

    a.   If Harry and Heinrick start eating at the same time, when will their ponds have the same number of lily pads remaining?

    b.   How many lily pads will be left in each hole at that time?

5-43. Graph each equation below on the same set of axes and label the point of intersection with its coordinates.

$$y = 2x + 3 \qquad\qquad y = x + 1$$

5-44. Shooter Magee is the Wolverines' best free-throw shooter. He normally makes three out of every four shots. In an upcoming charity event, Shooter will shoot 500 free throws. If he makes over 400 baskets, the school wins $1000. Should the Wolverines expect to win the cash for the school? Show and organize your work.

5.1.5 How can I change it to $y = mx + b$ form?

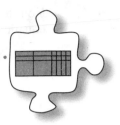

Working With Multi-Variable Equations

So far in this course, you have used your equation mat to find solutions for all types of linear equations with one variable. Today you will learn how to **apply** these skills to solving linear equations with two variables. As you work today, keep the following questions in mind:

What is a solution to an equation? What does it look like?

What is the growth factor?

What is the y-intercept?

5-45.   You now have a lot of experience working with equations that compare two quantities. For example, while working with the height of a tree, you found the relationship $y = 4x + 5$, which compared x (the number of years after it was planted) with y (its height in feet). For this tree:

a.   What was its starting height? How can you tell from the equation?

b.   What was its growth rate? That is, how many feet did the tree grow per year? **Justify** your answer.

5-46.   CHANGING FORMS

You could find the growth rate and starting value for $y = 4x + 5$ quickly because the equation is in $y = mx + b$ form. But what if the equation is in a different form? Explore this situation below.

a.   The line $-6x + 2y = 10$ is written in **standard form**. Can you tell what the growth rate of the line is? Its y-intercept? Predict these values.

b.   The equation $-6x + 2y = 10$ is shown on the equation mat at right. Set up this equation on your equation mat using tiles. Using only "legal" moves, rearrange the tiles to get y by itself on the left side of the mat. Record each of your moves algebraically.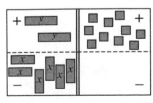

c.   Now use your result from part (b) to find the growth factor and y-intercept of the line $-6x + 2y = 10$. Did your result match your prediction in part (a)?

5-47.   Your teacher will assign you one of the linear equations listed below. For your equation:

- Use algebra tiles to set up the equation on your equation mat.

- Using only "legal" moves, rearrange your tiles to create an equation that starts with "$y = \ldots$" Be sure to record all of your moves algebraically and be prepared to share your steps with the class.

- What is the growth factor of your line? What is the y-intercept? How can you tell?

a. $2x + y = 3x - 7$ b. $x + 2y = 3x + 4$

c. $3y + 2 = 2y - 5x$ d. $2(y - 3) = 2x - 6$

e. $5 - 3(x + 1) = 2y - 3x + 2$ f. $x - (y + 2) = 2(2x + 1)$

5-48.   Solve each of the following equations for the indicated variable. Use your equation mat if it is helpful. Write down each of your steps algebraically.

a.   Solve for y: $2(y - 3) = 4$

b.   Solve for x: $2x + 5y = 10$

c.   Solve for y: $6x + 3y = 4y + 11$

d.   Solve for x: $3(2x + 4) = 2 + 6x + 10$

e.   Solve for x: $y = -3x + 6$

f.   Solve for p: $m = 8 - 2(p - m)$

g.   Solve for y: $x^2 + 4y = (x + 6)(x - 2)$

h.   Solve for q: $4(q - 8) = 7q + 5$

METHODS AND MEANINGS

Linear Equations

MATH NOTES

    A **linear equation** is an equation that forms a line when it is graphed. This type of equation may be written in several different forms. Although these forms look different, they are equivalent; that is, they all graph the same line.

STANDARD FORM: An equation in $ax + by = c$ form, such as $-6x + 3y = 18$.

$y = mx + b$ **FORM:** An equation in $y = mx + b$ form, such as $y = 2x - 6$.

You can quickly find the **growth factor** and **y-intercept** of a line in $y = mx + b$ form. For the equation $y = 2x - 6$, the growth factor is 2, while the y-intercept is $(0, -6)$.

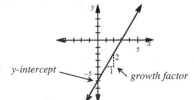

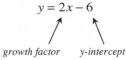

$$y = 2x - 6$$

growth factor   y-intercept

Review & Preview

5-49.   Use what you know about $y = mx + b$ to graph each of the following equations quickly on the same set of axes.

    a. $y = 3x + 5$ b. $y = -2x + 10$ c. $y = 1.5x$

5-50.   Multiply each of the following expressions. Show all of your work.

    a. $(x + 3)(4x + 5)$ b. $(-2x - 4)(3x + 4)$

    c. $(3y - 8)(-x + y)$ d. $(y - 4)(3x + 5y - 2)$

5-51.   Solve each of the following equations for the indicated variable. Show all of your steps.

a. $y = 2x - 5$ for x

b. $p = -3w + 9$ for w

c. $2m - 6 = 4n + 4$ for m

d. $3x - y = -2y$ for y

5-52.   Find the rule for the following tile pattern.

Figure 2   Figure 3   Figure 4

5-53.   Consider these two equations:
$$y = 3x - 2$$
$$y = 4 + 3x$$

a.   Graph both equations on the same set of axes.

b.   Solve this system using the Equal Values Method.

c.   Explain how the answer to part (b) agrees with the graph you made in part (a).

5-54.   Marta has made the following statements. Determine if each statement is true or false. If true, use algebraic properties to **justify** your conclusion. If false, explain how you know.

a. $(6x - 3) \cdot 1$ is equivalent to $4x - 3 + 2x$

b. $3 - 6x$ is equivalent to $6x - 3$

c. $3 + (1 - 6x)$ is equivalent to $(3 + 1) - 6x$

5.1.6 What kinds of equations can I solve now?

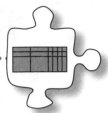

Solving Equations Without Manipulatives

So far, you have developed your equation-solving skills in three major sections of this course (Sections 2.1, 3.2, and 5.1). Today you will practice solving equations while moving away from using algebra tiles. At the end of the lesson, you will summarize everything you know about solving equations.

5-55.   Your teacher will explain the way you are working today on the problems below. As you work, be sure to record all of your steps carefully. Check your solutions, if possible.

a.   Solve for x: $5(4x + 3) = 75$

b.   Solve for y: $x - 2y = 4$

c.   Solve for x: $-6 = -6(3x - 8)$

d.   Solve for y: $3x + 6y = 24$

e.   Solve for x: $2 - 3(2x - 1) = 17$

f.   Solve for y: $5 + 2(x + y) = 11$

g.   Solve for x: $y = -3x + 4$

h.   Solve for x: $x(2x - 1) = 2x^2 + 5x - 12$

i.   Solve for w: $2(v - 3) = 1 - (w + 4)$

j.   Solve for x: $4x(x + 1) = (2x - 3)(2x + 5)$

5-56.   SUMMARY OF SOLVING EQUATIONS

Write a letter to Clarissa, a new student in class, explaining everything you have learned about how to solve equations. Clarissa does not have algebra tiles, so you will need to show her how to solve *without* the tiles. Make up examples that show all of the different equation-solving skills you have. Be sure to explain your ideas to her thoroughly so she will know what to do on her own.

5-57.   Solve each of the following equations. Be sure to show your work carefully and check your answers.

a. $2(3x-4)=22$

b. $6(2x-5)=-(x+4)$

c. $2-(y+2)=3y$

d. $3+4(x+1)=159$

5-58.   Find the dimensions of the generic rectangle at right. Then write an equivalency statement (length · width = area) of the area as a product and as a sum.

x^2	$-5x$
$3x$	-15

5-59.   Consider the rule $y=\frac{1}{3}x-2$.

a.   Without graphing, find the zero of $y=\frac{1}{3}x-2$. Remember that a zero of a rule is an input that makes the output zero.

b.   Make a table and graph $y=\frac{1}{3}x-2$ on graph paper.

c.   How could you find the zero of $y=\frac{1}{3}x-2$ with your graph from part (b)? What about with the table? Explain.

5-60.   One number is five more than a second number. The product of the numbers is 3300. Find the two numbers.

5-61.   Ms. B and Ms. D are writing problems for an algebra book. Ms. B started with 10 problems already written, and she can write 6 problems an hour. Ms. D had no problems written, but she writes 10 problems an hour.

a.   When will Ms. B have the same number of problems written as Ms. D?

b.   How many problems will they each have written at that time?

5-62.   How many yearbooks should your school order? Your student government surveyed three homeroom classes, and 55 of 90 students said that they would definitely buy a yearbook. If your school has 2000 students, approximately how many books should be ordered? Show and organize your work.

5.2.1 How can I write proportions?

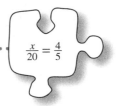

Setting Up and Solving Proportions

In Chapter 2, you studied proportional situations and used several strategies to solve problems involving such situations. Since then, you have learned to set up and solve equations to solve many types of problems. Today you will investigate methods for using equations to solve proportion problems.

5-63. Use what you know about solving equations to solve for x. Remember to check your solution to each equation. Be prepared to share your method with the class.

a. $\frac{x}{2} = 9$ b. $\frac{x}{18} = \frac{2}{3}$ c. $\frac{3}{2} = \frac{x+3}{5}$ d. $\frac{7}{3} = \frac{4}{x}$

5-64. POLITICAL POLL

Mr. Mears is running for mayor of Atlanta. His campaign managers are eager to determine how many citizens of Atlanta will vote for him in the upcoming election. They decided to pay a respected, impartial statistical company to survey potential voters (a process called "polling") in order to find out how many people will probably vote for Mr. Mears.

One afternoon, pollsters called 100 random potential voters in Atlanta to ask them how they would vote in the election. During that survey, 68 people indicated that they would vote for Mr. Mears.

a. If the pollsters had instead called 50 randomly selected potential voters, predict how many people would have said that they would vote for Mr. Mears.

b. Is this relationship proportional? Why or why not?

c. Carina decided to organize the information in a table like the one shown at right. She wants to figure out how many people will probably vote for Mr. Mears if 350,125 people vote in the election. Help her determine how many votes Mr. Mears will probably receive. Then complete her table on your paper. Be prepared to share your method with the class.

Number of Potential Voters	Number of Votes Expected for Mr. Mears
50	
100	68
350,125	

5-65.   Carina noticed a pattern in her table. If she makes a **ratio** (a fraction) of the two numbers of potential voters and another ratio of the two numbers of votes for Mr. Mears, the two ratios are equal! See her notes below:

Number of Potential Voters	Number of Votes Expected for Mr. Mears
50	34
100	68

$\dfrac{50}{100}\ \dfrac{\text{number of voters}}{\text{number of voters}} = \dfrac{1}{2}$ ← → $\dfrac{34}{68}\ \dfrac{\text{votes for Mears}}{\text{votes for Mears}} = \dfrac{1}{2}$

a.   Carina wonders what would happen if she created ratios with numbers in the same row. Write two ratios using the values in the rows circled at right. Are your ratios equal?

Number of Potential Voters	Number of Votes Expected for Mr. Mears
50	34
100	68

b.   What about diagonally? Will the ratios be equal? Set up some ratios and determine if they are equal.

c.   Why are some ratios equal and others not?

d.   Carina's neighborhood has 527 potential voters. If her neighborhood reflects the entire city, how many neighbors will probably vote for Mr. Mears? Since she does not know the answer to this question, she placed an x in the table at right.

Number of Potential Voters	Number of Votes Expected for Mr. Mears
50	34
100	68
527	x

Write an equation using two equal ratios and solve for x. Then answer her question.

5-66.   Make a table and set up an equation for each proportional situation below.

a.   In two minutes, Stacie can write her name 17 times. How long will it take her to write her name 85 times?

b.   Eight of 29 students in your class want to attend the Winter Ball. If your class represents the entire school, how many of the 1490 students will probably attend the dance?

METHODS AND MEANINGS

MATH NOTES

Ratios and Proportions

A **ratio** is a way to compare two related numbers, such as 68 expected votes for Mr. Mears out of 100 people surveyed. It can be written with a colon, such as 68:100, or it can be written as a fraction, such as:

$$\frac{68 \text{ votes for Mr. Mears}}{100 \text{ people surveyed}}$$

A ratio can compare any two quantities, such as comparing the number of boys and girls in your class (such as 17 boys:18 girls), or comparing the heights of two people (such as $\frac{62 \text{ inches}}{65 \text{ inches}}$).

An equation that sets two ratios equal is called a **proportion**. For example, the proportion below is an equation made up of two equal ratios:

$$\frac{68 \text{ votes for Mr. Mears}}{100 \text{ people surveyed}} = \frac{34 \text{ votes for Mr. Mears}}{50 \text{ people surveyed}}$$

Review & Preview

5-67.　Chi loves to read. He can speed-read 40 pages in 3 minutes. How long should it take him to read *The Scarlet Letter*, a 265-page novel?

5-68.　GETTING IN SHAPE

Frank weighs 160 pounds and is on a diet to gain two pounds a week so that he can make the football team. John weighs 208 pounds and is on a diet to lose three pounds a week so that he can be on the wrestling team in a lower weight class.

a.　If Frank and John can meet these goals with their diets, when will they weigh the same, and how much will they weigh at that time?

b.　Clearly explain your method.

5-69.   Below are two pairs of equal ratios. For each pair, find two more ratios that are equal.

a. $\dfrac{1}{5} = \dfrac{10}{50} = \dfrac{?}{?} = \dfrac{?}{?}$

b. $\dfrac{13}{20} = \dfrac{65}{100} = \dfrac{?}{?} = \dfrac{?}{?}$

5-70.   Find each of the following products by drawing and labeling a generic rectangle or by using the Distributive Property.

a. $(x+5)(x+4)$

b. $2y(y+3)$

5-71.   Simplify the expressions below. You may want to draw or visualize algebra tiles to help you rewrite these problems.

a. $(2x^2 + 3x + 5) + (x^2 + 2x + 8)$

b. $(3x^2 + 8x + 1) + (2x^2 + 8x + 4)$

c. $(3x^2 + 5x + 7) - (4x^2 + x + 1)$

d. $(x^2 + 9x + 8) - (x^2 + 4x + 8)$

e. $(7x^2 + x + 10) - (3x^2 + 12x + 12)$

5.2.2 What strategy can I use to solve?

Practice With Proportions

In the last lesson, you used equations to solve problems involving proportional situations. Today you will practice writing and solving these special equations, called **proportions**, while you help a student set up a recycling program for her school. As you work, focus on these questions:

What information can you use to answer this question?

How can you use that information to write an equation?

5-72.   Solve for x. Remember to check your solution to each equation.

a. $7.5 = \dfrac{x}{4}$

b. $\dfrac{x}{20} = \dfrac{4}{5}$

c. $\dfrac{x-4}{12} = \dfrac{7}{3}$

d. $\dfrac{100}{30} = \dfrac{4}{3x}$

5-73.   RECYCLING CLUB

Elsie is starting a recycling club at her school and
hopes to use the money earned from recycling cans
to buy recycling bins for the school.

Elsie first needs to figure out how much the cans
that can be collected at her school will weigh, so
she starts by weighing the cans in her recycling bin
at home. She finds that 50 cans weigh 0.77 kg. The
next day, Elsie counts cans at school and finds that
her fellow students throw away 1240 cans each day.

a.   Put all of Elsie's information into a table
      like the one shown at right. Let x represent
      anything Elsie does not know yet.

# of Cans	Weight (kg)

b.   Write and solve a **proportion** (an equation
      setting two ratios equal) from your table.
      How much do all of the school's cans weigh?

c.   Elsie's school just got a new soda machine in the cafeteria. Now the students at
      her school consume 2070 cans a day. Add this information to your table, and
      then use a proportion to find out how much all of those cans weigh.

5-74.   In order to buy recycling bins for her school, Elsie plans to collect empty aluminum
         cans in big plastic bags and drive them to a local recycling center. Elsie wants to
         figure out how many days she will need to use plastic bags before she can buy the
         recycling bins.

a.   The recycling center pays 25 cents per kg for
      aluminum cans. If her school recycles 2070 cans
      each day, how much money will Elsie earn each
      day by recycling?

b.   Elsie has a friend at a local store who can get her
      6 recycling bins for $14.99. Elsie thinks her
      school needs 30 recycling bins. Set up and solve
      a proportion to find out how much money Elsie
      needs in order to buy all of the bins for her
      school. Remember to check your answer.

c.   Now put it all together: Assuming Elsie recycles
      about 2070 cans each day, for how many days
      will Elsie have to recycle before she can buy her
      school new recycling bins?

5-75.   Jeremy enlarged the shape at right to create a similar shape. The side that was originally 34 units long became 51 units long. How long is the side that was originally 10 units long?

5-76.   Beth's favorite toy is a 4-inch-long scale model of a popular convertible. The full-sized convertible is 184 inches long and 74 inches wide. Use a proportion to find the width of Beth's model.

LOOKING DEEPER

Rational Numbers and Closure

Any number that can be written in the form $\frac{a}{b}$ (with a and b being integers and b not being zero) is called a **rational number**.

For example, -5, $2\frac{3}{4}$, and $0.\overline{6}$ are all rational numbers, as illustrated below.

$$-5 = \frac{-5}{1} \qquad\qquad 2\frac{3}{4} = \frac{11}{4} \qquad\qquad 0.\overline{6} = \frac{2}{3}$$

A set of numbers is called **closed** under an operation (like addition or multiplication) when using that operation with some of those numbers always results in one of those kinds of numbers. For example, odd numbers are closed under multiplication since $(odd) \cdot (odd) = odd$, but are not closed under addition since $(odd) + (odd) \neq odd$. The **closure properties** of rational numbers state that for all rational numbers a and b, $a + b$ and $a \cdot b$ are both rational numbers.

5-77.   Solve each equation below for the indicated variable, if possible. Show all steps.

a.   Solve for x: $2x + 22 = 12$

b.   Solve for y: $2x - y = 3$

c.   Solve for x: $2x + 15 = 2x - 15$

d.   Solve for y: $6x + 2y = 10$

Algebra Connections

5-78.   Janelle came to bat 464 times in 131 games. At this rate, how many times should she expect to have at bat in a full season of 162 games?

5-79.   Jung's car travels 32 miles per gallon of gas. For each question below, write an equation, and then solve it.

   a.   How far will Jung's car go on 8 gallons of gas?

   b.   If Jung drives 118 miles, how much gas will be used?

5-80.   The graph at right contains the lines for $y = x + 2$ and $y = 2x - 1$.

   a.   Using the graph, what is the solution to this system?

   b.   Solve the system algebraically to confirm your answer to part (a).

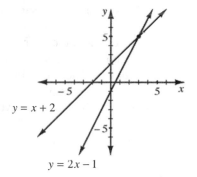

5-81.   The Math Notes box for this lesson explains that the set (or group) of odd numbers is closed under multiplication because (odd)(odd) = odd. However, the set of odd numbers is *not* closed under addition because (odd) + (odd) ≠ odd.

   a.   Examine the set of all even numbers. Is this set closed under addition? Show how you know.

   b.   Is the set of even numbers closed under multiplication? Show how you know.

5-82.   For each generic rectangle below, find the dimensions (length and width). Then write the area as a **product** of the dimensions and as a **sum**.

   a.

$2x^2$	$10x$

   b.

$2x^2$	$10x$
$3x$	15

5.2.3 How can I use proportionality?

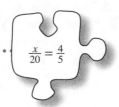

$\frac{x}{20} = \frac{4}{5}$

Applying Proportions

5-83.   ESTIMATING FISH POPULATIONS TEAM CHALLENGE

Fish biologists need to keep track of fish populations in the waters they monitor. They want to know, for example, how many striped bass there are in San Francisco Bay. This number changes throughout the year, however, as fish move in and out of the bay to spawn. Therefore, biologists need a way to gather current data fairly quickly and inexpensively.

Your team will be given a "lake" (paper bag) with "fish" (beans). How many fish are in your lake?

Your Task: Determine the number of fish in your lake as accurately as possible *without* actually counting the fish. Then count the fish and find out how accurate your method was. Be ready to share your process and solution with the class.

Discussion Points

What are you supposed to find? Explain in your own words.

How do you think fish biologists determine the population of fish in a lake?

What information can you gather to help you answer this question?

What tools will you need?

Can you use a proportion to determine the number of fish in your lake?
Why or why not?

Further Guidance

5-84.   Since it is impossible to count every animal, biologists use a process called "tag and recapture" to help them estimate the size of a population. Tag and recapture involves collecting a sample of animals, tagging them, and releasing them back into the wild. Later, biologists collect a new sample of the animals and count the number in the sample, distinguishing between first-time captures and recaptures. Then they use the data to estimate the population size.

Your team's task is to use the tag-and-recapture process to estimate the number of "fish" (beans) in your "lake" (paper bag).

a.   How many fish do you think are in your lake? Estimate.

b.   Use the "net" (small cup) to collect an initial sample. Carefully count the number of fish in the sample and record the data on your paper.

c.   In order to tag the fish, replace each fish in the sample with a fish of a different color. Add these tagged fish to the lake. Be careful not to let any of the fish jump out onto the floor! (Put the original fish from your sample aside. Do not return them to the lake, or else this will increase the number of fish in the lake.)

d.   Gently shake the bag to mix the fish thoroughly. Then collect another sample. Count the number of tagged and untagged fish in this new sample and record the information on your paper. Then return the entire sample to the lake.

e.   Look over the data you have collected. How many tagged fish are in the lake? How many tagged fish were in the second sample? What was the total number of fish in the second sample? Use this data to determine the total number of fish in the lake.

f.   Repeat the process outlined in parts (c) and (d) to get a second estimate of the total number of fish in the lake. Is this second estimate close to the first?

g.   **Extension:** Your solutions represent two estimates for the fish population of your lake. While it is important to get an accurate count, each time you net a sample, it costs the taxpayers $500 for your time and equipment. So far, your samples have cost a total of $1000. If you think your estimate is accurate at this point, record it on the class chart with your cost. If you think you should try another sample for better accuracy, do the same steps as before. Draw as many samples as you need, but remember that each sample costs $500.

h.   Count the fish in your lake to find the actual population. Then record your team's data on the class chart. Use the average of your estimates to represent your overall estimate of fish in the lake.

i.   Was your estimate close? Was it better than your estimate from part (a)? If not, what might have thrown it off? Is this method of counting populations accurate? Why or why not?

―――――   *Further Guidance*   ―――――
section ends here.

METHODS AND MEANINGS

Using Generic Rectangles to Multiply

A generic rectangle can be used to find products because it helps to organize the different areas that make up the total rectangle. For example, to multiply $(2x + 5)(x + 3)$, a generic rectangle can be set up and completed as shown below. Notice that each product in the generic rectangle represents the area of that part of the rectangle.

	$2x$	$+5$
x	$2x^2$	$5x$
$+3$	$6x$	15

$(2x + 5)(x + 3) = 2x^2 + 11x + 15$

area as a product   area as a sum

Note that while a generic rectangle helps organize the problem, its size and scale is not important.

5-85.   Find each of the following products by drawing and labeling a generic rectangle or by using the Distributive Property.

a. $(x + 2)(x + 8)$

b. $(2m + 30)(m + 20)$

c. $x(y + 10)$

d. $(2x + 3)(3x + 4)$

Algebra Connections

5-86.   Did you know that the Statue of Liberty was a gift
         from France? It was shipped to New York and
         reassembled on an island in New York Harbor. It was
         finished in 1886. The distance from the base to the
         torch is 152 feet. The gift store sells a scale model of
         the statue measuring 18 inches (1.5 feet) tall.

    a.   If the length of the index finger on the real statue
         is eight feet, what is its length on the scale
         model?

    b.   Alex wanted to know the length of the right arm
         on the statue. He measured the model, and the
         right arm was five inches long. What is the
         length of the arm on the statue?

5-87.   Solve each of the following equations for x. Then check each solution.

    a. $\frac{x}{16} = \frac{7}{10}$ b. $\frac{6}{15} = \frac{3}{x}$ c. $\frac{2x}{5} = \frac{12}{8}$ d. $-8 = \frac{2}{x}$

5-88.   Graph the lines $y = -4x + 3$ and $y = x - 7$ on the same set of axes. Then find their
         point of intersection.

5-89.   Change each equation below into $y = mx + b$ form.

    a. $y - 4x = -3$ b. $3y - 3x = 9$

    c. $3x + 2y = 12$ d. $2(x - 3) + 3y = 0$

Chapter 5 Closure   What have I learned?

Reflection and Synthesis

The activities below offer you a chance to reflect on what you have learned during this chapter. As you work, look for concepts that you feel very comfortable with, ideas that you would like to learn more about, and topics you need more help with. Look for **connections** between ideas as well as **connections** with material you learned previously.

① **TEAM BRAINSTORM**

With your team, brainstorm a list for each of the following topics. Be as detailed as you can. How long can you make your list? Challenge yourselves. Be prepared to share your team's ideas with the class.

Topics: What have you studied in this chapter? What ideas and words were important in what you learned? Remember to be as detailed as you can.

Connections: What topics, ideas, and words that you learned *before* this chapter are **connected** to the new ideas in this chapter? Again, make your list as long as you can.

②   MAKING CONNECTIONS

The following is a list of the vocabulary used in this chapter. The words that appear in bold are new to this chapter. Make sure that you are familiar with all of these words and know what they mean. Refer to the glossary or index for any words that you do not yet understand.

area	dimensions	**Distributive Property**
generic rectangles	growth	"legal" moves
linear equation	product	**proportion**
ratio	similar	solution
solve	**standard form**	starting value
sum	$y = mx + b$	

Make a concept map showing all of the **connections** you can find among the key words and ideas listed above. To show a **connection** between two words, draw a line between them and explain the **connection**, as shown in the example below. A word can be **connected** to any other word as long as there is a **justified connection**. For each key word or idea, provide a sketch that illustrates the idea (see the example below).

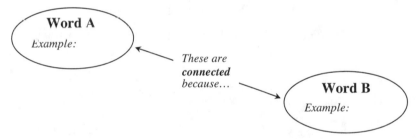

Your teacher may provide you with vocabulary cards to help you get started. If you use the cards to plan your concept map, be sure either to re-draw your concept map on your paper or to glue the vocabulary cards to a poster with all of the **connections** explained for others to see and understand.

While you are making your map, your team may think of related words or ideas that are not listed above. Be sure to include these ideas on your concept map.

③   SUMMARIZING MY UNDERSTANDING

This section gives you an opportunity to show what you know about certain math topics or ideas. Your teacher will give you directions for exactly how to do this.

WHAT HAVE I LEARNED?

This section will help you evaluate which types of problems you have seen with which you feel comfortable and those with which you need more help. This section appears at the end of every chapter to help you check your understanding. Even if your teacher does not assign this section, it is a good idea to try the problems and find out for yourself what you know and what you need to work on.

Solve each problem as completely as you can. The table at the end of the closure section has answers to these problems. It also tells you where you can find additional help and practice on problems like these.

CL 5-90. Two brothers, Martin and Morris, are in their backyard. Morris is taking down a wall on one side of the yard while Martin is building a wall on the other side. Martin starts from scratch and lays 2 bricks every minute. Meanwhile, Morris takes down 3 bricks each minute from his wall. It takes Morris 55 minutes to finish tearing down his wall.

    a.   How many bricks were originally in the wall that Morris started tearing down?

    b.   Represent this situation with equations, tables, and a graph.

    c.   When did the two walls have the same number of bricks?

CL 5-91. Rewrite each of these products as a sum.

    a. $6x(2x + y - 5)$ b. $(2x - 11)(x + 4)$

    c. $(7x)(2xy)$ d. $(x - 2)(3 + y)$

CL 5-92. Find the missing areas and dimensions for each generic rectangle below. Then write each area as a sum and as a product.

    a.

    b.

CL 5-93. For each equation below, solve for x.

    a. $(x - 1)(x + 7) = (x + 1)(x - 3)$ b. $2x - 5(x + 4) = -2(x + 3)$

CL 5-94. For each equation below, solve for y.

    a. $6x - 2y = 4$ b. $6x + 3y = 4x - 2y + 8$

    c.   Find the growth factors and y-intercepts for the equations in parts (a) and (b).

CL 5-95. For every 42 berries Samantha picks, her dog Clepto eats 7 berries. Samantha picked 462 berries last Saturday.

    a.   How many berries did Clepto eat last Saturday? Answer this question by writing and solving a proportion.

    b.   After Clepto was finished eating, how many berries did Samantha take home on Saturday?

CL 5-96. Solve for each variable.

    a. $\frac{x}{7} = \frac{3}{10}$ b. $\frac{8}{m} = \frac{3}{22}$ c. $\frac{11}{5} = \frac{2p}{3}$

CL 5-97. Kirstin enlarged her favorite picture at right on her computer so that the enlarged figure was similar to her original drawing. If the measurements of the original and new figure are as shown in the diagram at right, find x. Show all work.

CL 5-98. Find x and y for the system of equations at right:
$$y = 3x - 5$$
$$y = -x + 23$$

CL 5-99. Check your answers using the table at the end of the closure section. Which problems do you feel confident about? Which problems were hard? Use the table to make a list of topics you need help on and a list of topics you need to practice more.

HOW AM I THINKING?

This course focuses on five different **Ways of Thinking**: reversing thinking, justifying, generalizing, making connections, and applying and extending understanding. These are some of the ways in which you think while trying to make sense of a concept or to solve a problem (even outside of math class). During this chapter, you have probably used each Way of Thinking multiple times without even realizing it!

So far, each chapter of this course has focused on a different Way of Thinking, as you can see in the table below.

Chapter 1	**making connections**
Chapter 2	**justifying**
Chapter 3	**generalizing**
Chapter 4	**reversing thinking**

This closure activity will focus on the fifth Way of Thinking: **applying and extending**. Read the description of this Way of Thinking at right.

Think about the topics that you have learned during this chapter. When did you broaden your understanding of a concept? When did you apply an idea to solve a real-life problem? You may want to flip through the chapter to refresh your memory about the problems that you have worked on. Discuss any ideas you have with the rest of the class.

Once your discussion is complete, examine some of the ways you have **applied** and **extended** your understanding as you answer the questions below.

Applying and Extending

To extend understanding means to increase or expand what you know about an idea. You think this way when you try to apply your knowledge in new ways or consider new possibilities. An application is often the answer to a question like, *"How can I use this?"* When you catch yourself thinking, *"What if …"*, you are usually trying to extend your understanding.

a.   One way you **applied** your understanding of area was to use an area model to multiply expressions. For example, the area of the rectangle at right represents the product $(4x + 3)(2x - 7)$.

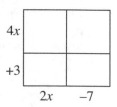

   i.   Copy and complete the generic rectangle and write its area as a sum.

Continues on next page →

Algebra Connections

⑤   *Continued from previous page.*

    ii.   Now **apply** your understanding to find two more products similar to $(4x + 3)(2x - 7)$. In other words, create your own products in the form $(ax + b)(cx + d)$ and use an area model to multiply.

    iii.   Now **extend** this idea: What if one of the expressions being multiplied has three terms? How can a generic rectangle be used to multiply two expressions such as $(x - 3)(3y + 2x + 1)$? Discuss this with your team. Then create and complete a generic rectangle for $(x - 3)(3y + 2x + 1)$ and write its area as a sum.

    iv.   Part (*iii*) was an **extension** because it considered a new "What If…?" question that came from the study of multiplying expressions. Now, as a team, write your own "What if…?" questions that come from this work. Be ready to share your questions with the class.

    b.   Now examine how you can **apply** proportional reasoning to solve different problems. With your team, answer the questions below.

    i.   The math club is sponsoring a math contest, and to prepare, Clarisse needs to sharpen 568 pencils. Luckily, the club has an electric pencil sharpener! When Clarisse started to sharpen the first 8 pencils, she noticed that it took her 2.5 minutes. Assuming she can continue sharpening pencils at the same rate, how long will it take her to sharpen the rest of the pencils? Write and solve a proportion to answer this question.

    ii.   To pay for trophies, the math club will sell 176 raffle tickets for $1 each. The club will randomly select 22 tickets to award prizes. If the club sponsor, Mr. Wallis, bought 40 tickets, will he probably win a prize? If so, how many prizes do you predict he would win? Show how you found our answer.

    iii.   Now, with your team, create at least two problems that would require someone to **apply** proportional reasoning to solve. Be creative! Be ready to share your problems with the class.

Answers and Support for Closure Activity #4
What Have I Learned?

Problem	Solution	Need Help?	More Practice

CL 5-90.

a. $55(3) = 165$ bricks

b. Martin's rule: $y = 2x$

Morris's rule: $y = 165 - 3x$

Martin's table:

Min.	Bricks
0	0
1	2
2	4
...	...
56	112
57	114

Morris's table:

Min.	Bricks
0	165
1	162
2	159
...	...
54	3
55	0

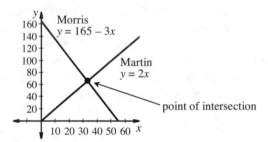

c. After 33 hours, they will each have 66 bricks.

Need Help? Lesson 5.1.5 Math Notes box

More Practice Problems 5-19, 5-31, 5-42, 5-45, 5-61, and 5-68

CL 5-91.

a. $12x^2 + 6xy - 30x$

b. $2x^2 - 3x - 44$

c. $14x^2y$

d. $3x + xy - 6 - 2y$

Need Help? Lessons 5.1.1 and 5.1.3 Math Notes boxes

More Practice Problems 5-11, 5-13, 5-21, 5-25, 5-27, 5-33, 5-50, 5-70, and 5-85

Problem	Solution	Need Help?	More Practice
CL 5-92.	a. $(2x+1)(1+8x) = 16x^2 + 10x + 1$ $$\begin{array}{c|c|c} & 16x^2 & 8x \\ \hline 8x & & \\ 1 & 2x & 1 \\ \hline & 2x & 1 \end{array}$$ b. $(2y-3)(4x+5) =$ $8xy - 12x + 10y - 15$ $$\begin{array}{c|c|c} 5 & 10y & -15 \\ \hline 4x & 8xy & -12x \\ \hline & 2y & -3 \end{array}$$	Lessons 5.1.1, 5.1.3, and 5.2.3 Math Notes boxes	Problems 5-16, 5-24, 5-26, 5-58, and 5-82
CL 5-93.	a. $x = \frac{1}{2}$ b. $x = -14$	Lesson 5.1.3 Math Notes box, Lesson 5.1.4	Problems 5-34, 5-37, 5-38, 5-48, 5-55, and 5-57
CL 5-94.	a. $y = 3x - 2$ b. $y = -\frac{2}{5}x + \frac{8}{5}$ c. part (a): $m = 3$, $b = -2$ part (b): $m = -\frac{2}{5}$, $b = \frac{8}{5}$	Lesson 5.1.5	Problems 5-46, 5-47, 5-48, 5-51, 5-55, 5-77, and 5-89
CL 5-95.	a. 77 berries b. 385 berries	Lesson 5.2.1 Math Notes box	Problems 5-54, 5-62, 5-66, 5-67, 5-75, 5-76, 5-78, 5-79, and 5-86

Problem	Solution	Need Help?	More Practice
CL 5-96.	a. $x = \frac{21}{10}$ or 2.1 b. $x = \frac{176}{3}$ or $58\frac{2}{3}$ c. $p = \frac{33}{10}$ or 3.3	Section 5.2	Problems 5-17, 5-28, 5-63, 5-72, and 5-87
CL 5-97.	$x = \frac{35}{3} \approx 11.7$	Lesson 5.2.1 Math Notes box	Problems 5-54, 5-62, 5-66, 5-67, 5-75, 5-76, 5-78, 5-79, and 5-86
CL 5-98.	$x = 7$ $y = 16$	Lesson 4.2.1 Math Notes box, Lesson 4.2.3, problem 4-86, and Lesson 4.2.4 Math Notes box	Problems 5-43, 5-53, 5-80, and 5-88

6

SYSTEMS OF
EQUATIONS

CHAPTER 6　Systems of Equations

In Chapter 4, you studied the **connections** between the multiple representations of data and learned how to write equations from situations. You also developed a way to solve a system of equations. In this chapter, you will learn how to solve word problems by writing an equation (or a system of equations). Also, unlike previous chapters, where you were limited to certain kinds of systems of equations, in this chapter you will learn how to solve *any* system of linear equations, regardless of its form.

Along the way, you will develop new ways to solve different forms of systems and will learn how to recognize when one method may be most efficient. By the end of this chapter, you will know multiple ways to find the point of intersection of two lines and will be able to solve systems that arise from different contexts.

In this chapter, you will learn:

➢ What a solution of a system of equations represents.

➢ How to solve contextual word problems by writing and solving equations.

➢ How to recognize systems of equations that have no solution or infinite solutions.

➢ How to solve different forms of systems quickly and efficiently.

Guiding Questions

Think about these questions throughout this chapter:

What is a solution?

How can I represent it algebraically?

How can I solve it?

Is there another way?

How can I check my answer?

Chapter Outline

Section 6.1 In this section, you will write and solve mathematical sentences (such as one- and two-variable equations) to solve contextual word problems.

Section 6.2 You will develop methods to solve systems of equations in different forms. You will learn which equations will result in lines when graphed. You will also find ways to know which solving method is most efficient and accurate.

Section 6.3 Section 6.3 provides an opportunity for you to review and **extend** what you learned in Chapters 1 through 6. You will make important **connections** between solving equations, multiple representations, proportional reasoning, and systems of equations.

6.1.1 How can I write it using algebra?

$b+g=23$

Mathematical Sentences

Spoken and written languages use *sentences* to convey information. A sentence has a subject and verb, follows the rules of grammar, and is structured with punctuation. Likewise, algebra uses **mathematical sentences**, such as $b + g = 23$, which also convey information and follow structural rules.

During this lesson, you will explore various mathematical sentences and learn how to interpret their meanings. Then you will write mathematical sentences of your own.

6-1.   How can variables give you new information? Suppose Mr. Titelbaum's class has b boys and g girls.

   a.   Mr. Titelbaum noticed that $b + g = 23$. What does that tell you about his class?

   b.   If $b = g - 3$, what statement can you make about the number of boys and girls?

   c.   How many girls are in Mr. Titelbaum's class? Explain how you know.

6-2.   The local commuter train has three passenger cars. When it is sold out, each passenger car can hold p people.

   a.   In addition to the passengers, the train has 8 employees. Write an expression that represents the total number of people on this commuter train.

   b.   When it is sold out, the train has a total of 176 people on board. Write an equation that represents this fact.

   c.   Solve your equation to determine how many people a passenger car can hold. Be sure to check your solution when you are finished.

6-3.   MATHEMATICAL SENTENCES

A **mathematical sentence** uses variables and mathematical operations to represent information. For example, if you know that b represents the number of boys in a class and g represents the number of girls in the same class, then the mathematical sentence "$b + g = 23$" states that if you add the number of boys to the number of girls, you get a result of 23. In other words, there are 23 students in the class.

Mathematical Sentence:

Same Sentence in English:

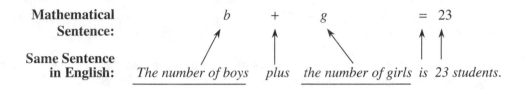

While many mathematical sentences contain more than one variable (such as $b + g = 23$ above), some only contain one variable. For example, if p represents the maximum number of people in a train's passenger car, then the mathematical sentence $3p + 8 = 176$ states that a train with 3 passenger cars and 8 additional people will have 176 people in all. This is shown below.

Mathematical Sentence:

Same Sentence in English:

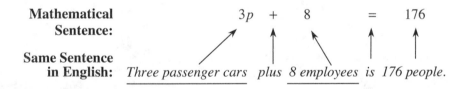

Mathematical sentences convey information once you understand what each variable represents. Sometimes the structure of the equation or the letter of the variable can reveal its possible meaning. With your team, study the two mathematical sentences below and decide what each could be trying to communicate. Be prepared to share your description with the class.

a. $0.25q + 0.05n = 5.00$ b. $l + w + l + w = 30$

6-4.   Mathematical sentences are easier to understand when everyone knows what the variables represent. For example, if you knew that l in part (b) of problem 6-3 represented the length of one side of a rectangle, then it would have been easier to understand that the mathematical sentence $l + w + l + w = 30$ could have been stating that the perimeter of a rectangle is 30 units.

A statement that describes what the variable represents is called a **"let" statement**. It is called this because it often is stated in the form "Let $l = ...$". While solving the problems below, examine how "let" statements are used.

a.   Let m = the number of students at Mountain View High School and let $m - 100$ = the number of students at neighboring Ferguson High School. Which school has more students? How can you tell?

b.   Based on the "let" statements in part (a) above, translate this mathematical sentence into English: $m + (m - 100) = 5980$.

c.   A book called *How I Love Algebra* has only three chapters. Let p = the number of pages in Chapter 1, $p + 12$ = the number of pages in Chapter 2, and $\frac{p}{2}$ = the number of pages in Chapter 3. Which is the longest chapter? Which is the shortest?

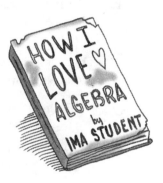

d.   Using the definitions in part (c) above, write and solve a mathematical sentence that states that *How I Love Algebra* has 182 pages. How many pages are in Chapter 1?

6-5.   With your team, practice translating words into mathematical symbols. For each problem below, write an expression or equation that best represents the given situation.

a.   Turner rode his bike m miles. If Carolyn rode 10 less than twice the number of miles that Turner rode, how many miles did Carolyn ride?

b.   Your teacher spent $9.50 on 5 boxes of chalk and 2 boxes of overhead pens. If c represents the price of a box of chalk and p represents the price of a box of overhead pens, write an equation to represent this purchase.

c.   Each fruit basket comes with a apples, p pears, and b bananas. Wendi orders 4 fruit baskets and gets 84 pieces of fruit. Write an equation that represents this order.

6-6.   In your Learning Log, write your own mathematical sentence. Be sure to state what any variables represent. Title this entry "Writing Mathematical Sentences" and include today's date.

ETHODS AND MEANINGS

Mathematical Sentences

A **mathematical sentence** uses variables and mathematical operations to represent information. An equation is one type of mathematical sentence. When the variables are defined, a mathematical sentence can be translated into a sentence with words.

For example, if b represents the number of boys in a class and if g represents the number of girls, then the mathematical sentence $b + g = 23$ states that the total number of boys and girls is 23.

Mathematical Sentence:	b	$+$	g		$=$	23

Same Sentence in English:	*The number of boys*	*plus*	*the number of girls*	*is*	*23.*

6-7.   Solve the problem below using a Guess and Check table. ***Note:*** *Be sure to put your work in a safe place, because you will need it for the next lesson.*

The perimeter of a triangle is 31 cm. Sides #1 and #2 have equal length, while Side #3 is one centimeter shorter than twice the length of Side #1. How long is each side?

6-8.   Write expressions to represent the quantities described below.

    a.   If Thompson Valley High School has x students and if Erwin Middle School has 342 fewer students, how many students does Erwin Middle School have?

    b.   If w represents the width of a rectangle and if its length is twice its width, how long is the rectangle?

    c.   When Mr. Van Exel bought his laptop, he paid $400 more than three times the amount he paid for his camera. If he paid c dollars for his camera, then how much did he pay for his laptop?

6-9.   Solve the system of equations below using the Equal Values Method.

$$a = 12b + 3$$
$$a = -2b - 4$$

6-10.   Ms. Cai's class is studying a tile pattern. The rule for the tile pattern is $y = 10x - 18$. Kalil thinks that Figure 12 of this pattern will have 108 tiles. Is he correct? **Justify** your answer.

6-11.   Angel is picking blackberries in her backyard for a delicious pie. She can pick 9 blackberries in 2 minutes. If she needs 95 blackberries for the pie, how long will it take her to pick the berries?

6-12.   Juan thinks that the graph of $6y + 12x = 4$ is a line.

    a.   Solve Juan's equation for y.

    b.   Is this equation **linear**? That is, is its graph a line? Explain how you know.

    c.   What are the growth factor and y-intercept of this graph?

6.1.2 How can I use variables to solve problems?

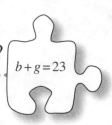

$b+g=23$

Solving Word Problems by Writing Equations

In Lesson 6.1.1, you examined mathematical sentences (equations that convey related information). Today you will learn more ways to translate written information into algebraic symbols and will then solve the equations that represent the relationships.

6-13.   Match each mathematical sentence on the left with its translation on the right.

a. $2z + 12 = 30$

1.   A zoo has two fewer elephants than zebras and five times more monkeys than elephants. The total number of elephants, monkeys, and zebras is 30.

b. $12z + 5(z + 2) = 30$

2.   Zola earned $30 by working two hours and receiving a $12 bonus.

c. $z + (z - 2) + 5(z - 2) = 30$

3.   Thirty ounces of metal is created by mixing zinc with silver. The number of ounces of silver needed is twelve times the number of ounces of zinc.

d. $z + 12z = 30$

4.   Eddie, who earns $5 per hour, worked two hours longer than Zach, who earns $12 per hour. Together they earned $30.

6-14.   In Lesson 6.1.1, you examined how to translate words into mathematical symbols to form expressions and equations. However, you can also use Guess and Check tables to help you write mathematical sentences. Find your solution for problem 6-7, reprinted below.

The perimeter of a triangle is 31 cm. Sides #1 and #2 have equal length, while Side #3 is one centimeter shorter than twice the length of Side #1. How long is each side?

a.   Add a row to your Guess and Check table. If x represents the length of Side #1, then what is the length of Side #2? Side #3? Fill in the columns for Sides #1, #2, and #3 with these variable expressions.

b.   Write a mathematical sentence that states that the perimeter is 31 cm.

c.   If you have not done so already, solve the equation you found in part (b) and determine the length of each side. Does this answer match the one you got for problem 6-7?

Algebra Connections

6-15.   For the following word problems, write one or two equations and then solve the problem. You may choose to use a Guess and Check table to help you set up equations, although it is not required. Regardless of your method, be sure to define your variable(s) with appropriate "let" statements.

a.   Herman and Jacquita are each saving money to pay for college. Herman currently has $15,000 and is working hard to save $1000 per month. Jacquita only has $12,000 but is saving $1300 per month. In how many months will they have the same amount of savings?

b.   There are 21 animals on Farmer Cole's farm – all sheep and chickens. If the animals have a total of 56 legs, how many of each type of animal lives on his farm?

c.   When ordering supplies, Mr. Williams accidentally ordered 12 more than twice his usual number of pencils. When the order arrived, he received 60 pencils! How many pencils does Mr. Williams usually order?

d.   George bought some CDs at his local store. He paid $15.95 for each CD. Nora bought the same number of CDs from a store online. She paid $13.95 for each CD, but had to pay $8 for shipping. In the end, both George and Nora spent the exact same amount of money buying their CDs! How many CDs did George buy?

e.   After the math contest, Basil noticed that there were four extra-large pizzas that were left untouched. In addition, another three slices of pizza were uneaten. If there were a total of 51 slices of pizza left, how many slices does an extra-large pizza have?

6-16.   Solve for x. Check your solutions, if possible.

a. $-2(4 - 3x) - 6x = 10$ b. $\frac{x-5}{-2} = \frac{x-1}{-3}$

6-17.   On the same set of axes, graph the two rules shown at right. $y = -x + 2$
         Then find the point(s) of intersection, if one (or more) exists. $y = 3x + 6$

6-18.   Evaluate the expression $6x^2 - 3x + 1$ for $x = -2$.

6-19.   The basketball coach at Washington High School normally starts each game with the
         following five players:

                    Melinda, Samantha, Carly, Allison, and Kendra

         However, due to illness, she needs to substitute Barbara for Allison and Lakeisha for
         Melinda at this week's game. What will be the starting roster for this upcoming
         game?

6-20.   When Ms. Shreve solved an equation in class, she checked her
         solution and it did not make the equation true! Examine her work
         below and find her mistake. Then find the correct solution.

$$5(2x - 1) - 3x = 5x + 9$$
$$10x - 5 - 3x = 5x + 9$$
$$7x - 5 = 5x + 9$$
$$12x = 4$$
$$x = \tfrac{1}{3}$$

6-21.   Determine if the statement below is true or false. **Justify** your conclusion.

$$2(3 + 5x) = 6 + 5x$$

6.1.3 How can I solve the system?

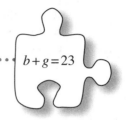

Solving Problems by Writing Equations

In Lessons 6.1.1 and 6.1.2, you created mathematical sentences that represented word problems. But how can you tell if you can use one variable or two? And is one method more convenient than another? Today you will compare the different ways to represent a word problem with mathematical symbols.

You will also explore how to use the Equal Values Method to solve systems containing equations that are not in $y = mx + b$ form.

6-22.   ONE EQUATION OR TWO?

Review what you learned in Lesson 6.1.2 by answering the questions below.

a.   Solve the problem below using Guess and Check.

Elsie took all of her cans and bottles from home to the recycling plant. The number of cans was one more than four times the number of bottles. She earned 10¢ for each can and 12¢ for each bottle, and ended up earning $2.18 in all. How many cans and bottles did she recycle?

b.   Use your Guess and Check table to help you write an equation that represents the information in part (a). Be sure to define your variable.

c.   If you have not done so already, solve your equation from part (b). Does this solution match your answer to part (a)? If not, look for and correct any errors.

d.   How can this problem be represented using two variables? With your team, write two mathematical sentences that represent this problem. Be sure to state what your variables represent. You do not need to solve the system.

e.   Show that your solution from part (a) makes both equations in part (d) true.

6-23.   Renard thinks that writing two equations for problem 6-22 was easy, but he's not sure if he knows how to solve the system of equations. He wants to use two equations with two variables to solve this problem:

> Ariel bought several bags of caramel candy and taffy. The number of bags of taffy was 5 more than the number of bags of caramels. Taffy bags weigh 8 ounces each, and caramel bags weigh 16 ounces each. The total weight of all of the bags of candy was 400 ounces. How many bags of candy did she buy?

a.   Renard lets t = the number of taffy bags and c = the number of caramel bags. Help him write two equations to represent the information in the problem.

b.   Now Renard is stuck. He says, "If both of the equations were in the form 't = something,' I could use the Equal Values Method to find the solution." Help him change the equations into a form he can solve.

c.   Solve Renard's equations to find the number of caramel and taffy bags that Ariel bought. Check to make sure your solution works.

6-24.   When you write equations to solve word problems, you sometimes end up with two equations like Renard's or like the system shown at right. Notice that the second equation is solved for y, but the first is not. Change the first equation into $y = mx + b$ form, and then solve this system of equations. Discuss with your team how you can make sure your solution is correct.

$$2y + 8x = 10$$
$$y = 5x + 23$$

6-25.   Solve each system below by first changing each equation so that it is in $y = mx + b$ form. Check that your answer makes both equations true.

a. $x - 2y = 4$
       $y = -\frac{1}{2}x + 4$

b. $x + 2y = 14$
       $-x + 3y = 26$

6-26.   Write expressions to represent the quantities described below.

a.   Geraldine is 4 years younger than Tom. If Tom is t years old, how old is Geraldine? Also, if Steven is twice as old as Geraldine, how old is he?

b.   150 people went to see "Ode to Algebra" performed in the school auditorium. If the number of children that attended the performance was c, how many adults attended?

c.   The cost of a new CD is $14.95, and the cost of a video game is $39.99. How much would c CDs and v video games cost?

6-27.   Nina has some nickels and 9 pennies in her pocket. Her friend, Maurice, has twice as many nickels as Nina. Together, these coins are worth 84¢. How many nickels does Nina have? Solve using any method, but show all of your work.

6-28.   To count the number of endangered falcons in the local county, Fernando first tagged each of the 8 falcons he saw one day. Then, days later, he counted 11 falcons and noticed that only 3 were tagged. What is a good estimate of how many falcons exist in his county? Show how you know.

6-29.   As Sachiko solved the equation $(x+2)+3=9$, she showed her work in the table below. Copy the table and provide justification for each step.

Statement	Reason
1. $(x+2)+3=9$	Given
2. $x+(2+3)=9$	
3. $x+5=9$	
4. $x+5-5=9-5$	
5. $x=4$	

6-30.   A **prime number** is defined as a number with exactly two integer factors: itself and 1. Jeannie thinks that all prime numbers are odd. Is she correct? If so, state how you know. If not, provide a counterexample.

6-31.   In an "If…then…" statement, the "if" portion is called the **hypothesis**, while the "then" portion is called the **conclusion**. For example, in the statement "*If $x = 3$, then $x^2 = 9$,*" the hypothesis is "$x = 3$" while the conclusion is "$x^2 = 9$."

Identify the hypothesis and conclusion of each of the following statements. Then decide if you think the statement is true or not. **Justify** your decision.

a.   If $-x = 8$ then $x = -8$.

b.   If $3x + y = -11$, then $6x + 2y = -22$.

c.   If Tomas runs at a constant rate of 4 meters every five seconds, then he will run 50 meters in 1 minute.

6.2.1 How can I solve the system?

Solving Systems of Equations Using Substitution

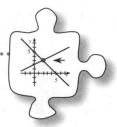

In Chapter 4, you learned that a set of two or more equations that go together is called a **system of equations**. In Lesson 6.1.3, you helped Renard develop a method for solving a system of equations when one of the equations was not solved for a variable. Today you will develop a more efficient method of solving systems that are too messy to solve with the Equal Values Method.

6-32.   Review what you learned in Lesson 6.1.3 as you solve the system of equations below. Check your solution.

$$y = -x - 7$$
$$5y + 3x = -13$$

6-33.   AVOIDING THE MESS

A new method, called the **Substitution Method**, can help you solve the system in problem 6-32 without getting involved in messy fractions. This method is outlined below.

a.   If $y = -x - 7$, then does $-x - 7 = y$? That is, can you switch the y and the $-x - 7$? Why or why not?

$$\widehat{y} = \widehat{-x - 7}$$
$$5y + 3x = -13$$

b.   Since you know that $y = -x - 7$, can you switch the y in the second equation with $-x - 7$ from the top equation? Why or why not?

$$y = \widehat{-x - 7}$$
$$5\,\widehat{y} + 3x = -13$$

c.   Once you replace the y in the second equation with $-x - 7$, you have an equation with only one variable, as shown below. This is called **substitution** because you are substituting for (replacing) y with an expression that it equals. Solve this new equation for x and then use that result to find y in either of the original equations.

$$5(-x - 7) + 3x = -13$$

6-34.   Use the Substitution Method to solve the systems of equations below.

a. $y = 3x$
      $2y - 5x = 4$

b. $x - 4 = y$
      $-5y + 8x = 29$

c. $2x + 2y = 18$
      $x = 3 - y$

d. $c = -b - 11$
      $3c + 6 = 6b$

6-35.   When Mei solved the system of equations below, she got the solution $x = 4$, $y = 2$.
         Without solving the system yourself, can you tell her whether this solution is correct?
         How do you know?

$$4x + 3y = 22$$
$$x - 2y = 0$$

6-36.   HAPPY BIRTHDAY!

You've decided to give your best
friend a bag of marbles for her
birthday. Since you know that your
friend likes green marbles better than
red ones, the bag has twice as many
green marbles as red. The label on
the bag says it contains a total of 84
marbles.

How many green marbles are in the
bag? Write an equation (or system
of equations) for this problem. Then solve the problem using any method you
choose. Be sure to check your answer when you are finished.

6-37.   Solve each equation for the variable. Check your solutions, if possible.

a. $8a + a - 3 = 6a - 2a - 3$

b. $8(3m - 2) - 7m = 0$

c. $\frac{x}{2} + 1 = 6$

d. $4t - 2 + t^2 = 6 + t^2$

6-38.   The Fabulous Footballers scored an incredible 55 points at
last night's game. Interestingly, the number of field goals
was 1 more than twice the number of touchdowns. The
Fabulous Footballers earned 7 points for each touchdown
and 3 points for each field goal.

a.   **Multiple Choice:** Which system of equations
below best represents this situation? Explain your
reasoning. Assume that t represents the number of
touchdowns and f represents the number of field goals.

i. $t = 2f + 1$ ii. $f = 2t + 1$
$7t + 3f = 55$ $7t + 3f = 55$

iii. $t = 2f + 1$ iv. $f = 2t + 1$
$3t + 7f = 55$ $3t + 7f = 55$

b.   Solve the system you selected in part (a) and determine how many touchdowns
and field goals the Fabulous Footballers earned last night.

6-39.   Yesterday Mica was given some information
and was asked to find a linear equation. But
last night her cat destroyed most of the
information! At right is all she has left:

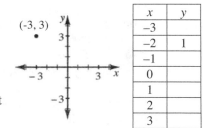

x	y
−3	
−2	1
−1	
0	
1	
2	
3	

a.   Complete the table and graph the line that
represents Mica's rule.

b.   Mica thinks the equation for this graph could be $2x + y = -3$. Is she correct?
Explain why or why not. If not, find your own algebraic rule to match the
graph and $x \to y$ table.

6-40.   Kevin and his little sister, Katy, are trying to solve the system of equations shown
below. Kevin thinks the new equation should be $3(6x - 1) + 2y = 43$, while Katy
thinks it should be $3x + 2(6x - 1) = 43$. Who is correct and why?

$$y = 6x - 1$$
$$3x + 2y = 43$$

6-41.   Create a table and graph the rule $y = 10 - x^2 + 3x$. Label its x- and y-intercepts.

6-42.   Maurice thinks that $x = -2$ is a solution to $x^2 - 3x - 8 = 0$. Is he correct? Explain.

6.2.2 How does a graph show a solution?

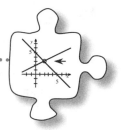

• •

Making Connections: Systems, Solutions, and Graphs

In this chapter you have practiced writing mathematical sentences to represent situations. Often, these sentences give you a system of equations, which you can solve using substitution. Today you will start to represent these situations in an additional way: on a graph. You will also examine more closely what makes a solution to a two-variable equation.

6-43.   THE HILLS ARE ALIVE

The Alpine Music Club is going on its annual music trip. The members of the club are yodelers, and they like to play the xylophone. This year they are taking their xylophones on a gondola to give a performance at the top of Mount Monch.

The gondola conductor charges $2 for each yodeler and $1 for each xylophone. It costs $40 for the entire club, including the xylophones, to ride the gondola. Two yodelers can share a xylophone, so the number of yodelers on the gondola is twice the number of xylophones.

How many yodelers and how many xylophones are on the gondola?

Your Task:

• Represent this problem with a system of equations. Solve the system and explain how its solution relates to the yodelers on the music trip.

• Represent this problem with a graph. Identify how the solution to this problem appears on the graph.

Discussion Points

How can the given information be represented with equations?

What is a solution to a two-variable equation?

How can this problem be represented on a graph?

How does the solution appear on the graph?

6-44.   Start by focusing on one aspect of the problem: the cost to ride the gondola. The conductor charges $2 for each yodeler and $1 for each xylophone. It costs $40 for the entire club, with instruments, to ride the gondola.

   a.   Write an equation with two variables that represents this information. Be sure to define your variables.

   b.   Find a combination of xylophones and yodelers that will make your equation from part (a) true. Is this is the only possible combination?

   c.   List five additional combinations of xylophones and yodelers that could ride the gondola if it costs $40 for the trip. With your team, decide on a good way to organize and share your list.

   d.   Jon says, "I think there could be 28 xylophones and 8 yodelers on the gondola." Is he correct? Use the equation you have written to explain why or why not.

   e.   Helga says, "Each correct combination we found is a *solution* to our equation." Is this true? Explain what it means for something to be a solution to a two-variable equation.

6-45.   Now consider the other piece of information: The number of yodelers is twice the number of xylophones.

   a.   Write an equation (mathematical sentence) that expresses this piece of information.

   b.   List four different combinations of xylophones and yodelers that will make this equation true.

   c.   Put the equation you found in part (a) together with your equation from problem 6-44 and use substitution to solve this system of equations.

   d.   Is the answer you found in part (c) a solution to the first equation you wrote (the equation in part (a) of problem 6-44)? How can you check? Is it a solution to the second equation you wrote (the equation in part (a) of this problem)? Why is this a solution to the *system* of equations?

6-46.   The solution to "The Hills are Alive" problem can also be represented graphically.

    a.   On graph paper, graph the equation you wrote in part (a) of problem 6-44. The points you listed for that equation may help. What is the shape of this graph? Label your graph with its equation.

    b.   Explain how each point on the graph represents a solution to the equation.

    c.   Now graph the equation you wrote in part (a) of problem 6-45 on the same set of axes. The points you listed for that equation may help. Label this graph with its equation.

    d.   Find the intersection point of the two graphs. What is special about this point?

    e.   With your team, find as many ways as you can to express the solution to "The Hills are Alive" problem. Be prepared to share all the different forms you found for the solution with the class.

—————— *Further Guidance*
section ends here. ——————

6-47.   Consider this system of equations:

$$2x + 2y = 18$$
$$y = x - 3$$

    a.   Use substitution to solve this system.

    b.   With your team, decide how to fill in the rest of the table at right for the equation $2x + 2y = 18$.

    c.   Use your table to make an accurate graph of the equation $2x + 2y = 18$.

    d.   Now graph $y = x - 3$ on the same set of axes. Find the point of intersection.

x	y
−2	11
−1	
0	
1	
2	
3	

    e.   Does the point of intersection you found in part (a) agree with what you see on your graph?

6-48.   If you had an equation with three variables, how would you write its solutions?

6-49.   What is a solution to a two-variable equation? Answer this question in complete sentences in your Learning Log. Then give an example of a two-variable equation followed by two different solutions to it. Finally, make a list of all of the ways to represent solutions to two-variable equations. Title your entry "Solutions to Two-Variable Equations" and label it with today's date.

METHODS AND MEANINGS

The Substitution Method

The **Substitution Method** is a way to change two equations with two variables into one equation with one variable. It is convenient to use when only one equation is solved for a variable.

For example, to solve the system:

$$x = -3y + 1$$
$$4x - 3y = -11$$

Use substitution to rewrite the two equations as one. In other words, replace x with $(-3y + 1)$ to get $4(-3y + 1) - 3y = -11$. This equation can then be solved to find y. In this case, $y = 1$.

$$x = \boxed{-3y + 1}$$

$$4(\ ) - 3y = -11$$

$$4(-3y + 1) - 3y = -11$$

To find the point of intersection, substitute to find the other value.

$$-12y + 4 - 3y = -11$$
$$-15y + 4 = -11$$
$$-15y = -15$$
$$y = 1$$

Substitute $y = 1$ into $x = -3y + 1$ and write the answer for x and y as an ordered pair.

To test the solution, substitute $x = -2$ and $y = 1$ into $4x - 3y = -11$ to verify that it makes the equation true. Since $4(-2) - 3(1) = -11$, the solution must be correct.

$$x = -3(1) + 1 = -2$$

$$(-2, 1)$$

Review & Preview

6-50.   Camila is trying to find the equation of a line that passes through the points $(-1, 16)$ and $(5, 88)$. Does the equation $y = 12x + 28$ work? **Justify** your answer.

6-51.   Solve the systems of equations below using the method of your choice. Check your solutions, if possible.

a. $y = 7 - 2x$
      $2x + y = 10$

b. $3y - 1 = x$
      $4x - 2y = 16$

Algebra Connections

6-52. Hotdogs and corndogs were sold at last night's football game. Use the information below to write mathematical sentences to help you determine how many corndogs were sold.

    a. The number of hotdogs sold was three fewer than twice the number of corndogs. Write a mathematical sentence that relates the number of hotdogs and corndogs. Let h represent the number of hotdogs and c represent the number of corndogs.

    b. A hotdog costs $3 and a corndog costs $1.50. If $201 was collected, write a mathematical sentence to represent this information.

    c. How many corndogs were sold? Show how you found your answer.

6-53. Examine the balanced scales in Figures 1 and 2 shown below. Figure 1 shows that two candies balance three dice. Figure 2 shows that one rubber ball balances two jacks.

    Figure 1   Figure 2   Figure 3

Determine what could be placed on the right side of the scale in Figure 3 to balance with the left side. **Justify** your solution in complete sentences.

6-54. Rianna thinks that if $a = b$ and if $c = d$, then $a + c = b + d$. Is she correct?

6-55. For each of the following generic rectangles, find the dimensions (length and width) and write the area as the product of the dimensions and as a sum.

a.

$3y^2$	$-12y$

b.

$3y^2$	$-12y$
$5y$	-20

6.2.3 Can I solve without substituting?

Solving Systems Using Elimination

In this chapter, you have learned the Substitution Method for solving systems of equations. In Chapter 4, you learned the Equal Values Method. But are these methods the best to use for all types of systems? Today you will develop a new solution method that can save time for systems of equations in standard form.

6-56.   Jeanette is trying to find the intersection point of these two equations:

$$2x + 3y = -2$$
$$5x - 3y = 16$$

She has decided to use substitution to find the point of intersection. Her plan is to solve the first equation for y, and then to substitute the result into the second equation. Use Jeanette's idea to solve the system.

6-57.   AVOIDING THE MESS: THE ELIMINATION METHOD

Your class will now discuss a new method, called the **Elimination Method**, to find the solution to Jeanette's problem without the complications and fractions of the previous problem. Your class discussion is outlined below.

a.   Verify that each equation mat at right represents one of Jeanette's equations.

$$2x + 3y = -2$$
$$5x - 3y = 16$$

b.   Can these two equations be merged onto one equation mat as shown below? That is, can the left sides and right sides of two equations be added together to create a new equation? Why or why not?

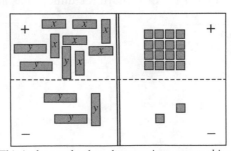

This is the result when the equations are combined.

Problem continues on next page →

6-57.   *Problem continued from previous page.*

    c.   Write a new equation for the result of merging Jeanette's equations. Simplify and then solve this new equation for the remaining variable. Notice that you now have only one equation with one variable. What happened to the *y*-terms?

    d.   Use your solution for *x* to find *y*. Check to be sure your solution makes both original equations true.

    e.   How can you record this process on paper? That is, when solving this type of system, how can you show that you are combining the equations?

    f.   Now use the Elimination Method to solve the system of equations at right for *x* and *y*. Check your solution.

$$2x - y = -2$$
$$-2x + 3y = 10$$

6-58.   Pat was in a fishing competition at Lake Pisces. She caught some bass and some trout. Each bass weighed 3 pounds, and each trout weighed 1 pound. Pat caught a total of 30 pounds of fish. She got 5 points in the competition for each bass, but since trout are endangered in Lake Pisces, she lost 1 point for each trout. Pat scored a total of 42 points.

    a.   Write a system of equations representing the information in this problem.

    b.   Is this system a good candidate for the Elimination Method? Why or why not?

    c.   Solve this system to find out how many bass and trout Pat caught. Be sure to record your work and check your answer by substituting your solution into the original equations.

6-59.   ANNIE NEEDS YOUR HELP

Annie was all ready to "push together" the two equations below to eliminate the *x*-terms when she noticed a problem: Both *x*-terms are positive!

$$2x + 7y = 13$$
$$2x + 3y = 5$$

With your team, figure out something you could do that would allow you to put these equations together and eliminate the *x*-terms. As you try out different ideas, ask your teacher for some algebra tiles and an equation mat if you think they will help. Once you have figured out a method, solve the system and check your solution. Be ready to share your method with the class.

6-60. Find the point of intersection of each pair of lines below. If you use an equation mat, be sure to record your process on paper. Otherwise, show your steps algebraically. Check each solution when you are finished.

a. $2y - x = 5$
$-3y + x = -9$

b. $2x - 4y = 14$
$4y - x = -3$

c. $3x + 4y = 1$
$2x + 4y = 2$

M ETHODS AND MEANINGS

Systems of Linear Equations

A **system of linear equations** is a set of two or more linear equations that are given together, such as the example at right:

$y = 2x$
$y = -3x + 5$

If the equations come from a real-world context, then each variable will represent some type of quantity in both equations. For example, in the system of equations above, y could stand for a number of dollars in *both* equations.

To represent a system of equations graphically, you can simply graph each equation on the same set of axes. The graph may or may not have a **point of intersection**, as shown circled at right.

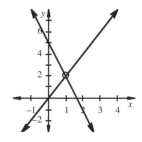

Sometimes two lines have *no* points of intersection. This happens when the two lines are parallel. It is also possible for two lines to have an *infinite* number of intersections. This happens if they are simply the same equation in different forms. Such lines are said to **coincide**.

Also notice that the point of intersection lies on *both* graphs in the system of equations. This means that the point of intersection is a **solution** to *both* equations in the system. For example, the point of intersection of the two lines graphed above is (1, 2). This point of intersection makes both equations true, as shown at right.

$y = 2x$ $\quad$ $y = -3x + 5$
$(2) = 2(1)$ $\quad$ $(2) = -3(1) + 5$
$2 = 2$ $\quad$ $2 = -3 + 5$
$\quad$ $2 = 2$

The point of intersection makes both equations true; therefore the point of intersection is a solution to both equations. For this reason, the point of intersection is sometimes called a **solution to the system of equations**.

6-61.   Find the point of intersection of each pair of lines, if one exists. If you use an equation mat, be sure to record your process on paper. Check each solution, if possible.

   a. $x = -2y - 3$
         $4y - x = 9$

   b. $x + 5y = 8$
         $-x + 2y = -1$

   c. $4x - 2y = 5$
         $y = 2x + 10$

6-62.   Jai was solving the system of equations below when something strange happened.

$$y = -2x + 5$$
$$2y + 4x = 10$$

   a.   Solve the system. Explain to Jai what the solution should be.

   b.   Graph the two lines on the same set of axes. What happened?

   c.   Explain how the graph helps to explain your answer in part (a).

6-63.   On Tuesday the cafeteria sold pizza slices and burritos. The number of pizza slices sold was 20 less than twice the number of burritos sold. Pizza sold for $2.50 a slice and burritos for $3.00 each. The cafeteria collected a total of $358 for selling these two items.

   a.   Write two equations with two variables to represent the information in this problem. Be sure to define your variables.

   b.   Solve the system from part (a). Then determine how many pizza slices were sold.

6-64.   A local deli sells 6-inch sub sandwiches for $2.95. It has decided to sell a "family sub" that is 50 inches long. How much should it charge? Show all work.

6-65.   Represent the tile pattern below with a table, a rule, and a graph.

  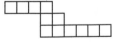

   Figure 1   Figure 2   Figure 3

6-66.   Use generic rectangles to multiply each of the following expressions.

   a. $(x + 2)(x - 5)$

   b. $(y + 2x)(y + 3x)$

   c. $(3y - 8)(-x + y)$

   d. $(x - 3y)(x + 3y)$

6.2.4 How can I eliminate a variable?

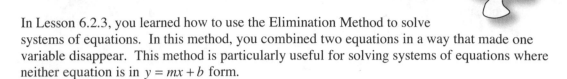

More Elimination

In Lesson 6.2.3, you learned how to use the Elimination Method to solve systems of equations. In this method, you combined two equations in a way that made one variable disappear. This method is particularly useful for solving systems of equations where neither equation is in $y = mx + b$ form.

Today you will practice using the Elimination Method while learning to deal with various complications that systems of equations sometimes present. As you solve these systems, ask your teammates these questions:

> How can you create one equation with only one variable?
>
> How can you eliminate one variable?
>
> How do you know your solution is correct?

6-67.   Which system of equations below would be easiest to solve using the Elimination Method? Once you have explained your decision, use the Elimination Method to solve this system of equations. (You do not need to solve the other system!) Record your steps and check your solution.

a. $5x - 4y = 37$
$-8x + 4y = -52$

b. $4 - 2x = y$
$3y + x = 11$

6-68.   Rachel is trying to solve this system:

$$2x + y = 10$$
$$3x - 2y = 1$$

a.   Combine these equations. What happened?

b.   Is $2x + y = 10$ the same line as $4x + 2y = 20$? That is, do they have the same solutions? Are their graphs the same? **Justify** your conclusion! Be ready to share your reasoning with the class.

c.   Since you can rewrite $2x + y = 10$ as $4x + 2y = 20$, perhaps this equivalent form of the original equation can help solve this system. Combine $4x + 2y = 20$ and $3x - 2y = 1$. Is a variable eliminated? If so, solve the system for x and y. If not, brainstorm another way to eliminate a variable. Be sure to check your solution.

d.   Why was the top equation changed? Would a variable have been eliminated if the bottom equation were multiplied by 2 on both sides? Test this idea.

Algebra Connections

6-69.   For each system below, determine:

- Is this system a good candidate for the Elimination Method? Why or why not?

- What is the best way to get one equation with one variable? Carry out your plan and solve the system for both variables.

- Is your solution correct? Verify by substituting your solution into both original equations.

a. $5m + 2n = -10$
    $3m + 2n = -2$

b. $6a - b = 3$
    $b + 4a = 17$

c. $7x + 4y = 17$
    $3x - 2y = -15$

d. $-18x + 3y = -12$
    $6x - y = 4$

6-70.   A NEW CHALLENGE

Carefully examine this system:

$$4x + 3y = 10$$
$$9x - 4y = 1$$

With your team, propose a way to combine these equations so that you eventually have one equation with one variable. Be prepared to share your proposal with the class.

METHODS AND MEANINGS

Coefficients and Constants

A **coefficient** is the numerical part of a term that includes a variable. For example, in the expression below, the coefficient of $7x^2$ is the number 7, the coefficient of $4x$ is 4, and the coefficient of $-y$ is -1. Note that the 9 in the expression below is called a **constant**. A constant is a term that does not include a variable.

$$7x^2 + 4x - y + 9$$

MATH NOTES

6-71.   Solve these systems of equations using any method. Check each solution, if possible.

   a. $2x + 3y = 9$
         $-3x + 3y = -6$

   b. $x = 8 - 2y$
         $y - x = 4$

   c. $y = -\frac{1}{2}x + 7$
         $y = x - 8$

   d. $9x + 10y = 14$
         $7x + 5y = -3$

6-72.   For each line below, make a table and graph. What do you notice?

   a. $y = \frac{2}{3}x - 1$

   b. $2x - 3y = 3$

6-73.   **Consecutive numbers** are integers that are in order without skipping, such as 3, 4, and 5. Find three consecutive numbers with a sum of 54.

6-74.   Identify the hypothesis and conclusion for each of the following statements. Then decide if the statement is true or false. Justify your decision. You may want to review the meanings of hypothesis and conclusion from problem 6-31.

   a.   If $y = \frac{2}{3}x - 5$, then the point $(6, -1)$ is a solution.

   b.   If Figure 2 of a tile pattern has 13 tiles and Figure 4 of the same pattern has 15 tiles, then the pattern grows by 2 tiles each figure.

   c.   If $(3x + 1)(x - 2) = 4$, then $3x^2 - 5x - 2 = 4$.

6-75.   Aimee thinks the solution to the system below is $(-4, -6)$. Eric thinks the solution is $(8, 2)$. Who is correct? Explain your reasoning.

$$2x - 3y = 10$$
$$6y = 4x - 20$$

6-76.   Figure 3 of a tile pattern has 11 tiles, while Figure 4 has 13 tiles. If the tile pattern grows at a constant rate, how many tiles will Figure 50 have?

6.2.5 What is the best method?

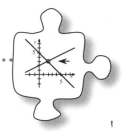

Choosing a Strategy for Solving Systems

When you have a system of equations to solve, how do you know which method to use? Focus today on how to choose a strategy that is the most convenient, efficient, and accurate for a system of equations.

6-77.   Erica works in a soda-bottling factory. As bottles roll past her on a conveyer belt, she puts caps on them. Unfortunately, Erica sometimes breaks a bottle before she can cap it. She gets paid 4 cents for each bottle she successfully caps, but her boss deducts 2 cents from her pay for each bottle she breaks.

Erica is having a bad morning. Fifteen bottles have come her way, but she has been breaking some and has only earned 6 cents so far today. How many bottles has Erica capped and how many has she broken?

    a.   Write a system of equations representing this situation.

    b.   Solve the system of equations using *two* different methods: substitution and elimination. Demonstrate that each method gives the same answer.

6-78.   For each system below, decide which strategy to use. That is, which method would be the most efficient, convenient, and accurate: the Substitution Method, the Elimination Method, or the Equal Values Method? Do not solve the systems yet! Be prepared to **justify** your reasons for choosing one strategy over the others.

    a. $x = 4 - 2y$
           $3x - 2y = 4$

    b. $3x + y = 1$
           $4x + y = 2$

    c. $x = -5y + 2$
           $x = 3y - 2$

    d. $2x - 4y = 10$
           $x = 2y + 5$

    e. $y = \frac{1}{2}x + 4$
           $y = -2x + 9$

    f. $-6x + 2y = 76$
           $3x - y = -38$

    g. $5x + 3y = -6$
           $2x - 9y = 18$

    h. $x - 3 = y$
           $2(x - 3) - y = 7$

6-79.   Your teacher will assign you a variety of systems from problem 6-78 to solve. With your team, use the best strategy to solve each system assigned by your teacher. Be sure to check your solution.

6-80.   In your Learning Log, write down everything you know about solving systems of equations. Include examples and explain your reasoning. Title this entry "Solving Systems of Equations" and label it with today's date.

METHODS AND MEANINGS

Intersection, Parallel, and Coincide

When two lines lie on the same flat surface (called a plane), they may **intersect** (cross each other) once, an infinite number of times, or never.

For example, if the two lines are **parallel**, then they never intersect. Examine the graph of two parallel lines at right. Notice that the distance between the two lines is constant.

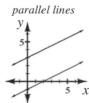

parallel lines

However, what if the two lines lie exactly on top of each other? When this happens, we say that the two lines **coincide**. When you look at two lines that coincide, they appear to be one line. Since these two lines intersect each other at all points along the line, coinciding lines have an infinite number of intersections.

intersecting lines

While some systems contain lines that are parallel and others coincide, the most common case for a system of equations is when the two lines intersect once, as shown at right.

Algebra Connections

6-81. Solve the following systems of equations using any method. Check each solution, if possible.

 a. $-2x + 3y = 1$
    $2x + 6y = 2$

 b. $y = \frac{1}{3}x + 4$
    $x = -3y$

 c. $3x - y = 7$
    $y = 3x - 2$

 d. $x + 2y = 1$
    $3x + 5y = 8$

6-82. The Math Club is baking pies for a bake sale. The fruit-pie recipe calls for twice as many peaches as nectarines. If it takes a total of 168 pieces of fruit for all of the pies, how many nectarines are needed?

6-83. Candice is solving this system:

$$2x - 1 = 3y$$
$$5(2x - 1) + y = 32$$

 a. She notices that each equation contains the expression $2x - 1$. Can she substitute $3y$ for $2x - 1$? Why or why not?

 b. Substitute $3y$ for $2x - 1$ in the second equation to create one equation with one variable. Then solve for x and y.

6-84. Examine the diagram at right. The smaller triangle is similar to the larger triangle. Write and solve a proportion to find x.

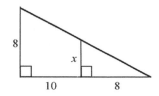

6-85. Figure 2 of a tile pattern is shown at right. If the pattern grows linearly and if Figure 5 has 15 tiles, then find a rule for the pattern.

Figure 2

6-86. Identify the hypothesis and conclusion for each of the following statements. Then decide if the statement is sometimes true, always true, or never true. **Justify** your decision. You may want to review the meanings of hypothesis and conclusion from problem 6-31.

 a. If line l is parallel to line m and line m is parallel to line n, then line l must be parallel to line n.

 b. If z is more than one, then $\frac{1}{z}$ is more than one.

 c. $y = 38$ if $y = 5x^3 - 2$ and $x = 2$.

6.3.1 What can I do now?

Pulling It All Together

This lesson contains many problems that will require you to use the algebra content you have learned so far in new ways. It will require you to use all five Ways of Thinking (justifying, making connections, applying and extending, reversing thinking, and generalizing) and will help you solidify your understanding.

Your teacher will describe today's activity. As you solve the problems below, remember to make **connections** between all of the different subjects you have studied in Chapters 1 through 6. If you get stuck, think of what the problem reminds you of. Decide if there is a different way to approach the problem. Most importantly, discuss your ideas with your teammates.

6-87. Brianna has been collecting insects and measuring the lengths of their legs and antennae. Below is the data she has collected so far.

	Ant	Beetle	Grasshopper
Length of Antenna (x)	2 mm	6 mm	20 mm
Length of Leg (y)	4 mm	10 mm	31 mm

a. Graph the data Brianna has collected. Put the antenna length on the x-axis and leg length on the y-axis.

b. Brianna thinks that she has found an algebraic rule relating antenna length and leg length: $4y - 6x = 4$. If x represents the length of the antenna and y represents the leg length, could Brianna's rule be correct? If not, find your own algebraic rule relating antenna length and leg length.

c. If a ladybug has an antenna 1 mm long, how long does Brianna's rule say its legs will be? Use both the rule and the graph to **justify** your answer.

6-88.   Barry is helping his friend understand how to solve systems of equations. He wants to give her a problem to practice. He wants to give her a problem that has two lines that intersect at the point (–3, 7). Help him by writing a system of equations that will have (–3, 7) as a solution and demonstrate how to solve it.

6-89.   Examine the generic rectangle at right. Determine the missing attributes and then write the area as a product and as a sum.

6-90.   One evening, Gemma saw three different phone-company ads. TeleTalk boasted a flat rate of 8¢ per minute. AmeriCall charges 30¢ per call plus 5¢ per minute. CellTime charges 60¢ per call plus only 3¢ per minute.

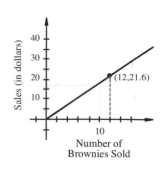

a.   Gemma is planning a phone call that will take about 5 minutes. Which phone plan should she use and how much will it cost?

b.   Represent each phone plan with a table and a rule. Then graph each plan on the same set of axes, where *x* represents time in minutes and *y* represents the cost of the call in cents. If possible, use different colors to represent the different phone plans.

c.   How long would a call need to be to cost the same with TeleTalk and AmeriCall? What about AmeriCall and CellTime?

d.   Analyze the different phone plans. How long should a call be so that AmeriCall is cheapest?

6-91.   Lashayia is very famous for her delicious brownies, which she sells at football games. The graph at right shows the relationship between the number of brownies she sells and the amount of money she earns.

a.   How much should she charge for 10 brownies? Be sure to demonstrate your reasoning.

b.   During the last football game, Lashayia made $34.20. How many brownies did she sell? Show your work.

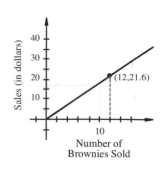

6-92.   How many solutions does each equation below have? How can you tell?

   a. $4x - 1 + 5 = 4x + 3$ b. $6t - 3 = 3t + 6$

   c. $6(2m - 3) - 3m = 2m - 18 + m$ d. $10 + 3y - 2 = 4y - y + 8$

6-93.   Anthony has the rules for three lines: A, B, and C. When he solves a system with lines A and B, he gets no solution. When he solves a system with lines B and C, he gets infinite solutions. What solution will he get when he solves a system with lines A and C? **Justify** your conclusion.

6-94.   Complete the Guess and Check table below and find a solution. Then write a possible word problem that would fit the table.

Stevie	Joan	Julio	Total	31.50? Check
3	5	8.50	16.50	Too low
10	19	22.50	51.50	Too high
7.50	14	17.50	39.00	Too high

6-95.   Normally, the longer you work for a company, the higher your salary per hour. Hector surveyed the people at his company and placed his data in the table below.

Number of Years at Company	1	3	6	7
Salary per Hour	$7.00	$8.50	$10.75	$11.50

   a.   Use Hector's data to estimate how much he makes, assuming he has worked at the company for 12 years.

   b.   Hector is hiring a new employee who will work 20 hours a week. How much should the new employee earn for the first week?

6-96. Dexter loves to find shortcuts. He has proposed a few new moves to help simplify and solve equations. Examine his work below. For each, decide if his move is "legal." That is, decide if the move creates an equivalent equation. **Justify** your conclusions using the "legal" moves you already know.

a.

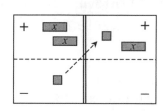

b.

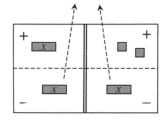

c.

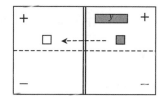

d.

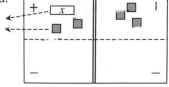

6-97. Solve the problem below using *two different methods*.

The Math Club sold roses and tulips this year for Valentine's Day. The number of roses sold was 8 more than 4 times the number of tulips sold. Tulips were sold for $2 each and roses for $5 each. The club made $414.00. How many roses were sold?

6-98. Use substitution to find where the two parabolas below intersect. Then confirm your solution by graphing both on the same set of axes.

$$y = x^2 + 5$$
$$y = x^2 + 2x + 1$$

METHODS AND MEANINGS

The Elimination Method for Solving Systems of Equations

One method of solving systems of equations is the **Elimination Method**. This method involves adding or subtracting both sides of two equations to eliminate a variable. Equations can be combined this way because balance is maintained when equal amounts are added to both sides of an equation. For example, if $a = b$ and $c = d$, then if you add a and c you will get the same result as adding b and d. Thus, $a + c = b + d$.

Consider the system of linear equations shown at right. Notice that when both sides of the equations are added together, the sum of the x-terms is zero and so the x-terms are eliminated. (Be sure to write both equations so that x is above x, y is above y, and the constants are similarly matched.)

$$3x + 2y = 14$$
$$-3x + 5y = 14$$
$$\frac{7y}{7} = \frac{28}{7}$$
$$y = 4$$

Now that you have one equation with one variable ($7y = 28$), you can solve for y by dividing both sides by 7. To find x, you can substitute the answer for y into one of the original equations, as shown at right. You can then test the solution for x and y by substituting both values into the other equation to verify that $-3x + 5y = 14$.

$$3x + 2(4) = 14$$
$$3x + 8 = 14$$
$$3x = 6$$
$$x = 2$$

$$-3(2) + 5(4) = 14 \checkmark$$

Since $x = 2$ and $y = 4$ is a solution to both equations, it can be stated that the two lines cross at the point (2, 4).

Review & Preview

6-99. Find the point of intersection for each set of equations below using any method. Check your solutions, if possible.

a. $6x - 2y = 10$
$3x - 5 = y$

b. $6x - 2y = 5$
$3x + 2y = -2$

c. $5 - y = 3x$
$y = 2x$

d. $y = \frac{1}{4}x + 5$
$y = 2x - 9$

6-100.   Consider the equation $-6x = 4 - 2y$.

        a.   If you graphed this equation, what shape would the graph have? How can you tell?

        b.   Without changing the form of the equation, find the coordinates of three points that must be on the graph of this equation. Then graph the equation on graph paper.

        c.   Solve the equation for y. Does your answer agree with your graph? If so, how do they agree? If not, check your work to find the error.

6-101.   A tile pattern has 10 tiles in Figure 2 and increases by 2 tiles for each figure. Find a rule for this pattern and then determine how many tiles are in Figure 100.

6-102.   Make a table and graph the rule $y = -x^2 + x + 2$ on graph paper. Label the x-intercepts.

6-103.   Mr. Greer solved an equation below. However, when he checked his solution, it did not make the original equation true. Find his error and then find the correct solution.

$$4x = 8(2x - 3)$$
$$4x = 16x - 3$$
$$-12x = -3$$
$$x = \frac{-3}{-12}$$
$$x = \frac{1}{4}$$

6-104.   Thirty coins, all dimes and nickels, are worth $2.60. How many nickels are there?

6-105. **Multiple Choice:** Martha's equation has the graph shown at right. Which of these are solutions to Martha's equation? (Remember that more than one answer may be correct.)

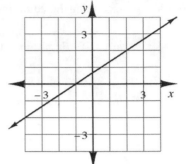

a. $(-4, -2)$

b. $(-1, 0)$

c. $x = 0$ and $y = 1$

d. $x = 2$ and $y = 2$

6-106. Copy and complete the table below. Then write the corresponding rule.

IN (x)	2	10	6	7	−3	0	−10	100	x
OUT (y)	−7				18	3			

6-107. Solve the following equations for x, if possible. Check your solutions.

a. $-(2 - 3x) + x = 9 - x$

b. $\frac{6}{x+2} = \frac{3}{4}$

c. $5 - 2(x + 6) = 14$

d. $\frac{1}{2}x - 4 + 1 = -3 - \frac{1}{2}x$

6-108. Using the variable x, write an equation that has no solution. Explain how you know it has no solution.

6-109. Identify the hypothesis and conclusion for each of the following statements. Then decide if the statement is sometimes true, always true, or never true. **Justify** your decision.

a. ab is odd if a and b are prime numbers.

b. If a and b are negative real numbers, then $a + b$ is positive.

6-110. **Multiple Choice:** Which equation below could represent a tile pattern that grows by 3 and has 9 tiles in Figure 2?

a. $3x + y = 3$

b. $-3x + y = 9$

c. $-3x + y = 3$

d. $2x + 3y = 9$

Chapter 6 Closure   What have I learned?

Reflection and Synthesis

The activities below offer you a chance to reflect on what you have learned during this chapter. As you work, look for concepts that you feel very comfortable with, ideas that you would like to learn more about, and topics you need more help with. Look for **connections** between ideas as well as **connections** with material you learned previously.

①   TEAM BRAINSTORM

With your team, brainstorm a list for each of the following topics. Be as detailed as you can. How long can you make your list? Challenge yourselves. Be prepared to share your team's ideas with the class.

Topics: What have you studied in this chapter? What ideas and words were important in what you learned? Remember to be as detailed as you can.

Connections: What topics, ideas, and words that you learned *before* this chapter are **connected** to the new ideas in this chapter? Again, make your list as long as you can.

②   MAKING CONNECTIONS

The following is a list of the vocabulary used in this chapter. The words that appear in bold are new to this chapter. Make sure that you are familiar with all of these words and know what they mean. Refer to the glossary or index for any words that you do not yet understand.

coefficients	**coincide**	**Elimination Method**
Equal Values Method	equation	graph
"let" statement	linear equation	**mathematical sentence**
ordered pair	**parallel**	point of intersection
situation	solution	standard form
Substitution Method	system of equations	variable
$y = mx + b$		

Make a concept map showing all of the **connections** you can find among the key words and ideas listed above. To show a **connection** between two words, draw a line between them and explain the **connection**, as shown in the example below. A word can be **connected** to any other word as long as there is a **justified connection**. For each key word or idea, provide a sketch that illustrates the idea (see the example on the following page).

Continues on next page →

Continued from previous page.

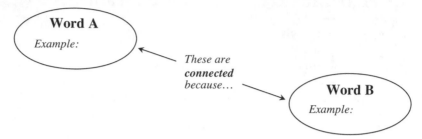

Your teacher may provide you with vocabulary cards to help you get started. If you use the cards to plan your concept map, be sure either to re-draw your concept map on your paper or to glue the vocabulary cards to a poster with all of the **connections** explained for others to see and understand.

While you are making your map, your team may think of related words or ideas that are not listed here. Be sure to include these ideas on your concept map.

③ SUMMARIZING MY UNDERSTANDING

This section gives you an opportunity to show what you know about certain math topics or ideas. Your teacher will give you directions for exactly how to do this. Your teacher may give you a "GO" page to work on. The "GO" stands for "Graphic Organizer," a tool you can use to organize your thoughts and communicate your ideas clearly.

④ WHAT HAVE I LEARNED?

This section will help you evaluate which types of problems you have seen with which you feel comfortable and those with which you need more help. Even if your teacher does not assign this section, it is a good idea to try these problems and find out for yourself what you know and what you need to work on.

Solve each problem as completely as you can. The table at the end of the closure section has answers to these problems. It also tells you where you can find additional help and practice on problems like these.

CL 6-111. Solve these systems of equations using any method.

a. $y = 3x + 7$
$y = -4x + 21$

b. $3x - y = 17$
$-x + y = -7$

c. $x = 3y - 5$
$2x + 12y = -4$

d. $2x - 3y = -16$
$-4x + 2y = -4$

CL 6-112. Bob climbed down a ladder from his roof, while Rob climbed up another ladder next to him. Each ladder had 30 rungs. Their friend Jill recorded the following information about Bob and Rob:

> Bob went down 2 rungs every second.
>
> Rob went up 1 rung every second.

At some point, Bob and Rob were at the same height. Which rung were they on?

CL 6-113. Solve for x.

    a. $6x - 11 = 4x + 12$ b. $2(3x - 5) = 6x - 4$

    c. $(x - 3)(x + 4) = x^2 + 4$ d. $\frac{x}{25} = \frac{7}{10}$

CL 6-114. Solve the equations in parts (a) and (b) for y. Then name the growth factor and the y-intercept of each equation in part (c).

    a. $-6x - 2y = 8$ b. $2x^2 + 2y = 4x + 2x^2 - 7$

    c.   For each of the two solved equations, find the y-intercept and growth factor. **Justify** your answers.

CL 6-115. Florida ecologists sampled Lake George to estimate the number of rainbow trout in the lake. Out of 156 fish, 18 were rainbow trout. About how many rainbow trout should they expect to find in a sample of 500 fish?

CL 6-116. As treasurer of his school's 4H club, Kenny wants to buy gifts for all 18 members. He can buy t-shirts for $9 and sweatshirts for $15. The club has only $180 to spend. If Kenny wants to spend all of the club's money, how many of each type of gift can he buy?

    a.   Write a system of equations representing this problem.

    b.   Solve your system of equations and figure out how many of each type of gift Kenny should buy.

CL 6-117. Simplify each expression.

    a. $3(x^2 - 7x) + 5xy - (x - 4xy) - 2x^2 + 21x$

    b. $3y - (4x + 7) - y + 11 + (2x - y + 12)$

CL 6-118. Rewrite each expression below as a product and as a sum.

a. $(x+7)(2x-5)$ b. $5x(y-7)$ c. $(3x-7)(x^2-2x+11)$

CL 6-119. Each part (a) through (d) below represents a different tile pattern. For each, find the growth factor and the number of tiles in Figure 0.

a.

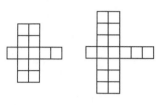

Figure 2   Figure 3   Figure 4

b.

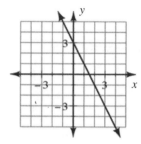

c. $y=3x-14$

d.

x	−3	−2	−1	0	1	2	3
y	18	13	8	3	−2	−7	−12

CL 6-120. Check your answers using the table at the end of the closure section. Which problems do you feel confident about? Which problems were hard? Use the table to make a list of topics you need help on and a list of topics you need to practice more.

⑤   HOW AM I THINKING?

This course focuses on five different **Ways of Thinking**: reversing thinking, justifying, generalizing, making connections, and applying and extending understanding. These are some of the ways in which you think while trying to make sense of a concept or to solve a problem (even outside of math class). During this chapter, you have probably used each Way of Thinking multiple times without even realizing it!

Review each of the Ways of Thinking that are described in the closure sections of Chapters 1 through 5. Then choose three of these Ways of Thinking that you remember using while working in this chapter. For each Way of Thinking that you choose, show and explain where you used it and how you used it. Describe why thinking in this way helped you solve a particular problem or understand something new. (For instance, explain why you wanted to **generalize** in this particular case, or why it was useful to see these particular **connections**.) Be sure to include examples to demonstrate your thinking.

Answers and Support for Closure Activity #4
What Have I Learned?

Problem	Solution	Need Help?	More Practice
CL 6-111.	a. $x = 2$, $y = 13$ b. $x = 5$, $y = -2$ c. $x = -4$, $y = \frac{1}{3}$ d. $x = \frac{11}{2}$, $y = 9$	Lessons 6.2.2, 6.2.3, and 6.3.1 Math Notes boxes	Problems 6-24, 6-25, 6-32, 6-34, 6-51, 6-56, 6-61, 6-62, 6-71, and 6-81
CL 6-112.	They were on the 10th rung.	Lessons 6.2.2, 6.2.3, and 6.3.1 Math Notes boxes	Problems 6-38, 6-43, 6-52, 6-58, 6-77, 6-90, and 6-97
CL 6-113.	a. $x = 11.5$ b. no solution c. $x = 16$ d. $x = 17.5$	Lesson 5.1.3 Math Notes box, Lesson 5.1.4	Problems 6-16, 6-37, and 6-107
CL 6-114.	a. $y = -3x - 4$ b. $y = 2x - \frac{7}{2}$ c. (a) y-intercept: $(0, -4)$, growth: -3 (b) y-intercept: $(0, -3.5)$, growth: 2	Lesson 5.1.5, Lesson 5.1.5 Math Notes box	Problems 6-12 and 6-100
CL 6-115.	approximately 58 rainbow trout	Lesson 5.2.1, Lesson 5.2.1 Math Notes box	Problems 6-11, 6-28, and 6-64
CL 6-116.	a. $9x + 15y = 180$, $x + y = 18$ b. 15 t-shirts, 3 sweatshirts	Lessons 6.2.2, 6.2.3, and 6.3.1 Math Notes boxes	Problems 6-38, 6-43, 6-52, 6-58, 6-77, 6-90, and 6-97

Problem	Solution	Need Help?	More Practice
CL 6-117.	a. $x^2 + 9xy - x$ b. $y - 2x + 16$	Lessons 2.1.5 and 5.1.3 Math Notes boxes	Problems 4-6, 3-15, and 3-75
CL 6-118.	a. $2x^2 + 9x - 35$ b. $5xy - 35x$ c. $3x^3 - 13x^2 + 47x - 77$	Lessons 5.1.3 and 5.2.3 Math Notes boxes	Problems 6-66 and 6-103
CL 6-119.	a. growth: 5, Figure 0: 3 tiles b. growth: –2, Figure 0: 3 tiles c. growth: 3, Figure 0: –14 tiles d. growth: –5, Figure 0: 3 tiles	Sections 3.1 and 4.1, Lesson 4.1.7 Math Notes box	Problems 6-10, 6-76, 6-85, 6-101, and 6-110

CHAPTER 7

Linear Equations

Chapter 7 will complete the focus on linear equations that began in Chapter 1 and continued through Chapters 3, 4, and 6. In this chapter, you will analyze the geometric meaning of slope and will explore the idea of slope as a rate of change. You will also use trend lines to make predictions from existing data about future events.

In this chapter, you will learn:

➢ How to find the slope (steepness) of a line given its equation, its graph, or any two points on the line.

➢ How the slopes of parallel and perpendicular lines are related.

➢ How slopes can represent rates of change in real-life applications.

➢ How to find the equation of a trend line to fit linear data.

➢ How to find the slope of a line without graphing it.

Guiding Questions

Think about these questions throughout this chapter:

What is slope?

What is a rate?

What information is necessary to find the equation of a line?

How are the slopes of two lines related?

Chapter Outline

Section 7.1 In this section, you will find equations of lines that fit data and will learn how to measure the steepness of a line on a graph. You will also study the difference between lines that point upward, lines that point downward, and lines that are horizontal.

Section 7.2 In this section, you will investigate situations where slope represents a rate in a real-life context, culminating in an activity called "The Big Race."

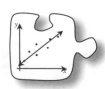

Section 7.3 In Section 7.3, you will develop a method for finding the equation of a line when given only two points on the line. This section ends with several activities for which you will pull together your understanding of slope and $y = mx + b$ to solve problems.

Algebra Connections

7.1.1 What's the equation of the line?

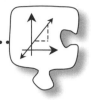

$y = mx + b$

Previously, you developed ways to find the growth of a line using its rule, table, and graph. You also learned how the y intercept is present in each of the multiple representations. In this chapter, you will complete your study of lines and will develop ways to find the equation of a line using different pieces of information about the line, such as two points that are on it. Today's lesson will help you review **connections** you made in previous chapters by challenging you to find equations for lines from multiple representations.

7-1. **GETTING TO KNOW YOU**, Part Three

Your teacher will give you a card with a representation of a line (a table, graph, rule, or situation). Consider what you know about the line represented on your card. Then find the other students in your class that have a representation of the same line. These students will be your teammates. Be prepared to **justify** how you know your representation matches those of your teammates.

7-2. **THE LINE FACTORY**, Part One

Congratulations! You have recently been hired to work at the city's premiere Line Factory. People from all over the country order lines from your factory because of their superior quality and excellent price.

However, lately the Line Factory is having a serious problem: Too many customers have placed orders and then received a line different from the one they wanted! The factory has hired your team to eliminate this problem.

Your Task: Review the recent orders (the bulleted items that follow) and decide if there is anything wrong with each customer's order. If the order is correct, then pass it on to your production department with a rule, a table, and a graph (on graph paper). However, if the order is incorrect, explain to the customer how you know the order is incorrect and suggest corrections.

Problem continues on next page →

7-2.   *Problem continued from previous page.*

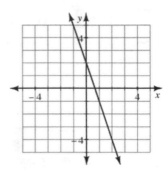

- **Customer A** wants a line that has y-intercept at $(0, -3)$ and grows by 4. She ordered the line $y = -3x + 4$.

- **Customer B** wants the line graphed at right. He ordered the line $y = 3x + 2$.

- **Customer C** wants a line that passes through the points $(2, -4)$ and $(5, 2)$. She ordered the line $y = 2x - 8$.

- **Customer D** wants the line that is represented by the table below.

IN (x)	-3	-2	-1	0	1	2	3
OUT (y)	-4	-1	2	4	7	10	13

- **Customer E** ordered the line $2x - y = 4$ and wants the line to grow by 2 and pass through the point $(5, 6)$.

- **Customer F** wants a line that starts at $(0, 1)$, grows first by 3, and then grows by 5.

7-3.   For the customer order that your team is assigned, prepare a team transparency or poster with your analysis from problem 7-2. Every team transparency or poster should include:

- The original customer order, complete with any given table, rule, graph, or statements.

- An explanation of any errors your team found in the order. If your team did not find any errors, the transparency or poster should **justify** this fact as well.

- Suggestions for how the customer can fix his or her order. You may want to suggest an equation that you suspect the customer wanted. If no mistake was made, then write a note to the company's production department with a rule, a table, and a graph for the order.

Review & Preview

7-4.   Examine the tile pattern shown at right.

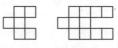

a.   On graph paper, draw Figure 0 and Figure 4.

Figure 1   Figure 2   Figure 3

b.   How many tiles will Figure 10 have? **Justify** your answer.

Algebra Connections

7-5.   Match the system of equations in the left column with its solution in the right column.

a. $6x - y = 4$ 1. $(0, -4)$
    $3x + y = 5$

b. $x = y + 4$ 2. $(3, 7)$
    $2x + 3y = -12$

c. $5x - 2y = 1$ 3. $(1, 2)$
    $y = 2x + 1$

7-6.   Use proportional reasoning to solve each of the problems below.

a. At the zoo, three adult lions eat 250 pounds of food a day. If two more adult lions joined the group, how much food would the zoo need to provide each day?

b. Byron can read 45 pages in an hour. How long will it take him to read the new 700-page Terry Cotter book?

7-7.   Graph $y = -\frac{1}{2}x + 6$. Find its x- and y-intercepts.

7-8.   Solve each equation below for the indicated variable.

a. $4x - 2 + y = 6 - 2x$ for y b. $4x - 2 + y = 6 - 2x$ for x

c. $3(6 - x) + 2x = 15$ for x

7-9.   Little Evan has 356 stuffed animals, all of which are either teddy bears or dogs. He has 17 more than twice as many dogs as teddy bears. How many teddy bears does he own? Write and solve an equation (or a system of equations) to solve this problem. Be sure to define your variable(s).

7.1.2 How can I use an equation?

Using Equations to Make Predictions

Previously, you have learned to find and **extend** patterns in data and to make predictions using rules, equations, and graphs. Today you will **apply** these math tools to a real situation in which your data does not make a perfect pattern.

7-10.   Today you will use your new knowledge of $y = mx + b$ to solve "Newton's Revenge," problem 1-15, which is summarized below.

Newton's Revenge, the new roller coaster, has a tunnel that thrills riders with its very low ceiling. The closest the ceiling of the tunnel ever comes to the seat of the roller-coaster car is 200 cm. Although no accidents have yet been reported, rumors have been spreading that very tall riders have been injured as they went through the tunnel with their arms raised over their heads. The management needs your help in convincing the public that the roller coaster is safe.

Your Task: To help determine whether the tunnel is safe for any rider, no matter how tall, plot the data collected in problem 1-15 into a grapher, such as a graphing calculator. The height and reach should both be measured in centimeters. If you do not have the data from Chapter 1, your teacher may instruct you to use the data provided at right. As you enter the data into the grapher, answer the questions below.

Height (cm)	Reach (cm)
166.4	127
169	133
172.8	133
179	139
170	139
183	137
162.5	121
165	126
157.5	128
165	123
169	132
156	119

a.   What window should you use to be able to see all of your data in a scatter plot? Set up the appropriate window and make a scatter plot with your grapher.

b.   Is this plot useful for making predictions? Why or why not? If not, how could you change the plot to make it more useful?

Algebra Connections

7-11. Use your grapher to help you find the **trend line** (the equation of the line that best approximates your data). Once you have an equation that can best represent the data, you will be able to use the equation to verify that the roller coaster is safe.

If you have not done so already, set the window on your grapher to show the x-axis from 0 to your highest x-value and the y-axis from 0 to your highest y-value.

a. Guess an equation that you think might come close to your data. Enter the equation into your grapher and graph it in the same window as your data. Did you come close?

b. Change the numbers in your equation to numbers you think might fit the data more closely. Graph the equation again and see what happens. Keep trying new numbers until you find an equation that you think comes close to fitting the data. What is your equation?

c. Now reset the window to zoom in on your data. Does your equation still seem to fit the data well? If not, adjust your equation until you are satisfied with how it fits the data.

d. Zoom back out and find the y-intercept. What does this point represent? Does this make sense? If necessary, change your equation so that your equation makes sense at $x = 0$.

7-12. The amusement park wants Newton's Revenge to be safe for tall riders. For example, the famous basketball player Yao Ming is 7 feet 6 inches (about 228.6 cm) tall. Is the roller coaster safe for him? Use your grapher to confirm your decision.

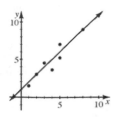

ETHODS AND MEANINGS

Trend Lines

A **trend line** is a line that represents a set of data. It does not need to intersect each data point. Rather, it needs to approximate the data. A trend line looks and "behaves" like the data, as shown in the example at right.

7-13.   Evaluate each expression below for a when $a = \frac{2}{3}$, if possible.

a. $24a$ b. $3a$ c. $\frac{a}{0}$ d. $\frac{0}{a}$

7-14.   Find the distance between each pair of points.

a.   (3, 7) and (8, 7)   b.   (–13, 7) and (8, 7)

c.   (x, 7) and (c, 7)   d.   (5, 2) and (5, 38)

e.   (5, –4) and (5, 34)   f.   (5, y) and (5, f)

7-15.   Solve each equation below for x. Check your solution.

a. $3x - 7(4 + 2x) = -x + 2$ b. $-5x + 2 - x + 1 = 0$

7-16.   Find the solution for each system of equations below, if a solution exists. If there is not a single solution, explain why not. Be sure to check your solution, if possible.

a. $x + 4y = 2$ b. $2x + 4y = -10$
        $3x - 4y = 10$ $x = -2y - 5$

7-17.   The figures below are **similar** (meaning they have the same shape). Use the information given about the lengths of the sides to solve for x and y.

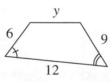
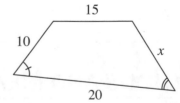

7-18.   Assume that a baby's length can be determined by the equation $l = 23 + 1.5t$, where l represents the length of the baby in inches and t represents the age of the baby in months.

a.   How fast is the baby growing each month? How can you tell?

b.   How long was the baby when it was born? How can you tell?

c.   How long will the baby be when it is 3 months old?

d.   If the baby was born in January, during what month will it be 39.5 inches long?

7.1.3 How can I measure steepness?

Measuring Steepness: An Introduction to Slope

You have been investigating what factors determine the steepness and position of a line and have seen that m in a $y = mx + b$ equation determines the direction of a line on a graph. In this lesson you will use all of your knowledge about m to determine the accurate value of m for an equation when you see the graph of a line.

During this lesson, ask your teammates the following focus questions:

What does m tell you about a line?

What makes lines steeper? What makes lines less steep?

How is growth related to steepness?

7-19.   In Chapter 4 you worked with tile patterns and **made connections** between tile patterns and graphs. Think back on your work from that chapter to answer these questions about the tile patterns A and B represented in the graph below.

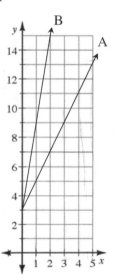

a.   By looking at the graph, what statements can you make about the two tile patterns? What do the patterns have in common? What is different? Be specific.

b.   On the Lesson 7.1.3 Resource Page you receive from your teacher, draw growth triangles for each line. If available, use different colors for the triangles on each line. Label each triangle with its dimensions.

c.   What does the steepness of a line tell you about the growth of the tile pattern?

d.   Write an equation (rule) for each tile pattern.

7-20.   The graph at right shows a line for a tile pattern you may recognize from Chapter 4. What is the growth factor for this line? That is, how many tiles are added each time the figure number is increased by 1? Explain how you found the growth factor.

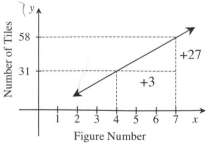

7-21. The growth triangles in problem 7-20 are also called **slope triangles**. **Slope** is a measure of the steepness of a line. It is the ratio of the vertical distance to the horizontal distance of a slope triangle. The vertical part of the triangle is called **Δy** (read "change in *y*"), while the horizontal part of the triangle is called **Δx** (read "change in *x*"). Note that "Δ" is the Greek letter "delta" that is often used to represent a difference or a change.

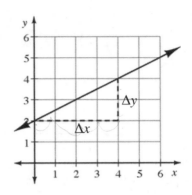

a. What is the vertical distance (Δ*y*) for this slope triangle?

b. What is the horizontal distance (Δ*x*) for this slope triangle?

c. Find this graph on the resource page. Draw miniature slope triangles for this line that have a horizontal distance (Δ*x*) of 1. Use one of these mini-triangles to find the slope (growth factor) for this line.

d. How could you use Δ*y* and Δ*x* to find the slope of this line?

e. What is the equation of this line?

7-22. Find the line graphed at right with slope triangles A, B, and C on the resource page.

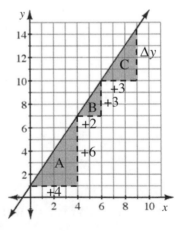

a. Find the slope using slope triangles A and B. What do you notice?

b. What is the vertical distance (Δ*y*) of slope triangle C? Explain your reasoning.

c. Draw a slope triangle on the line with a horizontal distance (Δ*x*) of 1 unit. Find the vertical distance (Δ*y*) of this new triangle. What do you notice?

7-23. What is special about the line that has Δ*y* = 0? How can you describe a line for which Δ*x* = 0? Draw a diagram for each case to demonstrate your answer.

7-24.　Michaela was trying to find the slope of the line shown at right, so she selected two **lattice points** (locations where the grid lines intersect) and then drew a slope triangle.

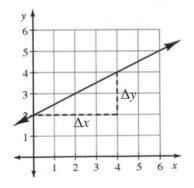

Her teammate, Cynthia, believes that $\Delta y = 3$ because the triangle is three units tall, while her other teammate, Essie, thinks that $\Delta y = -3$ because the triangle is three units tall and the line is pointing downward.

a.　With whom do you agree and why?

b.　When writing the slope of the line, Michaela noticed that Cynthia wrote $\frac{-3}{4}$ on her paper, while Essie wrote $-\frac{3}{4}$. She asked, "Are these ratios equal?" Discuss this with your team and answer her question.

c.　Find the equation of Michaela's line.

METHODS AND MEANINGS

Introduction to Slope

Slope is a measure of the steepness of a line. It is the ratio of the vertical distance to the horizontal distance of a slope triangle. The vertical part of the triangle is called Δy (read "change in y"), while the horizontal part of the triangle is called Δx (read "change in x").

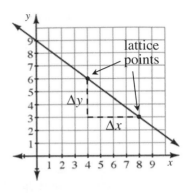

In the example at right, $\Delta y = 2$ and $\Delta x = 4$, so the slope is $\frac{2}{4} = \frac{1}{2}$.

Note that "Δ" is the Greek letter "delta" that is often used to represent a difference or a change.

7-25.   What shape will the graph of $y = x^2 + 2$ be? How can you tell? **Justify** your prediction by making a table and graphing $y = x^2 + 2$ on graph paper.

7-26.   Carol has two rose bushes: one with red flowers and another with yellow flowers. Her red rose bush has three times as many flowers as her yellow rose bush. Combined, they have 124 flowers. How many of each color flower does she have? Write an equation (or a system of equations) and solve.

7-27.   Artemis thinks that all lines eventually cross the x-axis. Do you agree? If not, provide a counterexample (that is, find a rule and a graph of a line that does not have an x-intercept).

7-28.   For each equation below, solve for x and check your answer.

   a. $10(2x - 1) = 100$ b. $\frac{1}{3}x - 6 = 8$

   c. $(x - 2)(x + 1) = x^2 + 4x$ d. $9x - 21 + 9 = 2(5 - x)$

7-29.   Write and solve an equation (or a system of equations) for the situation below. Define your variables and write your solution as a sentence.

   Kelly and Jack participated in a cross-country bicycle race sponsored by the school. They left school at the same time and rode their bikes on the same path. If Kelly traveled 15 kilometers per hour and Jack traveled 12 kilometers per hour, how long does it take for Kelly to be 18 kilometers ahead of Jack on the path?

7-30.   Use a generic rectangle to multiply the expressions below. Write each answer as a product and as a sum.

   a. $(5x + 3)(x - 7)$ b. $-6x(4x - 3)$

7.1.4 How steep is it?

Comparing Δy and Δx

In Lesson 7.1.3, you discovered how to use the dimensions of a slope triangle to measure the steepness of a line. Today you will use the idea of stairs to understand slope even better. You will examine the difference between positive and negative slopes and will learn how to draw a line when given information about Δx and Δy.

During the lesson, ask your teammates the following target questions:

How can you tell if m is positive or negative?

What makes lines steeper? What makes lines less steep?

What does a line with a slope of zero look like?

7-31.   One way to think about slope or growth triangles is as stair steps on a line.

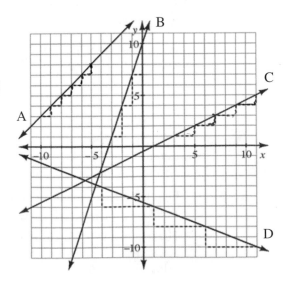

a.   Picture yourself climbing (or descending) the stairs from left to right on each of the lines on the graph (shown below, at right). Of lines A, B, and C, which is the steepest? Which is the least steep?

b.   Examine line D. What direction is it traveling from left to right? What number should be used for Δy to represent this direction?

c.   Find this graph on the Lesson 7.1.4 Resource Page and label the legs of one of the slope triangles on each line. Then find the slope of each line.

d.   How does the slope relate to the steepness of the graph?

e.   Cora answered part (d) with the statement, "The steeper the line, the greater the slope number." Do you agree? If so, use lines A through D to support her statement. If not, change her statement to make it correct.

7-32.   Find the graph shown below on the Lesson 7.1.4 Resource Page.

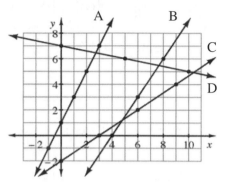

   a.   Which is the steepest line? Which is steeper, line B or line C?

   b.   Draw slope triangles for lines A, B, C, and D using the highlighted points on each line. Label Δx and Δy for each.

   c.   Match each line with its slope using the list below. Note: You will have slopes left over.

   $m = 6$ $\qquad$ $m = 2$ $\qquad$ $m = -\frac{1}{5}$ $\qquad$ $m = \frac{3}{2}$

   $m = 5$ $\qquad$ $m = -\frac{2}{3}$ $\qquad$ $m = -5$ $\qquad$ $m = \frac{2}{3}$

   d.   Viewed left to right, in what direction would a line with slope $-\frac{3}{5}$ point? How do you know?

   e.   Viewed left to right, in what direction would a line with slope $-\frac{5}{3}$ point? How do you know? How would it be different from the line in part (d)?

7-33.   Examine lines A, B, C, and D on the graph at right. For each line, decide if the slope is positive, negative, or zero. Then draw and label slope triangles on your resource page and calculate the slope of each line.

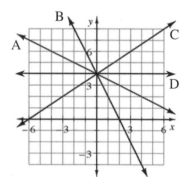

7-34.   On graph paper, graph a line to match each description below. List the slope of each line.

   a.   A line with $\Delta y = 6$ and $\Delta x = 1$.

   b.   A line that goes up 3 each time it goes over 5.

   c.   A line with $\Delta x' = 4$ and $\Delta y = -6$.

   d.   A line that has $\Delta y = 0$ and $\Delta x = 3$.

7-35.   What happens to the slope when the slope triangles are different sizes? For example, the line at right has three different slope triangles drawn as shown.

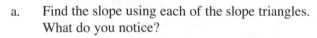

   a.   Find the slope using each of the slope triangles. What do you notice?

   b.   The triangle labeled A is drawn above the line. Does the fact that it is above the line instead of below it affect the slope of the line?

   c.   On the resource page provided by your teacher, draw another slope triangle for this line so that $\Delta x = 1$. What is the height (Δy) of this new slope triangle?

7-36.   Revisit the target questions for this lesson (reprinted below). Use the ideas you have developed in class to answer these questions in your Learning Log. Label this entry "Positive, Negative, and Zero Slope" and label it with today's date.

How can you tell if m is positive or negative?

What makes lines steeper? What makes lines less steep?

What does a line with slope zero look like?

MᴇᴛHODS AND Mᴇᴀɴɪɴɢs

MATH NOTES

More Solving Systems by Elimination

In Chapter 6, you learned how to solve systems of equations by eliminating a variable. Suppose you want to solve the system of equations shown at right.

$$3x + 2y = 11$$
$$4x + 3y = 14$$

multiply by 3

multiply by -2

The goal is to *eliminate* either x or y when you add the equations together. In this case, you need to do something to *both* equations before you add them. To eliminate y, you can multiply the first equation by 3 and multiply the second equation by -2.

$$9x + 6y = 33$$
$$-8x - 6y = -28$$

$$9x + 6y = 33$$
$$\underline{-8x - 6y = -28}$$
$$x = 5$$

Then eliminate the y-terms by adding the two new equations, as shown above.

Since you know that $x = 5$, you can substitute to find that $y = -2$. Therefore, the solution to the system of equations is $(5, -2)$.

You could also solve the system by multiplying the first equation by 4 and the second equation by -3. This would cause x to be eliminated when the equations are added together.

7-37. When Yoshi graphed the lines $y = 2x + 3$ and $y = 2x - 2$, she got the graph shown at right.

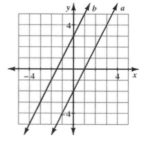

a. One of the lines at right matches the equation $y = 2x + 3$, and the other matches $y = 2x - 2$. Which line matches which equation?

b. Yoshi wants to add the line $y = 2x + 1$ to her graph. Predict where it would lie and sketch a graph to show its position. **Justify** your prediction.

c. Where would the line $y = -2x + 1$ lie? Again, **justify** your prediction and add the graph of this line to your graph from part (b).

7-38. Find the point of intersection for each system of linear equations below. Be sure to check your solutions. Which method did you use for each system and why?

a. $5x - y = 2$
$3x + y = -10$

b. $6x + 2y = 7$
$4x + y = 4$

c. $5x + 2y = 7$
$2y + 5x = 7$

7-39. Solve each of the following equations.

a. $2x + 8 = 3x - 4$

b. $1.5(w + 2) = 3 + 2w$

c. $8(x + 6) + 23 = 7$

d. $3(2x - 7) = 5x + 17 + x$

7-40. Copy and complete these generic rectangles on your paper. Then write the area of each rectangle as a product of the length and width and as a sum of the parts.

a.
6 | 13x | −21 |

b.
x | | |
−5 | | |
 | x | +3 |

c.
| 16x² | −24x | 4 |

d.
3x | | |
−2 | | |
 | x | +4 |

7-41. When Malcolm hops 15 times down the hallway, he travels 18 feet. How many times would he need to hop to travel to class (66 feet away)?

Algebra Connections

7-42. On graph paper, graph a line with *y*-intercept (0, –4) and *x*-intercept (3, 0). Find the equation of the line.

7.1.5   What information determines a line?

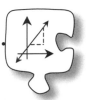

More on Slope

Today you will complete your focus on finding slope as well as using slope and the *y*-intercept to find the equation of a line. During this lesson, keep the following questions in mind:

Is there enough information to graph the line?

How are parallel lines related?

How can you find the slope of a line without graphing it?

7-43. WHAT'S MY LINE?

How much information is necessary to know where a line is on a graph? For example, if you only know two points on the line, is that enough information to know where the line is graphed? What if you only know one point? Consider each of the lines described in parts (a) through (e) below.

If possible, graph each line and find its equation. If you do not have enough information to draw one specific line, draw at least two lines that fit the given criteria. Then, for part (f), write a statement describing what information is necessary to determine a line.

a. Line A goes through the point (2, 5).

b. Line B has a slope of –3 and goes through the origin (the point (0, 0)).

c. Line C goes through points (2, 8) and (3, 10).

d. Line D has a slope of 4.

e. Line E goes through the point (8, –1) and has a slope of $-\frac{3}{4}$.

f. To graph a line and find its equation, what information do you need?

7-44. SLOPES OF PARALLEL LINES

How are the slopes of parallel lines related? How can this information be useful? Consider these questions as you answer the questions below.

a. On graph paper, graph the line $y = \frac{1}{2}x - 3$. Then, on the same set of axes, draw another line that is parallel to $y = \frac{1}{2}x - 3$. What is the slope of this line? Explain how you know.

b. What do you notice about the slope of parallel lines?

c. Use this idea to draw a line parallel to $y = -2x + 5$ that goes through the point $(0, -5)$.

d. Now draw a line parallel to $y = \frac{1}{2}x - 3$ that goes through the point $(2, -5)$. Find its rule.

7-45. FINDING THE SLOPE OF A LINE WITHOUT GRAPHING

While finding the slope of a line that goes through the points $(6, 5)$ and $(3, 7)$, Gloria figured that $\Delta y = -2$ and $\Delta x = 3$ without graphing.

a. Explain how Gloria could find the horizontal and vertical distance of the slope triangle without graphing. Draw a sketch of the line and validate her method.

b. What is the slope of the line?

c. Use Gloria's method (without graphing) to find the slope of the line that goes through the points $(4, 15)$ and $(2, 11)$.

d. Use Gloria's method to find the slope of the line that goes through the points $(28, 86)$ and $(34, 83)$.

e. Another student found the slope from part (d) to be 2. What error or errors did that student make?

7-46. SLOPE CHALLENGE

What is the steepest line possible? What is its slope? Be ready to **justify** your statements.

METHODS AND MEANINGS

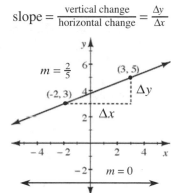

MATH NOTES

The Slope of a Line

The **slope** of a line is the ratio of the change in y (Δy) to the change in x (Δx) between any two points on the line. It indicates both how steep the line is and its direction, upward or downward, left to right.

Note that lines pointing upward from left to right have positive slope, while lines pointing downward from left to right have negative slope. A horizontal line has zero slope, while a vertical line has undefined slope. The slope of a line is denoted by the letter m when using the $y = mx + b$ equation of a line.

$$\text{slope} = \frac{\text{vertical change}}{\text{horizontal change}} = \frac{\Delta y}{\Delta x}$$

To calculate the slope of a line, pick two points on the line, draw a slope triangle (as shown in the example above), determine Δy and Δx, and then write the slope ratio. You can verify that your slope correctly resulted in a negative or positive value based on its direction.

7-47. Sam and Jimmica have both taken a speed-reading class and have been assigned to read a 300-page novel. Jimmica started reading at noon and read 10 pages per minute. Sam was on page 62 at noon and read 8 pages per minute. Will Jimmica ever catch up to Sam? Explain how you found your answer.

7-48.   Consider this system of equations:

$$y = 2x - 8$$
$$y = -\frac{2}{3}x$$

    a.   Use your knowledge of $y = mx + b$ to graph the lines without tables.

    b.   Use the graph to find the point of intersection.

    c.   Confirm this point of intersection by solving the system algebraically.

7-49.   Without graphing, find the slope of each line described below.

    a.   A line that goes through the points (4, 1) and (2, 5).

    b.   A line that goes through the origin and the point (10, 5).

    c.   A vertical line (one that travels "up and down") that goes through the point (6, –5).

    d.   A line that goes through the points (1, 6) and (10, 6).

7-50.   Solve the equations below for x. Check each solution by substituting the answer back into the equation.

    a. $4(2 - x) + 3x = x$ b. $x^2 - 5x + 2 = (x - 3)(x - 2)$

    c. $\frac{3}{x} = 6$ d. $-(-2x + 3) = -(-5)$

7-51.   Solve the equations below for the indicated variable.

    a. $6x - 3y = 12$ for y b. $y = -2x + 4$ for x

    c. $4 - 2(3x + 2) = 4x - 10$ for x d. $\frac{3-x}{4} = \frac{5}{2}$ for x

7-52.   Graph the curve $y = 3x^2 - 6x - 24$ using x-values between –3 and 5 on graph paper. What are the x- and y-intercepts?

7.2.1 What's the equation of the line?

Equation of a Line in Context

Today you will start to look at slope as a measurement of rate. Today's activity ties together the equation of a line and motion. Look for ways to **connect** what you know about *m* and *b* as you have fun.

7-53.   SLOPE WALK

Congratulations! The president of the Line Factory has presented your class with a special challenge: She now wants a way to find the equation of a line generated when a customer walks in front of a motion detector. That way, a customer can simply walk a line to order it from the factory.

Your Task: Once a motion detector has been set up with the correct software, have a volunteer walk **away** from the motion detector at a *constant* rate. In other words, he or she should walk the same speed the entire time. Then, once a graph is generated, find the equation of the line. Also find the equation of a line formed when a different volunteer walks **toward** the motion detector at a constant rate.

Discussion Points

What do you expect the first graph to look like? Why?

What will be different about the two graphs?

What would happen if the volunteer did not walk at a constant rate?

How does the volunteer's speed affect the graph?

7-54.   WALK THE WALK

To impress the president, you have decided to **reverse** the process: Write
instructions for a client on how to walk in front of the motion detector in order to
create a graph for a given rule.

Each team in the class will be assigned one or two rules from the list below. Then,
as a team, decide how to walk so that you will get the graph for your rule. After the
entire team understands how to walk, one member will try to graph the line by
walking in front of the motion detector. Pay close attention to detail! Your team
only has two tries!

a. $y = 3x + 2$ b. $y = -x + 10$

c. $y = 6$ d. $y = 2x + 4$

e. $y = -2x + 13$ f. $y = x + 5$

g. $y = -0.5x + 15$ h. $y = 1.5x + 3$

7-55.   Write a memo to the president of the Line Factory explaining why you cannot use a
motion detector to collect the data plotted below. The *x*-axis represents time in
seconds, and the *y*-axis represents the distance from the motion detector in feet.

a.      b.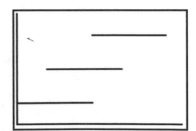

7-56.   On July 4th, Dizzyland had 67,000 visitors and collected approximately $2,814,000. How much money should Dizzyland expect to receive on New Year's Day, when park attendance reaches 71,000 people?

7-57.   The graph below represents the number of tiles in a tile pattern.

a.   Based on the information in the graph, how many tiles are being added each time (that is, what is the growth factor of the pattern)? Pay close attention to the scale of the axes.

b.   How many tiles are in Figure 0?

c.   How would the line change if the pattern grew by 12 tiles each time instead?

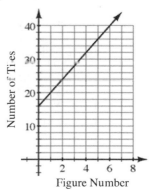

7-58.   Solve this system of equations:

$$y = \tfrac{2}{3}x - 4$$
$$2x - 3y = 10$$

a.   What does your solution tell you about the relationship between the lines?

b.   Solve the second equation for y.

c.   Does the slope of each line confirm your statement in part (a)? Explain how.

7-59.   Find the equation of each of the lines graphed at right. Then confirm algebraically that (1, 1) is the point of intersection.

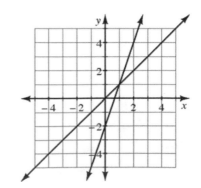

7-60.   Dominic simplified an expression using the Distributive Property and got this result: $15x^2 - 5x$. Can you find a possible expression that he started with?

7-61.   On graph paper, graph the line that goes through the points (–6, 3) and (–3, –1).

a.   What is the slope of the line?

b.   What is the y-intercept?

c.   Find the equation of the line.

7.2.2 What can slope represent?

Slope as a Measurement of Rate

Today you will focus on the meaning of slope in various contexts. What does a slope represent? How can you use it?

7-62. THE BIG RACE – HEAT 1

Before a big race, participants often compete in **heats**, which are preliminary races that determine who competes in the final race. Later, your class will compete in a tricycle race against the winners of these preliminary heats.

In the first heat, Leslie, Kristin, and Evie rode tricycles toward the finish line. Leslie began at the starting line and rode at a constant rate of 2 meters every second. Kristin got an 8-meter head start and rode 2 meters every 5 seconds. Evie rode 5 meters every 4 seconds and got a 6-meter head start.

a. On neatly scaled axes, graph and write an equation in terms of x and y for the distance Leslie travels. Let x represent time in seconds and y represent distance in meters. Then do the same for Kristin and Evie using the same set of axes.

b. After how many seconds did Leslie catch up to Evie? How far were they from the starting line when Leslie caught up to Evie? Confirm your answer algebraically.

c. If the race is 20 meters long, who won? Use both the graph and the rules to **justify** your answer.

d. What is the slope of Kristin's line? How does the slope of her line explain her rate of travel (also known as her speed)?

e. Kaye also rode in this heat. When her distance line is graphed, the rule is $y = \frac{2}{3}x + 1$. What was her speed? Did she get a head start?

7-63.   TAKE A WALK

The president of the Line Factory is so
impressed with your work that you have been
given a special assignment: to analyze the
graphs below, which were created when a
customer walked in front of a motion detector.
The motion detector recorded the distance
between it and the customer.

Working with your team, explain what motion each graph describes. In other words,
how did the customer need to walk in order to create each graph? **Note:** Time is
measured in 1-second increments along the *x*-axis, while distance from the detector
is measured in 1 foot increments along the *y*-axis

Make sure you describe:

- If the customer was walking **toward** or **away** from the motion detector.
- Where the customer began walking when the motion detector started
  collecting data.
- When the customer walked slowly and when he or she walked quickly.
- Any time the customer changed direction or stopped.

a. 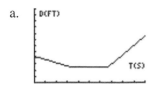   b. 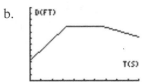   c.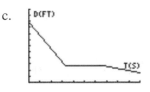

7-64.   OTHER RATES OF CHANGE

Problems 7-62 and 7-63 concentrated on situations where the slope of a line
represented speed. However, many other situations can be graphed that do not
involve motion. Examine the graphs below and explain what real-world quantities
the slope and *y*-intercepts represent. Find the slope and *y*-intercept. Write the
measurement units with each of your answers. (For example, the slopes in problem
7-63 would be expressed in feet per second.)

a. 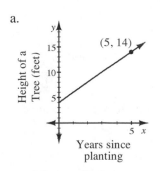   b. 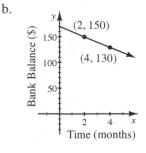   c.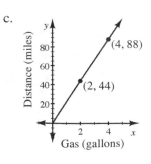

METHODS AND MEANINGS

Writing the Equation of a Line from a Graph

One of the ways to write the equation of a line directly from a graph is to find the slope of the line (m) and the y-intercept (b). These values can then be substituted into the general slope-intercept form of a line: $y = mx + b$.

For example, the slope of the line at right is $m = \frac{1}{3}$, while the y-intercept is $(0, 2)$. By substituting $m = \frac{1}{3}$ and $b = 2$ into $y = mx + b$, the equation of the line is:

$$y = mx + b \quad \rightarrow \quad y = \frac{1}{3}x + 2$$

slope y-intercept

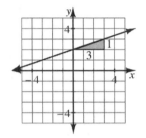

7-65.   THE BIG RACE – HEAT 2

Barbara, Elizabeth, and Carlos participated in the second heat of "The Big Race." Barbara thought she could win with a 3-meter head start even though she only pedaled 3 meters every 2 seconds. Elizabeth began at the starting line and finished the 20-meter race in 5 seconds. Meanwhile, Carlos rode his tricycle so that his distance (y) from the starting line in meters could be represented by the rule $y = \frac{5}{2}x + 1$, where x represents time in seconds.

a.   Using the given information, graph lines for Barbara, Elizabeth, and Carlos on the same set of axes. Who won the 20-meter race and will advance to the final race?

b.   Find rules that describe Barbara's and Elizabeth's motion.

c.   How fast did Carlos pedal?

d.   When did Carlos pass Barbara? Confirm your answer algebraically.

7-66. Salami and More Deli sells a 6-foot sandwich for parties. It weighs 8 pounds. Assume the weight per foot is constant.

a. How much does a sandwich 0 feet long weigh?

b. Draw a graph showing the weight of the sandwich (vertical axis) compared to the length of the sandwich (horizontal axis). Label the axes with appropriate units.

c. Use your graph to estimate the weight of a 1-foot sandwich.

d. Write a proportion to find the length of a 12-pound sandwich.

7-67. Create a table and a graph for the line $y = 5x - 10$. Find the x-intercept and y-intercept in the table and in the graph.

7-68. Match each expression in the left column with the equivalent expression on the right. Show and explain how you decided which ones matched.

a. $(x + 5)(2x - 1)$ 1. $2x^2 + 9x - 5$

b. $(2x - 5)(x + 1)$ 2. $2x^2 - 9x - 5$

c. $(2x + 1)(x - 5)$ 3. $2x^2 - 3x - 5$

7-69. Complete the missing entries in the table below. Then write the rule.

IN (x)	2	10	6	7	−3		−10	100	x
OUT (y)	4	28	16			10			

7-70. Write and solve an equation (or a system of equations) for the situation below. Define your variable(s) and write your solution as a sentence.

The Physical Education Department sells t-shirts for $12 and shorts for $8. One month, they sold 77 total items for $780 in total. How many t-shirts did they sell?

7.2.3 How can I use $y = mx + b$?

Rates of Change

Over the last four chapters you have found linear equations using many different strategies and starting from many different types of information. Today you are going to **apply** what you know about finding linear equations to solve a complicated puzzle: Who among you will win "The Big Race"?

7-71.   THE BIG RACE

Today is the final event of "The Big Race"! Your teacher will give you each a card that describes how you travel in the race. You and your study team will compete against Leslie and Elizabeth at today's rally in the gym. (Note: The information cards are also available at www.cpm.org.)

Your Task: As a team, do the following:

- Draw a graph (on graph paper) showing all of the racers' progress over time.

- Write an equation for each participant.

- Figure out who will win the race!

Rules:

- Your study team must work cooperatively to solve the problems. No team member has enough information to solve the puzzle alone!

- Each member of the team will select rider A, B, C, or D. You may not show your card to your team. You may only communicate the information contained on the card.

- Assume that each racer travels at a constant rate throughout the race.

- Elizabeth's and Leslie's cards will be shared by the entire team.

7-72.   Use your results from "The Big Race" to answer the following questions. You may answer the questions in any order, but be sure to **justify** each response.

a.   Who won "The Big Race"? Who came in last place?

b.   How fast was Rider D traveling? How fast was Elizabeth traveling?

c.   At one point in the race, four different participants were the same distance from the starting line. Who were they and when did this happen?

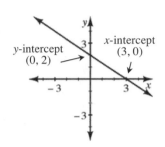

7-73. Find the point of intersection of the lines $3 = 6x - y$ and $3x - 2y = 24$.

7-74. Sometimes the quickest and easiest two points to use to graph a line that is not in slope-intercept form are the *x*- and *y*-intercepts. Find the *x*- and *y*-intercepts for the two lines below and use them to graph each line. Write the coordinates of the *x*- and *y*-intercepts on your graph.

    a. $x - 2y = 4$ b. $3x + 6y = 24$

7-75. Find the slope of the line passing through each pair of points below.

    a.   (1, 2) and (4, –1)   b.   (7, 3) and (5, 4)

    c.   (–6, 8) and (–8, 5)   d.   (55, 67) and (50, 68)

    e.   Azizah got 1 for the slope of the line through points (1, 2) and (4, –1). Explain to her the mistake she made and how to find the slope correctly.

7-76.   MATCH-A-GRAPH

Match the following graphs with their equations. Pay special attention to the scaling of each set of axes. Explain how you found each match.

a. $y = \frac{1}{4}x + 4$ b. $y = \frac{1}{2}x + 4$

c. $y = 2x + 4$ d. $y = -\frac{2}{3}x + 4$

1.
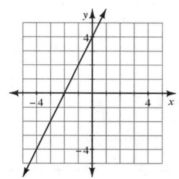

2.
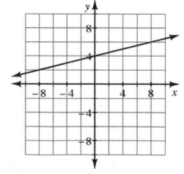

3.
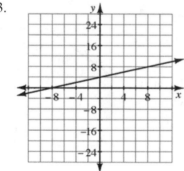

4.
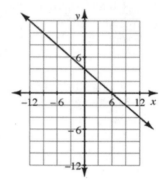

7-77.   Simplify the following expressions.

a. $15x^2 - 3x(4 + 5x)$ b. $\frac{1}{3}(24x - 9) + 10$

c. $(x - 3)(x + 1) + 2x$ d. $6x - 2 + 9 - 3y - x$

7-78.   **Multiple Choice:** The cost of a sweater is $3 less than the cost of a pair of jeans, while a hat is twice the cost of a sweater. If the pair of jeans costs j dollars, then which expression below represents the cost of the hat?

a. $2j$ b. $j - 3$ c. $2(j - 3)$ d. $2j - 3$

7.3.1 How can the solutions help find an equation?

Finding an Equation Given a Slope and a Point

To do well in "The Big Race," you had to find the equation of a line with a given rate (slope) that passed through a given point. Your method probably involved estimating the *y*-intercept of the line visually or working backward on a graph. What if the given point is far away from the *y*-axis? What if an estimate is not good enough in a particular situation?

During this lesson, you will develop an algebraic method for finding the equation of a line when given its slope and a point on the line.

7-79.   DOWN ON THE FARM

Colleen recently purchased a farm that raises chickens. Since she has never raised chickens before, Colleen wants to learn as much about her baby chicks as possible. In particular, she wants to know how much a baby chick weighs when it is hatched.

To find out, Colleen decided to track the weight of one of the chickens that was born just before she purchased the farm. She found that her chick grew steadily by about 5.2 grams each day, and she assumes that it has been doing so since it hatched. Nine days after it hatched, the chick weighed 98.4 grams.

Your Task: Determine how much the chick weighed the day it was hatched using two different representations of the chick's growth: a graph and an $x \rightarrow y$ table. Then, assuming the chicken will continue to grow at the same rate, determine when the chick will weigh 140 grams.

Discussion Points

What are you looking for?

What information are you given?

What do you expect the graph to look like? Why?

Which representation (graph or table) will give more accurate results? Why?

Further Guidance

7-80.   USING A GRAPH

Use the information in problem 7-79 to answer these questions.

a.   What is the baby chick's rate of growth? That is, how fast does the baby chick grow? How does this rate relate to the equation of the line?

b.   Before graphing, describe the line that represents the growth of the chicken. Do you know any points on the line? Does the line point upward or downward? How steep is it?

c.   Draw a graph for this situation. Let the horizontal axis represent the number of days since the chick hatched, and let the vertical axis represent the chick's weight. Label and scale your axes appropriately and title your graph "Growth of a Baby Chick."

d.   What is the y-intercept of your graph? According to your graph, how much did Colleen's chick weigh the day it hatched?

e.   When will the chick weigh 140 grams?

7-81.   USING A TABLE

Use the information in problem 7-79 to answer these questions.

a.   Now approach this problem using a table. Make a table with two columns, the first labeled "Days Since Birth" and the second labeled "Weight in Grams." In the first column, write the numbers 0 through 10.

b.   Use Colleen's measurements to fill one entry in the table.

c.   Use the chick's growth rate to complete the table.

d.   According to your table, how much did the chick weigh the day it was hatched? When will the chick weigh 140 grams? Do these answers match your answers from the graph? Which method do you think is more accurate? Why?

Further Guidance section ends here.

7-82.   FINDING AN EQUATION WITHOUT A TABLE OR GRAPH

Now you will explore another way Colleen could find the weight of her chick when it hatched without using a table or a graph.

a.   Since Colleen is assuming that the chick grows linearly, the equation will be in the form $y = mx + b$. Without graphing, what do m and b represent? Do you know either of these values?

b.   You already know the chicken's rate of growth. Place the slope into the equation of the line. What information is still unknown?

c.   In Lesson 7.1.5, you discovered that knowing the slope and a point is enough information to determine a line. Therefore, using the point (9, 98.4) should help you find the y-intercept. How can you use this point in your equation? Discuss this with your team and be ready to share your ideas with the rest of the class.

d.   Work together as a class to solve for b (the weight of the chick when it was hatched). Write the equation of the line that represents the weight of the chick.

e.   Does the y-intercept you found algebraically match the one you found using the graph? Does it match the one you found using the table? How accurate do you think your algebraic answer is?

f.   Use your equation to determine when Colleen's chicken will weigh 140 grams.

7-83.   Use this new algebraic method to find equations for lines with the following properties:

a.   A slope of –3, passing through the point (15, –50).

b.   A slope of 0.5 with an x-intercept of 28.

7-84.   MIGHTY MT. EVEREST

The Earth's surface is composed of gigantic plates that are constantly moving. Currently, India lies on a plate that is slowly drifting northward. India's plate is grinding into the rest of Asia. As it does so, it pushes up the Himalayan Mountains, which contain the world's highest peak, Mt. Everest. In 1999, mountain climbers measured Mt. Everest  with satellite gear and found it to be 8850 meters high. Geologists estimate that Mt. Everest may be growing by as much as 5 cm per year.

Your Task: Assuming a constant growth of 5 cm per year, determine how tall Mt. Everest was in the year 0. (The year 0 is the year that came 2000 years before the year 2000.) Write an equation for the height of Mt. Everest over time, with x representing the year and y representing the height of the mountain.

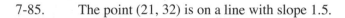

7-85.   The point (21, 32) is on a line with slope 1.5.

   a.   Find the equation of the line.

   b.   Find the coordinates of a third point on the line.

7-86.   Copy and complete each of the Diamond Problems below.
         The pattern used in the Diamond Problems is shown at right.

   a.   b.   c.   d.

7-87.   Solve the following systems of equations. Remember to check your solution in both
         equations to make sure it is the point of intersection.

   a. $y = 2x - 3$ b. $y - x = -2$
         $x - y = -4$ $-3y + 2x = 14$

7-88.   Solve each of the following equations for x.

   a. $\frac{x}{6} = \frac{7}{3}$ b. $3x + 2 = 7x - 8$

   c. $\frac{6}{x} = \frac{4}{x+1}$ d. $6(x - 4) = 42$

7-89.   The graph of the equation $2x - 3y = 7$ is a line.

   a.   Find the x- and y-intercepts and graph the line using these two points.

   b.   If a point on this line has an x-coordinate of 10, what is its y-coordinate?

7-90.   Without graphing, identify the slope and y-intercept of each equation below.

   a. $y = 3x + 5$ b. $y = \frac{5}{-4}x$ c. $y = 3$

   d. $y = 7 + 4x$ e. $3x + 4y = -4$ f. $x + 5y = 30$

7.3.2 What if the lines are perpendicular?

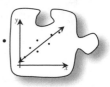

Slopes of Parallel and Perpendicular Lines

In Lesson 7.1.5, you found that the slopes of parallel lines are equal because lines with the same steepness grow at the same rate. What about the slopes of perpendicular lines (lines that form a right angle)? Today you will answer this question and then use parallel and perpendicular lines to find the equations of other lines.

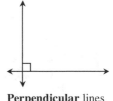

Perpendicular lines form a right angle.

7-91. SLOPES OF PERPENDICULAR LINES

To investigate the slopes of perpendicular lines, you will need some graph paper and a ruler or straightedge. You will also need a piece of transparency and an overhead pen (or tracing paper).

a. First place the transparency over the graph paper. Use the grid lines and ruler to draw two perpendicular lines, like the ones shown above. Label one line A and the other line B.

b. Now turn your transparency so that line A has a slope of $\frac{2}{3}$, as shown in the diagram at right. What is the slope of line B? Verify your results with your teammates and place your results in a table like the one shown at right.

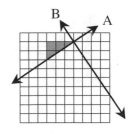

Slope of Line A	Slope of Line B
$\frac{2}{3}$	

c. Now collect data for at least three more pairs of perpendicular lines. For example, if line A has a slope of 2, what is the slope of the line perpendicular to it (line B)? What if line A has a slope of $-\frac{1}{4}$? Add each pair to your table from part (a). Share any patterns you find with your teammates.

d. Use inductive reasoning (using patterns) to find the relationship of the slopes of perpendicular lines. That is, based on your data, how do the slopes of perpendicular lines seem to be related? If you have two perpendicular lines, how can you get the slope of one from the other?

e. Test your conjecture from part (d). First find the slope of the line perpendicular to a line with slope $\frac{3}{5}$ without using graph paper. Then test it with graph paper.

7-92.   Use what you discovered about the slopes of parallel and perpendicular lines to find the equation of each line described below.

   a.   Find the equation of the line that goes through the point $(2, -3)$ and is perpendicular to the line $y = -\frac{2}{5}x + 6$.

   b.   Find the equation of the line that is parallel to the line $-3x + 2y = 10$ and goes through the point $(4, 7)$.

7-93.   Line L is perpendicular to the line $6x - y = 7$ and passes through the point $(0, 6)$. Line M is parallel to the line $y = \frac{2}{3}x - 4$ and passes through the point $(-3, -1)$. Where do these lines intersect? Explain how you found your solution.

7-94.   **EXTENSION**

   Suppose the rule for line A is $y = \frac{6}{5}x - 10$. Line A is parallel to line B, which is perpendicular to line C. If line D is perpendicular to line C and perpendicular to line E, what is the slope of line E? **Justify** your conclusion.

7-95.   In your Learning Log, summarize what you have learned today. Be sure to explain the relationship between the slopes of perpendicular lines and describe how to get the slope of one line when you know the slope of a line perpendicular to it. Title this entry "Slopes of Perpendicular Lines" and include today's date.

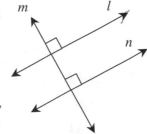

㉘ETHODS AND MEANINGS

Parallel and Perpendicular Lines

Parallel lines lie in the same plane (a flat surface) and never intersect. They have the same steepness, and therefore they grow at the same rate. Lines l and n at right are examples of parallel lines.

On the other hand, **perpendicular lines** are lines that intersect at a right angle. For example, lines m and n at right are perpendicular, as are lines m and l. Note that the small square drawn at the point of intersection indicates a right angle.

The **slopes of parallel lines** are the same. In general, the slope of a line parallel to a line with slope m is m.

The **slopes of perpendicular lines** are opposite reciprocals. For example, if one line has slope $\frac{4}{5}$, then any line perpendicular to it has slope $-\frac{5}{4}$. If a line has slope -3, then any line perpendicular to it has slope $\frac{1}{3}$. In general, the slope of a line perpendicular to a line with slope m is $-\frac{1}{m}$.

7-96.   Dean and Carlos decided to hold their own race. Dean estimates
         that he rides 3 meters every 4 seconds and wants a 5-meter head
         start. Carlos will ride 1 meter per second.

         a.   How many meters does Dean ride each second?

         b.   On one set of axes, graph and label lines to represent each
               rider's distance from the starting line. Find the equation for each rider.

         c.   Use the equations you wrote to determine when Carlos and Dean will be the
               same distance from the starting line.

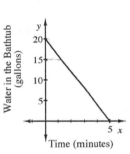

7-97.   Explain what the slope of each line below represents. Then find the slope.

         a. 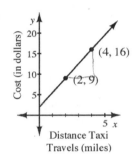   b.

7-98.   In the spring of 2005, there were 30 more Republicans than Democrats in the United
         States House of Representatives. There was also one member from an Independent
         Party. If there were 435 representatives in all, how many Republicans were there?
         Write and solve an equation (or a system of equations) to find your solution.

7-99.   Find the x-intercepts of the parabola $y = x^2 + 2x - 15$ using any representation you
         prefer. Then explain your method.

7-100.   Find the following products.

         a. $(2x - 1)(x + 3)$ b. $3x(5x - 11)$

         c. $(x - 5)(5x - 2)$ d. $100(3x - 0.5)$

7-101.   **Multiple Choice:** What is the slope of the line that goes through the points (–7, 10)
         and (1, 4)?

         a. $\frac{3}{4}$ b. $-\frac{3}{4}$ c.   1   d.   –1

Chapter 7: Linear Relationships

7.3.3 What if I only have two points?

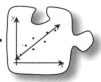

Finding the Equation of a Line through Two Points

So far, you know how to find the equation of a line with a given slope and a *y*-intercept or other point on the line. You have developed tools that help you find the equation using a graph, a table, or an algebraic process. Today you are going to expand your set of tools to include finding the equation of a line through two points. As you work on today's problems, keep these questions in mind:

What do you know about the line?

How can you use that information to find the equation?

How can you verify that your equation is correct?

7-102.   Without graphing, find the equation of the line that goes through the points (14, 52) and (29, 97). Use the questions below to help you organize your work.

   a.   What is the slope of the line?

   b.   How can you use a point to find the equation? Find the equation of the line.

   c.   Once you have the slope, does it matter which point you use to find your equation? Why or why not?

   d.   How can you verify that your equation is correct?

7-103.   In your Learning Log, describe the process you used in problem 7-102 to find the equation of a line through two points without graphing. Include an example. Title this entry "How to Find the Equation of a Line through Two Points" and include today's date.

7-104.   **WELCOME TO DIZZYLAND!**

Finding the equation of a line between two
points can be an effective method for finding
trend lines for data. Trend lines represent linear
data and can be used to make predictions about
an event or situation. In this problem, the
process you used in problem 7-102 will help
you make a prediction.

For over 50 years, Dizzyland has kept track of how many guests pass through its
entrance gates. Below is a table with the names and dates of some significant guests.
Predict when the 1 billionth guest will pass through Dizzyland's gates.

Name	Year	Guest
Elsa Marquez	1955	1 millionth guest
Leigh Woolfenden	1957	10 millionth guest
Dr. Glenn C. Franklin	1961	25 millionth guest
Mary Adams	1965	50 millionth guest
Valerie Suldo	1971	100 millionth guest
Gert Schelvis	1981	200 millionth guest
Brook Charles Arthur Burr	1985	250 millionth guest
Claudine Masson	1989	300 millionth guest
Minnie Pepito	1997	400 millionth guest
Mark Ramirez	2001	450 millionth guest

a.   With your team, represent the data on your grapher or on
graph paper. Let $x = 1955$ represent the year 1955.

b.   Select two points from the data that will make a good trend
line. You should choose your points so that when they are
connected by a line, that line will pass through the middle of
all the data and will resemble the overall trend of the data.
Every member of your team should use the same two points.
Be prepared to explain your choice of points and your
solution to the class.

c.   Use the two points you chose to find an equation for your trend line. Show
your algebraic thinking.

d.   Graph your line on the same axes as your data (either on your graph paper or
on your grapher). Does your line pass through the two points you chose? If
not, go back and check your work. Does the equation seem to do a good job of
fitting the data?

e.   What is the y-intercept of your line? Why does it make sense that it is
negative?

f.   Use your equation to make a prediction: If you want to be Dizzyland's
1 billionth guest, during what year should you go to the park? Remember that
1 billion is 1000 millions.

7-105. Find the equations of the lines described below.

  a. The line parallel to the line $y = \frac{1}{5}x - 6$ that goes through the point $(-5, 3)$.

  b. The line that goes through the points $(100, 76)$ and $(106, 58)$.

7-106. Find the equation of the line with x-intercept $(-4, 0)$ and y-intercept $(0, 9)$.

7-107. Find the point of intersection of the system of linear equations below.

$$8 - 3x = y$$
$$2y + 3x = 5$$

7-108. On graph paper, graph the parabola $y = x^2 - 6x + 10$.

  a. Label the x- and y-intercepts, if possible.

  b. The highest or lowest point on a parabola is called the **vertex**. What is the vertex of this parabola?

7-109. Evaluate the expressions below for the given values.

  a. $-2x^2 - 3x + 1$ for $x = -3$ b. $8 - (3x - 2)^2$ for $x = -2$

  c. $\frac{-3}{k+2}$ for $k = -3$ d. $\frac{15m}{n+1} - m^2 + n$ for $m = 1$, $n = 2$

7-110. Find the slope of each line below. Which pairs of lines are perpendicular? Which pairs are parallel?

  a. $y = \frac{-5}{6}x + 3$ b. $y = 3$ c. $5x + 6y = 9$ d. $x = -4$

  e. $y = -4x - 5$ f. $y = \frac{1}{4}x - 7$ g. $4x - y = 2$ h. $y = 5 - \frac{6}{5}x$

7.3.4 What's the equation of the line?

Applying $y = mx + b$ to Find Equations from Graphs

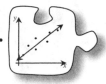

In past lessons, you learned facts about m and b by graphing lines from rules. In today's lesson, you will **reverse** the process used in Lesson 7.1.1 so that you can find the equation of a line when you know its graph.

7-111.   LINE FACTORY LOGO

The Line Factory needs a new logo for its pamphlet. After much work by the design staff, the two logos shown below were proposed.

The only problem is that the staff clerks need to have the equations of the lines in each design to program their pamphlet-production software.

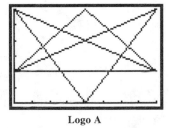

Logo A

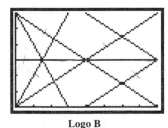

Logo B

Your Task: Find the equations of the lines in Logos A and B and recreate the graphs on your calculators. Split your team into two pairs so that one pair works on Logo A while the other pair works on Logo B.

Find the equations of the lines in your design and then use your grapher to check them. Assume that the axes shown above are scaled by ones. Also, be sure to set your window as shown at right so that the x-axis contains the values between 0 and 8 and the y-axis contains the values between 0 and 6. Once you have found all of the equations, draw all of the lines simultaneously on the same set of axes to recreate the logo on your grapher.

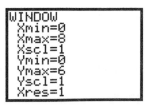

Discussion Points

How many equations should you have for each logo?

What is different about some of the lines? What is the same?

How can you find the equation of a line from its graph?

METHODS AND MEANINGS

Point-Slope Form of a Line

Another method for finding the equation of a line when given its slope and a point on the line uses the **point-slope form** of a line. This form is:

$$y - k = m(x - h)$$

In this form, (h, k) is a point on the line and m is the slope. For example, to find the equation of the line with slope $m = -3$ that goes through the point $(6, 1)$, substitute these values into $y - k = m(x - h)$ as shown below:

$$y - 1 = -3(x - 6)$$

This result can then be changed to $y = mx + b$ form:

$$y - 1 = -3(x - 6)$$
$$y - 1 = -3x + 18$$
$$y = -3x + 19$$

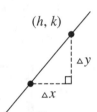

(h, k)

Δy

Δx

$\dfrac{\Delta y}{\Delta x} = m$

Thus, the equation of the line with slope $m = -3$ that goes through the point $(6, 1)$ can be written as $y - 1 = -3(x - 6)$ or $y = -3x + 19$.

Review & Preview

7-112. Complete each generic rectangle below and write the area as a sum and as a product.

a.

	$10xy$	
4		

3   5x

b.

5	$10x$	
	$4x^2$	

−3

7-113.   Peggy decided to sell brownies and cookies to raise
          money for her basketball uniform. She sold
          brownies for $3.00 and cookies for $2.50. If she
          sold 3 fewer cookies than brownies and collected
          $218 in all, then how many brownies did she sell?
          Write and solve an equation (or a system of
          equations) to find your solution.

7-114.   Use the point-slope formula (presented in the Math
          Notes box for this lesson) to find the equation of
          each line below.

          a.   The line with slope $m = -\frac{2}{3}$ that goes through the point (–6, 5).

          b.   A horizontal line that goes through the point (8, –11).

          c.   The line perpendicular to the line in part (a) above but going through the
                origin.

7-115.   Explain what the slope of each line below represents. Then find the slope.

    a.   b.
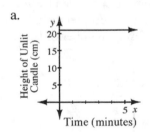   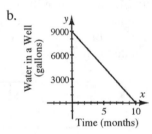

7-116.   Copy and complete each of the Diamond Problems below.
          The pattern used in the Diamond Problems is shown at right.

    a.   b.   c.   d.

7-117.   Simplify each expression below, if possible.

          a. $5x(3x)$ b. $5x + 3x$ c. $6x(x)$ d. $6x + x$

Extension Activity What's the equation of the line?

Finding $y = mx + b$ from Graphs and Tables

In past lessons, you learned facts about m and b by graphing lines from rules. In today's lesson, you will **reverse** the process to find the equation of a line when you know its graph.

7-118.   SAVE THE EARTH

The Earth Protection Service (EPS) has asked
your team to defend our planet against
dangerous meteors. Luckily, the EPS has
developed a very advanced protection system,
called the Linear Laser Cannon. This cannon
must be programmed with an equation that
dictates the path of a laser beam and destroys
any meteors in its path. Unfortunately, the
cannon uses a huge amount of energy, making
it very expensive to fire.

Your Mission: Using the technology (or resource page) provided by your teacher,
find equations of lines that will eliminate the meteors as efficiently as possible. The
EPS offers big rewards for operators who use the fewest number of lasers possible to
eliminate the meteors.

Game #1

X	Y
6	-5
2	8
-6	8
9	-9
4	-7
-4	4

Game #2

X	Y
9	-2
3	-7
-4	-5
-8	7
9	-2
-6	2

Game #3

X	Y
-1	-5
-4	2
6	2
9	6
0	5
-2	-1

Chapter 7 Closure   What have I learned?

Reflection and Synthesis

The activities below offer you a chance to reflect on what you have learned during this chapter. As you work, look for concepts that you feel very comfortable with, ideas that you would like to learn more about, and topics you need more help with. Look for **connections** between ideas as well as **connections** with material you learned previously.

①   TEAM BRAINSTORM

With your team, brainstorm a list for each of the following topics. Be as detailed as you can. How long can you make your list? Challenge yourselves. Be prepared to share your team's ideas with the class.

Topics: What have you studied in this chapter? What ideas and words were important in what you learned? Remember to be as detailed as you can.

Ways of Thinking: What Ways of Thinking did you use in this chapter? When did you use them?

Connections: What topics, ideas, and words that you learned *before* this chapter are **connected** to the new ideas in this chapter? Again, make your list as long as you can.

MAKING CONNECTIONS

The following is a list of the vocabulary used in this chapter. The words that appear in bold are new to this chapter. Make sure that you are familiar with all of these words and know what they mean. Refer to the glossary or index for any words that you do not yet understand.

coefficients	graph	growth
linear equation	parallel	**perpendicular**
prediction	**rate of change**	**slope**
slope triangle	solution	**steepness**
trend line	Δx	x-intercept
$y = mx + b$	Δy	y-intercept

Make a concept map showing all of the **connections** you can find among the key words and ideas listed above. To show a **connection** between two words, draw a line between them and explain the **connection**, as shown in the example below. A word can be **connected** to any other word as long as there is a **justified connection**. For each key word or idea, provide a sketch that illustrates the idea (see the following example).

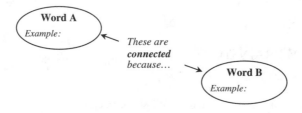

Your teacher may provide you with vocabulary cards to help you get started. If you use the cards to plan your concept map, be sure either to re-draw your concept map on your paper or to glue the vocabulary cards to a poster with all of the **connections** explained for others to see and understand.

While you are making your map, your team may think of related words or ideas that are not listed here. Be sure to include these ideas on your concept map.

SUMMARIZING MY UNDERSTANDING

Congratulations! You are now the owner of the city's premiere Line Factory. However, instead of raking in huge profits, you've noticed that you are only breaking even because many customers are ordering the incorrect line. After your company has produced the customer's line (at great expense!), they have refused to pay for it, saying it was not the line that they wanted!

Your Task: To prevent your customers from ordering the wrong lines, you need to produce a pamphlet to explain how to order a line. Carefully determine what information should be in the pamphlet so that customers will know how to write their equation in $y = mx + b$ form to get the line they want.

You can view some examples of fliers to help determine the layout of your pamphlet. A sample is shown at right. Your pamphlet can contain some advertisements, but remember that it needs to include *everything* you know about equations and graphs of lines so that your customers can order wisely. Remember to be specific and show examples!

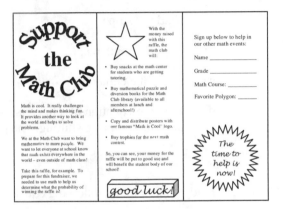

Discussion Points

How do *m* and *b* affect the equation of a line?

What information does a customer need to know to order a line correctly?

How could a customer figure out what line to order if he or she only knew two points on the line? One point and the slope?

Does the equation of a line always appear in the same form?

④ WHAT HAVE I LEARNED?

This section will help you evaluate which types of problems you have seen with which you feel comfortable and those with which you need more help. Even if your teacher does not assign this section, it is a good idea to try these problems and find out for yourself what you know and what you need to work on.

Solve each problem as completely as you can. The table at the end of the closure section has answers to these problems. It also tells you where you can find additional help and practice on problems like these.

CL 7-119. For the line graphed at right:

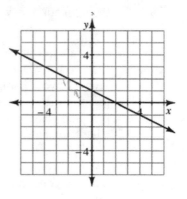

a. Find the slope.

b. Find the y-intercept.

c. Write the equation.

d. Find the equation of a line parallel to the one at right that passes through the point (0, 7).

CL 7-120. Find m and b in the following equations.

a. $y = 2x + 1$

b. $y = \frac{2}{5}x - 4$

c. $3x + 2y = 4$

CL 7-121. For each system of equations, find the point of intersection.

a. $3x + 4y = 25$
$y = x + 1$

b. $5x - 2y = 23$
$-4x + 2y = -18$

CL 7-122. Shirley starts with $85 in the bank and saves $15 every 2 months. Joshua starts with $212.50 and spends $20 every 3 months.

a. Write equations for the balances of Shirley's and Joshua's bank accounts.

b. When will Shirley and Joshua have the same amount of money? How much money will they have then?

CL 7-123. Shannon wants to estimate how many people live in her neighborhood. She knows that there are 56 houses on four blocks and that there are 62 blocks in her neighborhood.

    a.   How many houses are in her neighborhood?

    b.   Shannon estimates that on average, 4 people live in each house. About how many people live in her neighborhood?

CL 7-124. Louis and Max are contestants in a jellybean-eating contest. Louis eats 18 jellybeans in 30 seconds. Max eats 24 jellybeans in 40 seconds.

    a.   Who is eating jellybeans faster?

    b.   Because Max was also in a pie-eating contest today, he gets a 5-jellybean head start. If the contest lasts 3 minutes (180 seconds), who will win?

CL 7-125. Solve for m: $6m - 5 + 8m - (2m + 3) = 3(3m - 8)$.

CL 7-126. Match each situation to its equation and its graph. Explain how you know that all three go together.

Situations for each person:

1. Has $5 after 6 days.
2. Has no money after 7 days.
3. Has $9 after 1 day.
4. Has $10 after 2 days.
5. Started with $15.

Equations:

i. $-x + 2y = 18$

ii. $y = \frac{2}{3}x + 1$

iii. $x + 3y = 45$

iv. $y = 4x + 5$

v. $y = -x + 7$

Graphs:

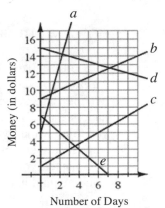

CL 7-127. Rewrite each product below as a sum.

    a. $(x + 3)(2x - 5)$

    b. $(3x - 6)(x - 4)$

CL 7-128. For each equation below, write the equation of a line that is **parallel** and passes through the origin. Then find another that is **perpendicular** and passes through the origin.

    a. $y = \frac{4}{3}x - 7$

    b. $y = 5x - 1$

    c. $y = x + 6$

CL 7-129. Copy and complete the table below for the rule $y = x^2 - 3x - 10$. Then graph the rule on graph paper.

x	−4	−3	−2	−1	0	1	2	3	4	5	6	7
y												

CL 7-130. Each box of tennis balls contains 3 tennis balls, while each box of baseballs only contains 2 baseballs. A sporting-goods store sold 26 boxes of tennis balls and baseballs. If a total of 70 balls were sold, how many boxes of tennis balls were sold? Write and solve an equation (or a system of equations) to find your answer.

CL 7-131. Find the equation of the line that passes through the points $(-5, 7)$ and $(10, 1)$.

CL 7-132. Check your answers using the table at the end of the closure section. Which problems do you feel confident about? Which problems were hard? Use the table to make a list of topics you need help on and a list of topics you need to practice more.

⑤   HOW AM I THINKING?

This course focuses on five different **Ways of Thinking**: reversing thinking, justifying, generalizing, making connections, and applying and extending understanding. These are some of the ways in which you think while trying to make sense of a concept or to solve a problem (even outside of math class). During this chapter, you have probably used each Way of Thinking multiple times without even realizing it!

Choose three of these Ways of Thinking that you remember using while working in this chapter. For each Way of Thinking that you choose, show and explain where you used it and how you used it. Describe why thinking in this way helped you solve a particular problem or understand something new. (For instance, explain why you wanted to **generalize** in this particular case, or why it was useful to see these particular **connections**.) Be sure to include examples to demonstrate your thinking.

Answers and Support for Closure Activity #4
What Have I Learned?

Problem	Solution	Need Help?	More Practice
CL 7-119.	a. The slope is $-\frac{1}{2}$. b. The y-intercept is $(0, 1)$. c. $y = -\frac{1}{2}x + 1$ d. $y = -\frac{1}{2}x + 7$	Lessons 7.1.3, 7.1.5, 7.2.2, 7.2.3, and 7.3.2 Math Notes boxes	Problems 7-59, 7-61, 7-76, 7-92, and 7-105
CL 7-120.	a. $m = 2,\ b = 1$ b. $m = \frac{2}{5},\ b = -4$ c. $m = -\frac{3}{2},\ b = 2$	Lesson 7.2.2 Math Notes box	Problems 7-76, 7-82, and 7-90
CL 7-121.	a. $(3, 4)$ b. $(5, 1)$	Lesson 7.1.4 Math Notes box	Problems 7-5, 7-38, 7-48, 7-58, 7-59, 7-73, 7-87, and 7-107
CL 7-122.	a. Let x = # of months that have passed Let y = amount of money in the account For Shirley: $y = \frac{15}{2}x + 85$ For Joshua: $y = -\frac{20}{3}x + 212.5$ b. They will have the same amount of money after 9 months. They will each have \$152.50 in their accounts.	Lesson 7.1.4 Math Notes box	Problems 7-9, 7-26, 7-29, 7-47, 7-70, 7-96, 7-98, and 7-113
CL 7-123.	a. There are 868 houses in the neighborhood. b. There are 3472 people in the neighborhood.	Lesson 5.2.1 Math Notes box	Problems 7-6, 7-41, 7-57, and 7-66
CL 7-124.	a. They are eating jellybeans at the same rate (36 jellybeans per minute). b. Max will win. After 3 minutes, Louis will have eaten 108 jellybeans and Max will have eaten 113 jellybeans.	Lesson 7.2.2	Problems 7-65 and 7-96

Problem	Solution	Need Help?	More Practice
CL 7-125.	$m = -\frac{16}{3}$	Lesson 5.1.3 Math Notes box, Lesson 5.1.4	Problems 7-15, 7-28, 7-39, 7-50, and 7-88
CL 7-126.	Situation 1, Equation *ii*, Graph (c) Situation 2, Equation *v*, Graph (e) Situation 3, Equation *iv*, Graph (a) Situation 4, Equation *i*, Graph (b) Situation 5, Equation *iii*, Graph (d)	Lesson 7.2.1, Lessons 7.2.2 and 7.2.3 Math Notes boxes	Problems 7-32, 7-37, 7-64, 7-76, 7-90, 7-97, and 7-115
CL 7-127.	a. $2x^2 + x - 15$ b. $3x^2 - 18x + 24$	Lesson 5.1.3 Math Notes box	Problems 7-30, 7-68, and 7-100
CL 7-128.	a. parallel: $y = \frac{4}{3}x$ perpendicular: $y = -\frac{3}{4}x$ b. parallel: $y = 5x$ perpendicular: $y = -\frac{1}{5}x$ c. parallel: $y = x$ perpendicular: $y = -x$	Lesson 7.3.2 Math Notes box	Problems 7-44, 7-92, 7-93, 7-105, and 7-110
CL 7-129.	*y*-values in table: 18, 8, 0, –6, –10, –12, –12, –10, –6, 0, 8, and 18	Lesson 3.1.4, Lessons 3.1.4 and 4.1.7 Math Notes boxes	Problems 7-25 and 7-108
CL 7-130.	If t = number of boxes of tennis balls and b = number of boxes of baseballs, then $3t + 2b = 70$ and $t + b = 26$; $t = 18$, so 18 boxes of tennis balls were sold.	Lesson 7.1.4 Math Notes box	Problems 7-9, 7-26, 7-29, 7-47, 7-70, 7-96, 7-98, and 7-113
CL 7-131.	$y = -\frac{2}{5}x + 5$	Lesson 7.3.3, Lesson 7.3.4 Math Notes box	Problems 7-102 and 7-106

CHAPTER 8   Quadratics

In Chapter 4, you used a web to organize the connections you found between each of the different representations of lines. These connections enabled you to use any representation (such as a graph, rule, situation, or table) to find any of the other representations.

In this chapter, a quadratics web will challenge you to find connections between the different representations of a parabola. Through this endeavor, you will learn how to rewrite quadratic equations by using a process called factoring. You will also discover and use a very important property of zero.

In this chapter, you will learn:

> How to factor a quadratic expression completely.

> How to find the roots of a quadratic equation, if they exist.

> How to move from all representations of a parabola (rule, graph, table, and situation) to each of the other representations directly.

Guiding Questions

Think about these questions throughout this chapter:

How can I rewrite it?

What's the connection?

What's special about zero?

What information do I need?

Is there another method?

Chapter Outline

Section 8.1 In this section, you will develop a method to change a quadratic equation written as a sum into its product form (also called its factored form).

Section 8.2 Through a fun application, you will find ways to generate each representation of a parabola from each of the others. You will also develop a method to solve quadratic equations using the Zero Product Property.

Section 8.3 In this section, you will be introduced to another method to solve quadratic equations called the Quadratic Formula.

8.1.1 How can I find the product?

Introduction to Factoring Quadratics

In Chapter 5 you learned how to multiply algebraic expressions using algebra tiles and generic rectangles. This section will focus on **reversing** this process: How can you find a product when given a sum?

8-1.   Review what you know about products and sums below.

    a.   Write the area of the rectangle at right as a product and as a sum. Remember that the product represents the area found by multiplying the length by the width, while the sum is the result of adding the areas inside the rectangle.

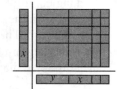

    b.   Use a generic rectangle to multiply $(6x - 1)(3x + 2)$. Write your solution as a sum.

8-2.   The process of changing a sum to a product is called **factoring**. Can every expression be factored? That is, *does every sum have a product that can be represented with tiles?*

Investigate this question by building rectangles with algebra tiles for the following expressions. For each one, write the area as a sum and as a product. If you cannot build a rectangle, be prepared to convince the class that no rectangle exists (and thus the expression cannot be factored).

    a. $2x^2 + 7x + 6$ b. $6x^2 + 7x + 2$

    c. $x^2 + 4x + 1$ d. $2xy + 6x + y^2 + 3y$

8-3. Work with your team to find the sum and the product for the following generic rectangles. Are there any special strategies you discovered that can help you determine the dimensions of the rectangle? Be sure to share these strategies with your teammates.

a.

$2x$	5
$6x^2$	$15x$

b.

$-2y$	-6
$5xy$	$15x$

c.

$-9x$	-12
$12x^2$	$16x$

8-4. While working on problem 8-3, Casey noticed a pattern with the diagonals of each generic rectangle. However, just before she shared her pattern with the rest of her team, she was called out of class! The drawing on her paper looked like the diagram below. Can you figure out what the two diagonals have in common?

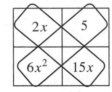

8-5. Does Casey's pattern always work? Verify that her pattern works for all of the 2-by-2 generic rectangles in problem 8-3. Then describe Casey's pattern for the diagonals of a 2-by-2 generic rectangle in your Learning Log. Be sure to include an example. Title this entry "Diagonals of a Generic Rectangle" and include today's date.

MᴇᴛHODS AND Mᴇᴀɴɪɴɢꜱ

New Vocabulary to Describe Algebraic Expressions

Since algebraic expressions come in many different forms, there are special words used to help describe these expressions. For example, if the expression can be written in the form $ax^2 + bx + c$ and if a is not 0, it is called a **quadratic** expression. Study the examples of quadratic expressions below.

Examples of quadratic expressions:

$$x^2 - 15x + 26$$
$$16m^2 - 25$$
$$12 - 3k^2 + 5k$$

The way an expression is written can also be named. When an expression is written in product form, it is described as being **factored**. When factored, each of the expressions being multiplied is called a **factor**. For example, the factored form of $x^2 - 15x + 26$ is $(x - 13)(x - 2)$, so $x - 13$ and $x - 2$ are each factors of the original expression.

Finally, the number of terms in an expression can help you name the expression to others. If the expression has one term, it is called a **monomial**, while an expression with two terms is called a **binomial**. If the expression has three terms, it is called a **trinomial**. Study the examples below.

Examples of monomials: $15xy^2$ and $-2m$

Examples of binomials: $16m^2 - 25$ and $7h^9 + \frac{1}{2}h$

Examples of trinomials: $12 - 3k^2 + 5k$ and $x^2 - 15x + 26$

8-6.   Write the area of the rectangle at right as a sum and as a product.

$-3x$	$-6y$	12
$2x^2$	$4xy$	$-8x$

8-7.   Multiply the expressions below using a generic rectangle. Then verify Casey's
        pattern (that the product of one diagonal equals the product of the other diagonal).

        a. $(4x - 1)(3x + 5)$ b. $(2x - 7)^2$

8-8.   Remember that a Diamond Problem is a pattern for which
        the **product** of two numbers is placed on top, while the
        sum of the same two numbers is placed on bottom. (This
        pattern is demonstrated in the diamond at right.) Copy and
        complete each Diamond Problem below.

        a.   b.   c.   d.

        e.   f.

8-9.   For each line below, name the slope and y-intercept.

        a. $y = \frac{-1+4x}{2}$ b. $3x + y = -7$

        c. $y = \frac{-2}{3}x + 8$ d. $y = -2$

8-10.   On graph paper, graph $y = x^2 - 2x - 8$.

        a.   Name the y-intercept. What is the connection between the y-intercept and the
              rule $y = x^2 - 2x - 8$?

        b.   Name the x-intercepts.

        c.   Find the lowest point of the graph, the vertex.

8-11.   Calculate the value of each expression below.

        a. $5 - \sqrt{36}$ b. $1 + \sqrt{39}$ c. $-2 - \sqrt{5}$

8.1.2 Is there a shortcut?

Factoring with Generic Rectangles

Since mathematics is often described as the study of patterns, it is not surprising that generic rectangles have many patterns. You saw one important pattern in Lesson 8.1.1 (Casey's pattern from problem 8-4). Today you will continue to use patterns while you develop a method to factor trinomial expressions.

8-12.　Examine the generic rectangle shown at right.

$-35x$	14
$10x^2$	$-4x$

　　a.　Review what you learned in Lesson 8.1.1 by writing the area of the rectangle at right as a sum and as a product.

　　b.　Does this generic rectangle fit Casey's pattern for diagonals? Demonstrate that the product of each diagonal is equal.

8-13.　FACTORING QUADRATICS

To develop a method for factoring without algebra tiles, first study how to factor with algebra tiles, and then look for connections within a generic rectangle.

　　a.　Using algebra tiles, factor $2x^2 + 5x + 3$; that is, use the tiles to build a rectangle, and then write its area as a product.

　　b.　To factor with tiles (like you did in part (a)), you need to determine how the tiles need to be arranged to form a rectangle. Using a generic rectangle to factor requires a different process.

　　　　Miguel wants to use a generic rectangle to factor $3x^2 + 10x + 8$. He knows that $3x^2$ and 8 go into the rectangle in the locations shown at right. Finish the rectangle by deciding how to place the ten x-terms. Then write the area as a product.

	8
$3x^2$	

　　c.　Kelly wants to find a shortcut to factor $2x^2 + 7x + 6$. She knows that $2x^2$ and 6 go into the rectangle in the locations shown at right. She also remembers Casey's pattern for diagonals. Without actually factoring yet, what do you know about the missing two parts of the generic rectangle?

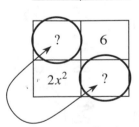

　　d.　To complete Kelly's generic rectangle, you need two x-terms that have a sum of $7x$ and a product of $12x^2$. Create and solve a Diamond Problem that represents this situation.

product

sum

　　e.　Use your results from the Diamond Problem to complete the generic rectangle for $2x^2 + 7x + 6$, and then write the area as a product of factors.

8-14.   Factoring with a generic rectangle is especially convenient when algebra tiles are not available or when the number of necessary tiles becomes too large to manage. Using a Diamond Problem helps avoid guessing and checking, which can at times be challenging. Use the process from problem 8-13 to factor $6x^2 + 17x + 12$. The questions below will guide your process.

a.   When given a trinomial, such as $6x^2 + 17x + 12$, what two parts of a generic rectangle can you quickly complete?

b.   How can you set up a Diamond Problem to help factor a trinomial such as $6x^2 + 17x + 12$? What goes on the top? What goes on the bottom?

product

sum

c.   Solve the Diamond Problem for $6x^2 + 17x + 12$ and complete its generic rectangle.

d.   Write the area of the rectangle as a product.

8-15.   Use the process you developed in problem 8-13 to factor the following quadratics, if possible. If a quadratic cannot be factored, justify your conclusion.

a. $x^2 + 9x + 18$ b. $4x^2 + 17x - 15$

c. $4x^2 - 8x + 3$ d. $3x^2 + 5x - 3$

METHODS AND **M**EANINGS

MATH NOTES

Diagonals of Generic Rectangles

Why does Casey's pattern from problem 8-4 work? That is, why does the product of the terms in one diagonal of a 2-by-2 generic rectangle always equal the product of the terms in the other diagonal?

Examine the generic rectangle at right for $(a + b)(c + d)$. Notice that each of the resulting diagonals have a product of $abcd$. Thus, the product of the terms in the diagonals are equal.

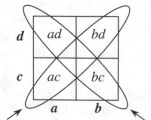

Product $= abcd$ Product $= abcd$

8-16.   Use the process you developed in problem 8-13 to factor the following quadratics, if possible.

a. $x^2 - 4x - 12$ b. $4x^2 + 4x + 1$

c. $2x^2 - 9x - 5$ d. $3x^2 + 10x - 8$

8-17.   For each rule represented below, state the x- and y-intercepts, if possible.

a.   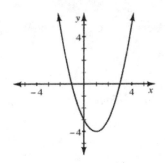   b.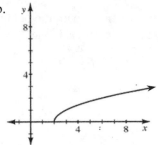

c.

x	−5	−4	−3	−2	−1	0	1	2
y	8	4	0	−4	0	2	0	−4

d. $5x - 2y = 40$

8-18.   Graph $y = x^2 - 9$ on graph paper.

a.   Name the y-intercept. What is the connection between the y-intercept and the rule $y = x^2 - 9$?

b.   Name the x-intercepts. What is the connection between the x-intercepts and the rule $y = x^2 - 9$?

8-19.   Find the point of intersection for each system.

a. $y = 2x - 3$ b. $3x = y - 2$
      $x + y = 15$ $6x = 4 - 2y$

8-20.   Solve each equation below for the given variable, if possible.

a. $\frac{4x}{5} = \frac{x-2}{7}$ b. $-3(2b - 7) = -3b + 21 - 3b$ c. $6 - 2(c - 3) = 12$

8-21.   Find the equation of the line that passes through the points (−800, 200) and (−400, 300).

8.1.3 How can I factor this?

Factoring with Special Cases

Practice your new method for factoring quadratic expressions without tiles as you consider special types of quadratic expressions.

8-22.   Factor each quadratic below, if possible. Use a Diamond Problem and generic rectangle for each one.

a. $x^2 + 6x + 9$ b. $2x^2 + 5x + 3$

c. $x^2 + 5x - 7$ d. $3m^2 + m - 14$

8-23.   SPECIAL CASES

Most quadratics are written in the form $ax^2 + bx + c$. But what if a term is missing? Or what if the terms are in a different order? Consider these questions while you factor the expressions below. Share your ideas with your teammates and be prepared to demonstrate your process for the class.

a. $9x^2 - 4$ b. $12x^2 - 16x$

c. $3 + 8k^2 - 10k$ d. $40 - 100m$

8-24.   Now turn your attention to the quadratic below. Use a generic rectangle and Diamond Problem to factor this expression. Compare your answer with your teammates' answers. Is there more than one possible answer?

$$4x^2 - 10x - 6$$

8-25.   The multiplication table below has factors along the top row and left column. Their
         product is where the row and column intersect. With your team, complete the table
         with all of the factors and products.

Multiply	$x - 2$	
$x + 7$		
	$3x^2 - 5x - 2$	$6x^2 + 5x + 1$

8-26.   In your Learning Log, explain how to factor a quadratic
         expression. Be sure to offer examples to demonstrate your
         understanding. Include an explanation of how to deal with special
         cases, such as when a term is missing or when the terms are not in
         standard order. Title this entry "Factoring Quadratics" and
         include today's date.

METHODS AND MEANINGS

Standard Form of a Quadratic

A quadratic expression in the form $ax^2 + bx + c$ is said to be in **standard
form**. Notice that the terms are in order from greatest exponent to least.

Examples of quadratic expressions in standard form: $3m^2 + m - 1$, $x^2 - 9$, and
$3x^2 + 5x$. Notice that in the second example, $b = 0$, while in the third example,
$c = 0$.

8-27.   At 3:25pm, two trains left Kalamazoo, Michigan. One train traveled westward at a constant rate of 82 miles per hour, while the other traveled eastward at a constant rate of 66 miles per hour. If they are now 111 miles apart, what time is it now? Write and solve an equation (or system of equations) to answer this question.

8-28.   Remember that a square is a rectangle with four equal sides.

   a.   If a square has an area of 81 square units, how long is each side?

   b.   Find the length of the side of a square with area 225 square units.

   c.   Find the length of the side of a square with area 10 square units.

   d.   Find the area of a square with side 11 units.

8-29.   Factor the following quadratics, if possible.

   a. $k^2 - 12k + 20$

   b. $6x^2 + 17x - 14$

   c. $x^2 - 8x + 16$

   d. $9m^2 - 1$

8-30.   Examine the two equations below. Where do they intersect?

$$y = 4x - 3$$
$$y = 9x - 13$$

8-31.   Find the equation of a line perpendicular to the one graphed at right that passes through the point (6, 2).

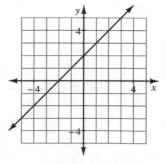

8-32.   Solve each equation below for x. Check each solution.

   a. $2x - 10 = 0$

   b. $x + 6 = 0$

   c. $(2x - 10)(x + 6) = 0$

   d. $4x + 1 = 0$

   e. $x - 8 = 0$

   f. $(4x + 1)(x - 8) = 0$

Algebra Connections

8.1.4 Can it still be factored?

Factoring Completely

There are many ways to write the number 12 as a product of factors. For example, 12 can be rewritten as $3 \cdot 4$, as $2 \cdot 6$, as $1 \cdot 12$, or as $2 \cdot 2 \cdot 3$. While each of these products is accurate, only $2 \cdot 2 \cdot 3$ is considered to be **factored completely**, since the factors are prime and cannot be factored themselves.

During this lesson you will learn more about what it means for a quadratic expression to be factored completely.

8-33.   Review what you have learned by factoring the following expressions, if possible.

    a. $9x^2 - 12x + 4$ b. $81m^2 - 1$

    c. $28 + x^2 - 11x$ d. $3n^2 + 9n + 6$

8-34.   Compare your solutions for problem 8-33 with the rest of your class.

    a.   Is there more than one factored form of $3n^2 + 9n + 6$? Why or why not?

    b.   Why does $3n^2 + 9n + 6$ have more than one factored form while the other quadratics in problem 8-33 only have one possible answer? Look for clues in the original expression ($3n^2 + 9n + 6$) and in the different factored forms.

    c.   **Without factoring**, predict which quadratic expressions below may have more than one factored form. Be prepared to defend your choice to the rest of the class.

        i. $12t^2 - 10t + 2$ ii. $5p^2 - 23p - 10$

        iii. $10x^2 + 25x - 15$ iv. $3k^2 + 7k - 6$

8-35.   FACTORING COMPLETELY

In part (c) of problem 8-34, you should have noticed that each term in $12t^2 - 10t + 2$ is divisible by 2. That is, it has a **common factor** of 2.

a.   What is the common factor for $10x^2 + 25x - 15$?

b.   For an expression to be **completely factored**, each factor must have all common factors separated out. Sometimes it is easiest to do this first. Since 5 is a common factor of $10x^2 + 25x - 15$, you can factor $10x^2 + 25x - 15$ using a special generic rectangle, which is shown below. Find the length of this generic rectangle and write its area as a product of its length and width.

$$5 \; \boxed{10x^2} \; \boxed{+\,25x} \; \boxed{-15}$$

c.   Can the result be factored even more? That is, can either factor from the result from part (b) above also be factored? Factor any possible expressions and write your solution as a product of all three factors.

8-36.   Factor each of the following expressions as completely as possible.

a. $5x^2 + 15x - 20$ b. $3x^3 - 6x^2 - 45x$

c. $2x^2 - 50$ d. $x^2y - 3xy - 10y$

METHODS AND MEANINGS

Factoring Quadratic Expressions

MATH NOTES

Review the process of factoring quadratics developed in problem 8-13 and outlined below. This example demonstrates how to factor $3x^2 + 10x + 8$.

1. Place the x^2 - and constant terms of the quadratic expression in opposite corners of the generic rectangle. Determine the sum and product of the two remaining corners: The sum is simply the x-term of the quadratic expression, while the product is equal to the product of the x^2 - and constant terms.

2. Place this sum and product into a Diamond Problem and solve it.

3. Place the solutions from the Diamond Problem into the generic rectangle and find the dimensions of the generic rectangle.

4. Write your answer as a product: $(3x + 4)(x + 2)$.

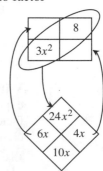

8-37.   Factor the quadratic expressions below. If the quadratic is not factorable, explain why not.

   a. $2x^2 + 3x - 5$ b. $x^2 - x - 6$

   c. $3x^2 + 13x + 4$ d. $2x^2 + 5x + 7$

8-38.   A line has intercepts (4, 0) and (0, –3). Find the equation of the line.

8-39.   As Jhalil and Joman practice for the SAT, their scores on practice tests rise. Jhalil's current score is 850, and it is rising by 10 points per week. On the other hand, Joman's current score is 570 and is growing by 50 points per week.

   a.   When will Joman's score catch up to Jhalil's?

   b.   If the SAT test is in 12 weeks, who will score highest?

8-40.   Mary says that you can find an *x*-intercept by substituting 0 for *x*, while Michelle says that you need to substitute 0 for *y*.

   a.   Who, if anyone, is correct and why?

   b.   Use the correct approach to find the *x*-intercept of $-4x + 5y = 16$.

8-41.   Find three consecutive numbers whose sum is 138 by writing and solving an equation.

8-42.   Match each rule below with its corresponding graph. Can you do this without making any tables? Explain your selections.

   a. $y = -x^2 - 2$ b. $y = x^2 - 2$ c. $y = -x^2 + 2$

   1.   2.   3.

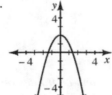   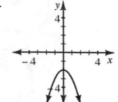   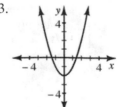

8.2.1 What do I know about a parabola?

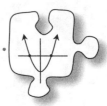

Investigating a Parabola

In previous chapters, you have investigated linear equations. In Section 8.2, you will study parabolas. You will learn all you can about their shape, study different equations used to graph them, and see how they can be used in real-life situations.

8-43.   FUNCTIONS OF AMERICA

Congratulations! Your work at the Line Factory was so successful that the small local company grew into a national corporation called Functions of America. Recently your company has had some growing pains, and your new boss has turned to your team for help. See her memo below.

MEMO

To: *Your study team*
From: *Ms. Freda Function, CEO*
Re: *New product line*

I have heard that while lines are very popular, there is a new craze in Europe to have non-linear designs. I recently visited Paris and Milan and discovered that we are behind the times!

Please investigate a new function called a parabola. I'd like a full report at the end of today with any information your team can give me about its shape and equation. Spare no detail! I'd like to know everything you can tell me about how the rule for a parabola affects its shape. I'd also like to know about any special points on a parabola or any patterns that exist in its table.

Remember, the company is only as good as its employees! I need you to uncover the secrets that our competitors do not know.

Sincerely,
Ms. Function, CEO

Problem continues on next page →

8-43.   *Problem continued from previous page.*

Your Task: Your team will be assigned its own parabola to study. Investigate your team's parabola and be ready to describe everything you can about it by using its graph, rule, and table. Answer the questions below to get your investigation started. You may answer them in any order; however, do not limit yourselves to these questions!

- Does your parabola have any **symmetry**? That is, can you fold the graph of your parabola so that each side of the fold exactly matches the other? If so, where would the fold be? Do you think this works for all parabolas? Why or why not?

- Is there a highest or lowest point on the graph of your parabola? If so, where is it? This point is called a **vertex**. How can you describe the parabola at this point?

- Are there any special points on your parabola? Which points do you think are important to know? Are there any special points that you expected but do not exist for your parabola? What connection(s) do these points have with the rule of your parabola?

- How would you describe the shape of your parabola? For example, would you describe your parabola as pointing up or down? Do the sides of the parabola ever go straight up or down (vertically)? Why or why not? Is there anything else special about its shape?

List of Parabolas:

$$y = x^2 - 2x - 8 \qquad\qquad y = -x^2 + 4$$

$$y = x^2 - 4x + 5 \qquad\qquad y = x^2 - 2x + 1$$

$$y = x^2 - 6x + 5 \qquad\qquad y = -x^2 + 3x + 4$$

$$y = -x^2 + 2x - 1 \qquad\qquad y = x^2 + 5x + 1$$

8-44.   Prepare a poster for the CEO detailing your findings from your parabola investigation. Include any insights you and your teammates found. Explain your conclusions and justify your statements. Remember to include a complete graph of your parabola with all special points carefully labeled.

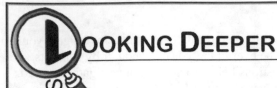 **OOKING DEEPER**

MATH NOTES

Symmetry

When a graph or picture can be folded so that both sides of the fold will perfectly match, it is said to have **symmetry**. The line where the fold would be is called the **line of symmetry**. Some shapes have more than one line of symmetry. See the examples below.

This shape has
one line of
symmetry.

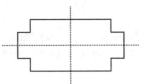

This shape has
two lines of
symmetry.

This shape has
eight lines of
symmetry.

This graph has
two lines of
symmetry.

Review & Preview

8-45.   Calculate the value of each expression below.

a. $\frac{2+\sqrt{16}}{3}$

b. $\frac{-1+\sqrt{49}}{-2}$

c. $\frac{-10-\sqrt{5}}{2}$

8-46.   Find the equation of the line that goes through the points (–15, 70) and (5, 10).

8-47.   Change $6x - 2y = 10$ to slope-intercept ($y = mx + b$) form.

a.   State the slope (m) and the y-intercept (b).

b.   Use the point-slope formula to find an equation of the line parallel to $6x - 2y = 10$ through the point $(3, 6)$.

8-48.   Copy the figure at right onto your paper. Then draw any lines of symmetry.

8-49.   For each rule represented below, state the x- and y-intercepts.

a.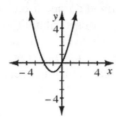

b.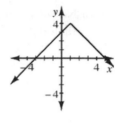

c.

x	-3	-2	-1	0	1	2	3
y	8	3	0	-1	0	3	8

d. $2x + 3y = 18$

8-50.   Use a generic rectangle to multiply each expression below.

a. $(3x - 4)(2x + 3)$

b. $(5x - 2)^2$

$8.2.2$ What's the connection?

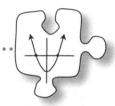

• •

Multiple Representations for Quadratics

In Chapter 4 you completed a web for the different
representations of linear equations. You discovered
special shortcuts to help you move from one
representation to another. For example, given a linear
equation, you can now draw the corresponding graph as
well as determine an equation from a graph.

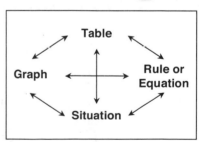

Today you will explore the connections between the
different representations for quadratics. As you work,
keep in mind the following questions:

What representations are you using?

What is the connection between the various representations?

What do you know about a parabola?

8-51.   WATER-BALLOON CONTEST

Every year Newtown High School holds a water-balloon competition during halftime of their homecoming game. Each contestant uses a catapult to launch a water balloon from the ground on the football field. This year you are the judge! You must decide which contestants win the prizes for *Longest Distance* and *Highest Launch*. Fortunately, you have a computer that will collect data for each throw. The computer uses *x* to represent horizontal distance in yards from the goal line and *y* to represent the height in yards.

The announcer shouts, "Maggie Nanimos, you're up first!" She runs down and places her catapult at the 3-yard line. After Maggie's launch, the computer reports that the balloon traveled along the parabola $y = -x^2 + 17x - 42$.

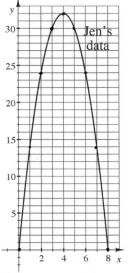

Then you hear, "Jen Erus, you're next!" Jen runs down to the field, places her catapult at the goal line, and releases the balloon. The tracking computer reports the path of the balloon with the graph at right.

The third contestant, Imp Ecable, accidentally launches the balloon before you are ready. The balloon launches, you hear a roar from the crowd, turn around, and...SPLAT! The balloon soaks you and your computer! You only have time to write down the following partial information about the balloon's path before your computer fizzles:

x (yards)	2	3	4	5	6	7	8	9
y (yards)	0	9	16	21	24	25	24	21

Finally, the announcer calls for the last contestant, Al Truistic. With your computer broken, you decide to record the balloon's height and distance by hand. Al releases the balloon from the 10-yard line. The balloon reaches a height of 27 yards and lands at the 16-yard line.

a.   Obtain the Lesson 8.2.2 Resource Page from your teacher. For each contestant, create a table and graph using the information provided for each toss. Determine which of these contestants should win the *Longest Distance* and *Highest Throw* contests.

b.   Find the *x*-intercepts of each parabola. What information do the *x*-intercepts tell you about each balloon toss?

c.   Find the vertex of each parabola. What information does the vertex tell you about each balloon throw?

8-52.   Today you have explored the four different representations of
         quadratics: table, graph, equation, and a description of a
         physical situation involving motion. Draw the representations
         of the web as shown below in your Learning Log and label it
         "Quadratic Web."

    a.   Draw in arrows showing the connections
          that you currently know how to make
          between different representations. Be
          prepared to **justify** a connection for the
          class.

    b.   What connections are still missing?

```
┌──────────────────────────────────────┐
│           QUADRATIC WEB                │
│                                        │
│               Table                    │
│                                        │
│                            Rule or     │
│   Graph                    Equation    │
│                                        │
│              Situation                 │
└──────────────────────────────────────┘
```

8-53.   SITUATION TO RULE

         Review how to write a rule from a situation by
         examining the tile pattern below.

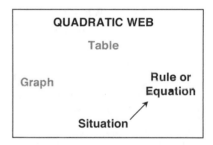

```
┌──────────────────────────────────────┐
│           QUADRATIC WEB                │
│                                        │
│               Table                    │
│                            Rule or     │
│   Graph                    Equation    │
│                                  ↗     │
│              Situation                 │
└──────────────────────────────────────┘
```

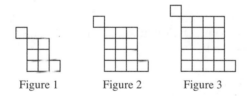

Figure 1   Figure 2   Figure 3

    a.   Write a rule to represent the number of tiles in Figure x.

    b.   Is the rule from part (a) **quadratic**? Explain how you know.

    c.   If you have not done so already, add this pathway to your web from problem
          8-52.

8-54.   Graph $y = x^2 - 8x + 7$ and label its vertex, x-intercepts, and y-intercepts.

8-55.   What is special about the number zero? Think about this as you answer the
         questions below.

    a.   Find each sum:

          $0 + 3 =$ $-7 + 0 =$ $0 + 6 =$ $0 + (-2) =$

    b.   What is special about adding zero? Write a
          sentence that begins, "When you add zero to a
          number, …"

    c.   Julia is thinking of two numbers a and b. When she
          adds them together, she gets a sum of b. Does that
          tell you anything about either of Julia's numbers?

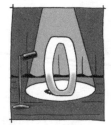

    d.   Find each product:

          $3 \cdot 0 =$ $(-7) \cdot 0 =$ $0 \cdot 6 =$ $0 \cdot (-2) =$

    e.   What is special about multiplying by zero? Write a sentence that begins,
          "When you multiply a number by zero, …"

8-56.   Based on the tables below, say as much as you can about the x- and y-intercepts of
         the corresponding graphs.

a.

x	y
2	0
0	18
−4	0
−1	−8
6	22
3	0

b.

x	y
7	−4
3	0
10	8
0	−3
8	0
−7	−1

c.

x	y
0	−4
−5	11
3	−2
1	0
13	27
−6	14

8-57.   For the line described by the equation $y = 2x + 6$:

    a.   What is the x-intercept?

    b.   What is the slope of any line perpendicular to the given line?

8-58.   Solve the following systems of equations using any method. Check your solution if
         possible.

    a. $6x - 2y = 10$
          $3x - y = 2$

    b. $x - 3y = 1$
          $y = 16 - 2x$

8.2.3 How are quadratic rules and graphs connected?

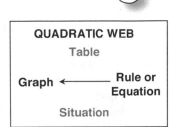

Zero Product Property

You already know a lot about quadratics and parabolas, and you have made several connections between their different representations on the quadratic web. Today you are going to develop a method to sketch a parabola from its equation without a table.

QUADRATIC WEB
Table
Graph ⟵——— Rule or Equation
Situation

8-59.   **WHAT DO YOU NEED TO SKETCH A PARABOLA?**

How many points do you need in order to sketch a parabola? 1? 10? 50? Think about this as you answer the questions below. (Note: A sketch does not need to be exact. The parabola merely needs to be reasonably placed with important points clearly labeled.)

a.   Can you sketch a parabola if you only know where its y-intercept is? For example, if the y-intercept of a parabola is at $(0, -15)$, can you sketch its graph? Why or why not?

b.   What about the two x-intercepts of the parabola? If you only know where the x-intercepts are, can you draw the parabola? For example, if the x-intercepts are at $(-3, 0)$ and $(5, 0)$, can you predict the path of the parabola?

c.   Can you sketch a parabola with only its x-intercepts and y-intercept? To test this idea, sketch the graph of a parabola $y = x^2 - 2x - 15$ with x-intercepts $(-3, 0)$ and $(5, 0)$ and y-intercept $(0, -15)$.

8-60.   In problem 8-59, you learned that if you can find the intercepts of a parabola from a rule, then you can sketch its graph without a table.

a.   What is true about the value of y for all x-intercepts? What is true about the value of x for all y-intercepts? Review your knowledge of intercepts and describe it here.

b.   If $x = 0$ at the y-intercept, find the y-intercept of the graph of $y = 2x^2 + 5x - 12$.

c.   Since the x-intercept occurs when $y = 0$, write the equation that you would need to solve to find the x-intercepts of the graph of $y = 2x^2 + 5x - 12$.

d.   The solutions of the equation $2x^2 + 5x - 12 = 0$ are called its **roots** and are the **zeros** of $2x^2 + 5x - 12$. At this point, can you solve $2x^2 + 5x - 12 = 0$ for x? Explain why or why not.

8-61.   ZERO PRODUCT PROPERTY

The equation you wrote in part (c) of problem
8-60 is called a **quadratic equation**. To solve it,
you need to examine what you know about zero.
Study the special properties of zero below.

Nathan, Nancy, and Gaston are playing a
game where Nathan and Nancy each think
of a number and then give Gaston a clue
about their numbers. Using the clue,
Gaston must tell them everything that he
knows about their numbers.

a.   Nathan and Nancy's first clue for Gaston is that when you multiply their
      numbers together, the result is zero. What conclusion can Gaston make?

b.   Disappointed that Gaston came so close to figuring out their numbers, Nathan
      and Nancy invite Nadia over to make things harder. Nathan, Nancy, and Nadia
      all think of secret numbers. This time Gaston is told that when their *three*
      secret numbers are multiplied together, the answer is zero. What can Gaston
      conclude this time?

c.   Does it matter how many numbers are multiplied? If the
      product is zero, what do you know about one of the numbers?
      This property is called the **Zero Product Property**. With the
      class, write a description of this property in your Learning
      Log. Title this entry "Zero Product Property" and include
      today's date.

8-62.   How can you use the Zero Product Property to help you solve the quadratic equation
         $0 = 2x^2 + 5x - 12$ from part (c) of problem 8-60?

a.   Examine the quadratic equation. Is there a product that equals zero? If not,
      how can you rewrite the quadratic expression as a product?

b.   Now that the equation is written as a product of factors equaling zero, you can
      use the Zero Product Property to solve it. Since you know that one of the
      factors must be zero, you can set up two smaller equations to help you solve for
      x. Use one factor at a time and determine what *x*-value makes it equal to zero.

c.   What do these solutions represent? What do they tell you?

d.   You now know the roots of the equation $0 = 2x^2 + 5x - 12$ (also called the
      zeros of $2x^2 + 5x - 12$). Use the roots to find the *x*-intercepts of the graph of
      the parabola $y = 2x^2 + 5x - 12$. Then sketch a graph of the parabola.

8-63.   Use a similar process to sketch the parabola $y = x^2 + x - 6$ by using its intercepts.

8-64.   Sketch the parabola $y = 2x^2 + 6x + 4$ by using its intercepts.

METHODS AND MEANINGS

Zero Product Property

MATH NOTES

When the product of two or more numbers is zero, one of those numbers must be zero. This is known as the **Zero Product Property**. If the two numbers are a and b, this property can be written as follows:

If a and b are two numbers where $a \cdot b = 0$, then $a = 0$ or $b = 0$.

For example, if $(2x - 3)(x + 5) = 0$, then $2x - 3 = 0$ or $x + 5 = 0$. Solving yields the solutions $x = \frac{3}{2}$ or $x = -5$. This property helps you solve quadratic equations when the equation can be written as a product of factors.

Review & Preview

8-65.   Compare the two equations below.

$$(x + 2)(x - 1) = 0 \text{ and } (x + 2) + (x - 1) = 0$$

a.   How are the equations different?

b.   Solve both equations.

8-66.   For each equation below, solve for x.

    a. $(x - 2)(x + 8) = 0$ b. $(3x - 9)(x - 1) = 0$

    c. $(x + 10)(2x - 5) = 0$ d. $(x - 7)^2 = 0$

Chapter 8: Quadratics   349

8-67.　　Examine the system of equations below.

$$5x - 2y = 4$$
$$x = 0$$

a.　Before solving this system, Danielle noticed that the point of intersection is also the y-intercept of $5x - 2y = 4$. Explain how she knows this.

b.　Find the point of intersection of the two rules above.

8-68.　　The x-intercepts of the graph of $y = 2x^2 - 16x + 30$ are $(3, 0)$ and $(5, 0)$.

a.　What is the x-coordinate of the vertex? How do you know?

b.　Use your answer to part (a) above to find the y-coordinate of the vertex. Then write the vertex as a point (x, y).

8-69.　　Factor each quadratic below completely.

a.　$2x^2 - 2x - 4$　　　　　　　　　b.　$4x^2 - 24x + 36$

8-70.　　The "≤" symbol represents "less than or equal to," while the "<" symbol represents "less than."

a.　Similarly, translate "≥" and ">."

b.　How can you write an expression that states that 5 is greater than 3?

c.　Write another expression that states that x is less than or equal to 9.

d.　Translate the expression $-2 < 7$ into words.

8.2.4　What new connection can I make?

Solving Quadratic Equations by Factoring

In Lesson 8.2.3, you developed a method for finding the x-intercepts of a parabola given by $y = ax^2 + bx + c$ by finding the roots of the corresponding quadratic equation, $ax^2 + bx + c = 0$, or the zeros of $ax^2 + bx + c$. Today you will learn how to use that skill to solve a wide variety of quadratic equations.

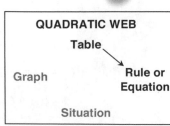

QUADRATIC WEB

Table

Graph　　　　　　　Rule or Equation

Situation

You will also revisit the quadratic web, make a connection between the table and rule of a parabola, and then apply this connection to the water-balloon competition you analyzed in problem 8-51.

8-71.   Review what you learned in Lesson 8.2.3 by sketching the graph of $y = x^2 + 3x + 2$ without a table. Specifically, find the x-intercepts and the y-intercept of the parabola and sketch its graph.

8-72.   Part of finding the x-intercepts of a parabola involves creating a quadratic equation of the form $ax^2 + bx + c = 0$ and finding its roots (which are also the zeros of the expression $ax^2 + bx + c$). Practice using the Zero Product Property to solve the quadratic equations below.

   a. $x^2 + 6x + 8 = 0$ b. $0 = 3x^2 - 7x + 4$

   c. $(x + 5)(-2x + 3) = 0$ d. $x^2 + 6x = 0$

   e. $0 = 3(x - 5)(2x + 3)$ f. $x^2 + 4x - 9 = 3$

8-73.   TABLE TO RULE

You know how to make a table for a quadratic rule, but how can you write an equation when given the table? Examine this new connection that requires you to **reverse** your understanding of the Zero Product Property as you find a rule for each table below. What clues in the tables helped you find the rule?

   a.

x	−4	−3	−2	−1	0	1	2	3	4
y	6	0	−4	−6	−6	−4	0	6	14

   b.

x	−6	−5	−4	−3	−2	−1	0	1	2	3	4
y	7	0	−5	−8	−9	−8	−5	0	7	16	27

8-74.   WATER-BALLOON CONTEST REVISITED

Remember Imp's water-balloon toss? Since the water balloon was thrown on the computer, you were given only a table of data, shown again below. Find a rule that represents the height of Imp's balloon as it traveled through the air.

x (yards)	2	3	4	5	6	7	8	9
y (yards)	0	9	16	21	24	25	24	21

8-75.   Find the quadratic web in your Learning Log entry from Lesson 8.2.3. In this entry, add a short explanation for how to find a quadratic equation from its table. Then add an arrow to your web for the connection you made today.

8-76.   Jamie was given the problem, "Find the result when the factors of
         $65x^2 + 212x - 133$ are multiplied together." Before she could answer, her sister,
         Lauren, said, "I know the answer without factoring or multiplying!" What was
         Lauren's answer and how did she know?

8-77.   Solve the equations below for x. Check your solutions.

         a. $(6x - 18)(3x + 2) = 0$ b. $x^2 - 7x + 10 = 0$

         c. $2x^2 + 2x - 12 = 0$ d. $4x^2 - 1 = 0$

8-78.   Sketch each parabola below with the given information.

         a.   A parabola with x-intercepts (2, 0) and (7, 0) and y-intercept (0, –8).

         b.   A parabola with exactly one x-intercept at (–1, 0) and y-intercept (0, 3).

         c.   The parabola represented by the equation $y = (x + 5)(x - 1)$.

8-79.   Review the meanings of the inequality symbols in
         the box at right. Then decide if the statements
         below are true or false.

         | < less than |
         | ≤ less than or equal to |
         | > greater than |
         | ≥ greater than or equal to |

         a. $5 < 7$ b. $-2 \geq 9$

         c. $0 \leq 0$ d. $-5 > -10$

         e. $16 \leq -16$ f. $1 > 1$

8-80.   Calculate the expressions below with a scientific calculator.

         a. $\dfrac{-10 + \sqrt{25}}{5}$ b. $\dfrac{8 + \sqrt{40}}{3 \cdot 3}$ c. $\dfrac{8 + \sqrt{3^2 + 2 \cdot 3 + 1}}{-4}$

8-81.   Find the slope of the line through the points (6, –8) and (3, –4).

         a.   Use the point-slope formula to find the equation of the line through (6, –8) and
               (3, –4).

         b.   Is the point (–3, 4) on the line you found in part (a)? How can you tell?

8.2.5 What's the connection?

Completing the Quadratic Web

In just three lessons you have almost completed the
quadratic web. Revisit the web posted in your classroom.
What connections, if any, still need to be made?

Today you will focus on how to get a quadratic rule from
a graph and a situation. As you work, ask yourself the
following questions:

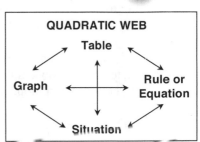

Which representation am I given?
Which representation am I looking for?

How can I reverse this process?

Is there another way?

8-82.   Several parabolas and quadratic rules are shown below. Match each graph with its
rule. Justify your choices and share any shortcuts you find with your teammates.
(Note: Not every rule will be matched with a parabola.)

Graphs:

(1)

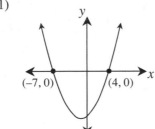

(2)

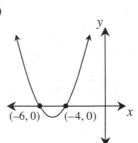

(3)

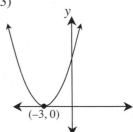

(4)

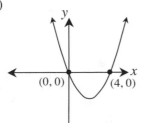

(5)

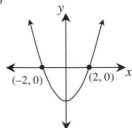

(6)

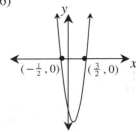

Rules:

a. $y = (x+3)^2$ b. $y = x^2 + 3x - 28$ c. $y = x^2 - 11x + 28$

d. $y = x^2 - 4$ e. $y = x^2 + 10x + 24$ f. $y = 2x^2 + 11x + 5$

g. $y = x^2 - 4x$ h. $y = (x-3)^2$ i. $y = 4x^2 - 4x - 3$

8-83.   QUALITY CONTROL, Part One

Congratulations! With your promotion, you are
now the Quality Assurance Representative of the
Function Factory. Your job is to make sure your
clients are happy. Whenever a client writes to the
company, you must reply with clear directions
that will solve his or her problem.

Your boss has provided graphing technology and
a team of fellow employees to help you fulfill
your job description.

Your Task:

1.   Carefully read the complaints below. Study each situation with your grapher.
      Work with your team to resolve each situation.

2.   Write each customer a friendly response that offers a solution to his or her
      problem. Remember that the customers are not parabola experts! Do not
      assume that they know anything about parabolas.

Dear Ms. Quadratic,   **A**

*I followed all of the directions given in your brochure on how
to order a parabola. I tried to order a parabola that passed
through the points (1, 0) and (–6, 0), only to have you send me
the wrong one!*

*Please tell me how to order
the correct parabola. Your
immediate reply is
appreciated.*

Perturbed in Pennsylvania

Dear Ms. Quadratic,   **C**

*Please help! I have
searched through your
entire brochure and did not
see a parabola that would
fit my needs. All I want is a
parabola that looks like
this:*

*Every time I order an equation to give me this
parabola you always send me a different one!
I refuse to pay for any parabola but the one
shown above. Please tell me how I should find
the equation of this parabola or I will take my
business elsewhere!*

Thank you,

Agitated in Alaska

Dear Ms. Quadratic,   **B**

*I am a very dissatisfied customer. I
want a parabola that hits the x-axis
only <u>once</u> at (5, 0), yet I see NO
mention of this type of parabola in
your pamphlet. Your company mission
statement assures me that "my needs
will be met no matter what." How
should I order my special parabola?*

Sincerely,

Troubled in Texas

8-84. **EXTRA! EXTRA!**

A journalist from the school newspaper wants to publish the results from the water-balloon contest. She wants a rule for each toss so that she can program her computer to create a graph for her article. You already have rules for the tosses made by Maggie and Imp from problems 8-51 and 8-74.

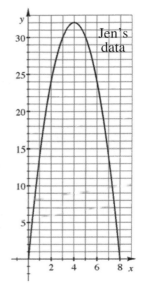

a. Examine the graph at right that represents the height of Jen's toss. Find the rule for this parabola.

b. Al released his balloon from the 10-yard line, and it landed at the 16-yard line. If the ball reached a height of 27 yards, what equation represents the path of his toss?

8-85. **QUALITY CONTROL, Part Two**

Lots O'Dough, a wealthy customer, would like to order a variety of parabolas. However, he is feeling pressed for time and said that he will pay you *lots* of extra money if you complete his order for him. Of course you agreed! He sent you sketches of each parabola that he would like to receive. Determine a possible equation for each parabola so that you can pass this information on to the Manufacturing Department.

a.

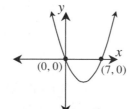

b.

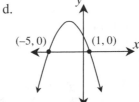

c.

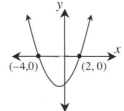

d.

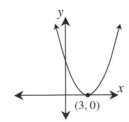

8-86.　Find the slope and y-intercept of the graph of $6y - 3x = 24$.

8-87.　Examine the graph of $y = 2x^2 + 2x - 1$ at right.

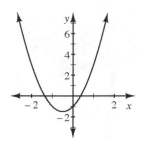

a.　Estimate the zeros of $2x^2 + 2x - 1$ from the graph.

b.　What happens if you try to use the Zero Product Property to find the roots of $2x^2 + 2x - 1 = 0$?

8-88.　Solve the equations below for x. Check your solutions.

a.　$x^2 + 6x - 40 = 0$　　　　b.　$2x^2 + 13x - 24 = 0$

8-89.　Calculate the expressions below. Then compare your answers from (a) and (b) to those in problem 8-88. What do you notice?

a.　$\dfrac{-6 + \sqrt{6^2 - (4)(1)(-40)}}{2 \cdot 1}$　　　　b.　$\dfrac{-6 - \sqrt{6^2 - (4)(1)(-40)}}{2 \cdot 1}$

c.　$\dfrac{-13 - \sqrt{13^2 - (4)(2)(-24)}}{2 \cdot 2}$　　　　d.　$\dfrac{-13 + \sqrt{13^2 - (4)(2)(-24)}}{2 \cdot 2}$

8-90.　Use any method to solve the systems of equations below.

a.　$2x - 3y = 5$　　　　b.　$m = -3 + 2n$
　　　$4x + y = 3$　　　　　　　$4m + 6n = -5$

8.3.1　What if it's not factorable?

Introduction to the Quadratic Formula

In Section 8.2 you developed a method to find the x-intercepts of a parabola by factoring and using the Zero Product Property. Today you will learn a new method to solve quadratic equations.

8-91.　Use the Zero Product Property to find the roots of $x^2 - 3x - 7 = 0$.

a.　What happened?

b.　What does this result tell you about the roots?

c.　Your teacher will display the graph of $y = x^2 - 3x - 7$ for the class. Did the graph confirm your answer to part (b)? Estimate the roots using the graph.

　　　　　　　　　　　　　　　　　　　　　　　　　Algebra Connections

8-92.   QUADRATIC FORMULA

Since a parabola can have x-intercepts even when its
corresponding quadratic equation is not factorable,
another way to find the roots of a quadratic equation is
needed.

a.   One way to find the roots of a quadratic
equation is by using the **Quadratic Formula**,
shown below. This formula uses values a, b,
and c from a quadratic equation written in
standard form (explained in the next paragraph).

$$x = \frac{-b \pm \sqrt{b^2 - 4ac}}{2a}$$

When the quadratic equation is written in **standard form** (i.e., it looks like
$ax^2 + bx + c = 0$), then a is the number of x^2-terms, b is the number of
x-terms, and c is the constant. If $x^2 - 3x - 7 = 0$, then what are a, b, and c?

b.   The Quadratic Formula calculates *two* possible answers by using the "$\pm$"
symbol. This symbol (read as "plus or minus") is shorthand notation that tells
you to calculate the formula twice: once with addition and once with
subtraction in the numerator. Therefore, every Quadratic Formula problem is
really two different problems unless the value of $\sqrt{b^2 - 4ac}$ is 0.

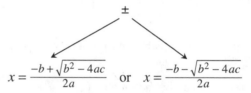

$$x = \frac{-b + \sqrt{b^2 - 4ac}}{2a} \quad \text{or} \quad x = \frac{-b - \sqrt{b^2 - 4ac}}{2a}$$

Carefully substitute a, b, and c from $x^2 - 3x - 7 = 0$ into the Quadratic
Formula. Evaluate each expression (once using addition and once using
subtraction) to solve for x. Do these solutions match those from part (c) of
problem 8-91?

8-93.   The Quadratic Formula is only one of the tools you can use to solve quadratic
equations.

a.   What are the other methods that you can use?

b.   You may be thinking, "Where did this formula come from? Why does it
work?" You can find the formula by starting with a generic quadratic
$ax^2 + bx + c = 0$ and using your algebra skills to solve for x. See the Math
Notes box for this lesson to learn about one way this formula can be derived.
Later, in Chapter 12, you will learn another formal method to derive the
Quadratic Formula.

8-94.   Use the Quadratic Formula to solve the equations below for x, if possible. Check
your solutions.

a. $3x^2 + 7x + 2 = 0$ b. $2x^2 - 9x - 35 = 0$

c. $8x^2 + 10x + 3 = 0$ d. $x^2 - 5x + 9 = 0$

8-95.   In your Learning Log, describe how to use the Quadratic Formula.
Be sure to include an example. Title this entry "Quadratic
Formula" and include today's date.

$\bigodot$OOKING DEEPER

MATH NOTES

Deriving the Quadratic Formula

Why is $x = \frac{-b \pm \sqrt{b^2 - 4ac}}{2a}$ a solution of $ax^2 + bx + c = 0$? One way to
derive this formula is shown below.

1. Begin with the quadratic equation in
    standard form. $ax^2 + bx + c = 0$

2. Multiply each side by $4a$. $4a(ax^2 + bx + c) = 0$

3. Add $b^2 - 4ac$ to each side in order to $4a^2x^2 + 4abx + 4ac = 0$
    get a factorable quadratic on the left.
                                                    $4a^2x^2 + 4abx + b^2 = b^2 - 4ac$

4. The left side can be factored as $(2ax + b)^2$,
    which is demonstrated in the generic
    rectangle shown at right.

	b	$2abx$	b^2
$2ax$		$4a^2x^2$	$2abx$
		$2ax$	b

5. Take the square root of each side. Since
    both the positive and negative values of a
    number can be squared to give the same
    result (for example, 4^2 and $(-4)^2$ both
    equal 16), then there are two possible square $(2ax + b)^2 = b^2 - 4ac$
    root values: $\sqrt{b^2 - 4ac}$ and $-\sqrt{b^2 - 4ac}$.

6. Now continue to solve for x by subtracting b $2ax + b = \pm\sqrt{b^2 - 4ac}$
    from both sides and dividing by $2a$. Notice
    that a cannot equal zero or else you will get $2ax = -b \pm \sqrt{b^2 - 4ac}$
    an error! However, if $a = 0$, then this equation
    would not be quadratic and you would not use $x = \frac{-b \pm \sqrt{b^2 - 4ac}}{2a}$
    this formula.

7. Thus, $x = \frac{-b \pm \sqrt{b^2 - 4ac}}{2a}$ are solutions of the equation $ax^2 + bx + c = 0$.

8-96. Solve the following quadratic equations by factoring and using the Zero Product Property. Be sure to check your solutions.

    a. $x^2 - 13x + 42 = 0$ b. $0 = 3x^2 + 10x - 8$

    c. $2x^2 - 10x = 0$ d. $4x^2 + 8x - 60 = 0$

8-97. Use the Quadratic Formula to solve $x^2 - 13x + 42 = 0$. Did your solution match the solution from part (a) of problem 8-96?

8-98. Does a quadratic equation always have two solutions? That is, does a parabola always intersect the x-axis twice?

    a.   If possible, draw an example of a parabola that only intersects the x-axis once.

    b.   What does it mean if the quadratic equation has no solution? Draw a possible parabola that would cause this to happen.

8-99. Find the equation of the line through the point $(-2, 8)$ with slope $\frac{1}{2}$.

8-100. For each of the following equations, indicate whether its graph would be a line or a parabola.

    a. $5x + 2y = 7$ b. $y = 3x^2$

    c. $y = 3$ d. $4x^2 + 3x = 7 + y$

8-101. **Multiple Choice:** Which equations below are equivalent to:

$$\tfrac{1}{2}(6x - 14) + 5x = 2 - 3x + 8 ?$$

    a. $3x - 7 + 5x = 10 - 3x$ b. $3x - 14 + 5x = 2 - 3x + 8$

    c. $8x - 14 = 10 - 3x$ d. $6x - 14 + 10x = 4 - 6x + 16$

8-102. Review the descriptions for the inequality symbols $<$, $\le$, $>$, and $\ge$ in problem 8-79. Then decide if the statements below are true or false.

    a. $11 < -13$ b. $5 \cdot 2 \ge 10$ c. $13 > -3(2 - 6)$ d. $4 \le 4$

    e. $9 \ge -9$ f. $-2 > -2$ g. $-16 < -15$ h. $0 > 6$

8.3.2 What if the equation is not in standard form?

More Solving Quadratic Equations

Today you will **apply** and **extend** what you know about solving quadratic equations.

8-103. For the quadratic equation $6x^2 + 11x - 10 = 0$:

    a. Solve it using the Zero Product Property.

    b. Solve it using the Quadratic Formula.

    c. Did the solutions from parts (a) and (b) match? If not, why not?

8-104. As the Math Notes box from Lesson 8.3.1 demonstrated, the Quadratic Formula can solve any quadratic equation $ax^2 + bx + c = 0$ if $a \neq 0$. But what if the equation is not in standard form? What if terms are missing? Consider these questions as you solve the quadratic equations below. Share your ideas with your teammates and be prepared to demonstrate your process for the class.

    a. $4x^2 - 121 = 0$ b. $2x^2 - 2 - 3x = 0$

    c. $15x^2 - 165x = 630$ d. $36x^2 + 25 = 60x$

8-105. **THE SAINT LOUIS GATEWAY ARCH**

The Saint Louis Gateway Arch (pictured at right) has a shape much like a parabola. Suppose the Gateway Arch can be approximated by $y = 630 - 0.00635x^2$, where both x and y represent distances in feet and the origin is the point on the ground directly below the arch's apex (its highest point).

    a. Find the x-intercepts of the Gateway Arch. What does this information tell you? Use a calculator to evaluate your answers.

    b. How wide is the arch at its base?

    c. How tall is the arch? How did you find your solution?

    d. Draw a quick sketch of the arch on graph paper, labeling the axes with all of the values you know.

METHODS AND MEANINGS

Solving a Quadratic Equation

So far in this course, you have learned two algebraic methods to solve a quadratic equation of the form $ax^2 + bx + c = 0$.

One of these methods, the Zero Product Property, requires the equation to be a product of factors that equal zero. In this case, the quadratic equation must be factored, as shown in Example 1 below. Another strategy uses the Quadratic Formula, as demonstrated in Example 2 below. Notice that each strategy results in the same answer.

Example 1: Solve $3x^2 + x - 14 = 0$ for x using the Zero Product Property.

Solution: First, factor the quadratic so it is written as a product: $(3x + 7)(x - 2) = 0$. The Zero Product Property states that if the product of two terms is 0, then at least one of the factors must be 0. Thus, $3x + 7 = 0$ or $x - 2 = 0$.

Solving these equations for x reveals that $x = -\frac{7}{3}$ or that $x = 2$.

Example 2: Solve $3x^2 + x - 14 = 0$ for x using the Quadratic Formula.

Solution: First, identify a, b, and c. a equals the number of x^2-terms, b equals the number of x terms, and c equals the constant. For $3x^2 + x - 14 = 0$, $a = 3$, $b = 1$, and $c = -14$. Substitute the values of a, b, and c into the Quadratic Formula and evaluate the expression twice: once with addition and once with subtraction. Examine this method below:

$$x = \frac{-1 + \sqrt{1^2 - 4(3)(-14)}}{2 \cdot 3} \qquad x = \frac{-1 - \sqrt{1^2 - 4(3)(-14)}}{2 \cdot 3}$$

$$= \frac{-1 + \sqrt{169}}{6} \qquad\qquad = \frac{-1 - \sqrt{169}}{6}$$

$$= \frac{-1 + 13}{6} \qquad \text{or} \qquad = \frac{-1 - 13}{6}$$

$$= \frac{12}{6} \qquad\qquad\qquad = \frac{-14}{6}$$

$$= 2 \qquad\qquad\qquad = -\frac{7}{3}$$

8-106.   Solve the following quadratic equations by factoring and using the Zero Product
          Property. Then check your solutions.

   a. $x^2 - 10x + 25 = 0$ b. $0 = 3x^2 + 17x - 6$

   c. $3x^2 - 2x = 5$ d. $16x^2 - 9 = 0$

8-107.   Use the Quadratic Formula to solve part (b) of problem 8-106 above. Did your
          solution match the solution you got by factoring and using the Zero Product Property
          (in part (b) of problem 8-106)?

8-108.   Find the equation of each parabola below based on the given information.

   a.   b.

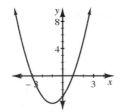

x	−4	−3	−2	−1	0	1	2	3	4
y	12	5	0	−3	−4	−3	0	5	12

8-109.   Solve the following problem using any method. Write your solution as a sentence.

          The length of a rectangle is 5 cm longer than twice the length of the width. If the
          area of the rectangle is 403 square centimeters, what is the width?

8-110.   Which of the points below is a solution to $4x - 3y = 10$? Note: More than one point
          may make this equation true.

   a.   (1, 2)   b.   (4, 2)   c.   (7, 6)   d.   (4, −3)

8-111.   Kristen loves shortcuts. She figured out that she can find x- and y-intercepts for any
          line without graphing! For example, she knows that the x-intercept for $5x - 3y = 15$
          is (3, 0) just by examining the rule.

   a.   What is her shortcut?

   b.   Does this shortcut work for the y-intercept? Try it and then test your result by
          changing $5x - 3y = 15$ into $y = mx + b$ form.

   c.   Use this shortcut to find the x- and y-intercepts of $3x - 2y = 24$.

8.3.3 Which method should I use?

Choosing a Strategy

You now have two algebraic methods to solve quadratic equations: using the Zero Product Property and using the Quadratic Formula. How can you decide which strategy is best to try first? By the end of this lesson, you should have some strategies to help you determine which method to try first when solving a quadratic equation.

8-112. Examine the quadratic equations below with your team. For each equation:

- Decide which strategy is best to try first.

- Solve the equation. If your first strategy does not work, switch to the other strategy.

- Check your solution(s).

Be prepared to share your process with the class.

a. $x^2 + 12x + 27 = 0$

b. $0.5x^2 + 9x + 3.2 = 0$

c. $(3x + 4)(2x - 1) = 0$

d. $x^2 + 16 = 8x$

e. $x^2 + 5 - 2x = 0$

f. $20x^2 - 30x = 2x + 45$

8-113. With the class, decide when it is best to solve a quadratic by factoring and when you should go directly to the Quadratic Formula. Copy your observations in your Learning Log. Title this entry "Choosing a Strategy to Solve Quadratics" and include today's date.

8-114.   While solving $(x-5)(x+2) = -6$, Kyle decided that x must equal 5 or –2. "Not so fast!" exclaimed Stanton, "The product does not equal zero. We need to change the equation first."

a.   What is Stanton talking about?

b.   How can the equation be rewritten? Discuss this with your team and use your algebraic tools to rewrite the equation so that it can be solved.

c.   Solve the resulting equation from part (b) for x. Do your solutions match Kyle's?

8-115.   MOE'S YO

Moe is playing with a yo-yo. He throws the yo-yo down and then pulls it back up. The motion of the yo-yo is represented by the equation $y = 2x^2 - 4.8x$, where x represents the number of seconds since the yo-yo left Moe's hand, and y represents the vertical height in inches of the yo-yo with respect to Moe's hand. Note that when the yo-yo is in Moe's hand, $y = 0$, and when the yo-yo is below his hand, y is negative.

a.   How long is Moe's yo-yo in the air before it comes back to Moe's hand? Write and solve a quadratic equation to find the times that the yo-yo is in Moe's hand.

b.   At what time does the yo-yo turn around? Use what you know about parabolas to help you.

c.   How long is the yo-yo's string? That is, what is y when the yo-yo changes direction?

d.   Draw a sketch of the graph representing the motion of Moe's yo-yo. On the sketch, label the important points: when the yo-yo is in Moe's hand and when it changes direction.

LOOKING DEEPER

MATH NOTES

Simplifying Square Roots

Before calculators were universally available, people who wanted to use approximate decimal values for numbers like $\sqrt{45}$ had a few options:

1. Carry around copies of long square-root tables.

2. Use Guess and Check repeatedly to get desired accuracy.

3. "Simplify" the square roots. A square root is **simplified** when there are no more perfect square factors (square numbers such as 4, 25, and 81) under the radical sign.

Simplifying square roots was by far the fastest method. People factored the number as the product of integers hoping to find at least one perfect square number. They memorized approximations of the square roots of the integers from one to ten. Then they could figure out the decimal value by multiplying these memorized facts with the roots of the square numbers. Here are some examples of this method.

Example 1: Simplify $\sqrt{45}$.

First rewrite $\sqrt{45}$ in an equivalent factored form so that one of the factors is a perfect square. Simplify the square root of the perfect square. Verify with your calculator that both $3\sqrt{5}$ and $\sqrt{45} \approx 6.71$.

Example 1
$$\sqrt{45} = \sqrt{9 \cdot 5}$$
$$= \sqrt{9} \cdot \sqrt{5}$$
$$= 3\sqrt{5}$$

Examine **Example 2** and **Example 3** at right. Note that in Example 3, $\sqrt{72}$ was rewritten as $\sqrt{36} \cdot \sqrt{2}$, rather than as $\sqrt{9} \cdot \sqrt{8}$ or $\sqrt{4} \cdot \sqrt{18}$, because 36 is the largest perfect square factor of 72. However, since

Example 2	Example 3
$\sqrt{27}$	$\sqrt{72}$
$= \sqrt{9} \cdot \sqrt{3}$	$= \sqrt{36} \cdot \sqrt{2}$
$= 3\sqrt{3}$	$= 6\sqrt{2}$

$$\sqrt{4} \cdot \sqrt{18} = 2\sqrt{9 \cdot 2} = 2\sqrt{9} \cdot \sqrt{2} = 2 \cdot 3\sqrt{2} = 6\sqrt{2} \quad \text{and}$$
$$\sqrt{9} \cdot \sqrt{8} = 3\sqrt{4 \cdot 2} = 3\sqrt{4} \cdot \sqrt{2} = 3 \cdot 2\sqrt{2} = 6\sqrt{2} \,,$$

you can still get the same answer if you simplify it using different methods.

When you take the square root of an integer that is not a perfect square, the result is a decimal that never repeats itself and never ends. This result is called an **irrational number**. The irrational numbers and the rational numbers together form the numbers we use in this course, which are called **real numbers**.

Generally, since it is now the age of technology, when a decimal approximation of an irrational square root is desired, a calculator is used. However, for an exact answer, the number must be written using the $\sqrt{}$ symbol.

8-116. Write and solve an equation (or system of equations) for the situation described below. Define your variable(s) and write your solution as a sentence.

Daria has 18 coins that are all nickels and quarters. The number of nickels is 3 more than twice the number of quarters. If she has $1.90 in all, how many nickels does Daria have?

8-117. Solve the following quadratic equations using any method.

a. $10000x^2 - 64 = 0$

b. $9x^2 - 8 = -34x$

c. $2x^2 - 4x + 7 = 0$

d. $3.2x + 0.2x^2 - 5 = 0$

8-118. Find a rule that represents the number of tiles in Figure x for the tile pattern at right.

 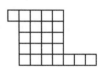

Figure 1   Figure 2   Figure 3

8-119. Solve the equations below for x. Check your solutions.

a. $3x^2 + 3x = 6 + 3x^2$

b. $\frac{5}{x} = \frac{1}{3}$

c. $5 - (2x - 3) = -3x + 6$

d. $6(x - 3) + 2x = 4(2x + 1) - 22$

8-120. Line L passes through the points $(-44, 42)$ and $(-31, 94)$, while line M has the rule $y = 6 + 3x$. Which line is steeper? **Justify** your answer.

8-121. **Multiple Choice:** Which line below is perpendicular to the line $2x - 5y = 3$?

a. $2x + 5y = 7$

b. $-2x + 5y = 4$

c. $5x - 2y = -1$

d. $5x + 2y = 3$

Chapter 8 Closure   What have I learned?

Reflection and Synthesis

The activities below offer you a chance to reflect on what you have learned during this chapter. As you work, look for concepts that you feel very comfortable with, ideas that you would like to learn more about, and topics you need more help with. Look for **connections** between ideas as well as **connections** with material you learned previously.

①   TEAM BRAINSTORM

With your team, brainstorm a list for each of the following topics. Be as detailed as you can. How long can you make your list? Challenge yourselves. Be prepared to share your team's ideas with the class.

Topics: What have you studied in this chapter? What ideas and words were important in what you learned? Remember to be as detailed as you can.

Ways of Thinking: What Ways of Thinking did you use in this chapter? When did you use them?

Connections: What topics, ideas, and words that you learned *before* this chapter are **connected** to the new ideas in this chapter? Again, make your list as long as you can.

② MAKING CONNECTIONS

The following is a list of the vocabulary used in this chapter. The words that appear in bold are new to this chapter. Make sure that you are familiar with all of these words and know what they mean. Refer to the glossary or index for any words that you do not yet understand.

binomial	**factor**	generic rectangle
graph	**monomial**	parabola
product	**quadratic equation**	**Quadratic Formula**
root	solution	**standard form for quadratics**
sum	**symmetry**	**trinomial**
vertex	x-intercept	$x \rightarrow y$ table
y-intercept	**Zero Product Property**	

Make a concept map showing all of the **connections** you can find among the key words and ideas listed above. To show a **connection** between two words, draw a line between them and explain the **connection**, as shown in the example below. A word can be **connected** to any other word as long as there is a **justified connection**. For each key word or idea, provide a sketch that illustrates the idea (see the example below).

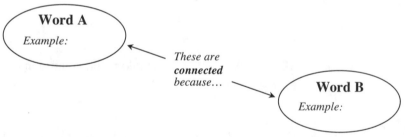

Your teacher may provide you with vocabulary cards to help you get started. If you use the cards to plan your concept map, be sure either to re-draw your concept map on your paper or to glue the vocabulary cards to a poster with all of the **connections** explained for others to see and understand.

While you are making your map, your team may think of related words or ideas that are not listed above. Be sure to include these ideas on your concept map.

③ SUMMARIZING MY UNDERSTANDING

This section gives you an opportunity to show what you know about certain math topics or ideas. Your teacher will give you directions for exactly how to do this. Your teacher may also provide a "GO" page to work on. The "GO" stands for "Graphic Organizer," a tool you can use to organize your thoughts and communicate your ideas clearly.

WHAT HAVE I LEARNED?

This section will help you evaluate which types of problems you have seen with which you feel comfortable and those with which you need more help. Even if your teacher does not assign this section, it is a good idea to try these problems and find out for yourself what you know and what you need to work on.

Solve each problem as completely as you can. The table at the end of the closure section has answers to these problems. It also tells you where you can find additional help and practice on problems like these.

CL 8-122. For the graph of the line at right:

a. Find the slope.

b. Find the y-intercept.

c. Find the equation.

d. Find the equation of a line perpendicular to this one that passes through $(0,7)$.

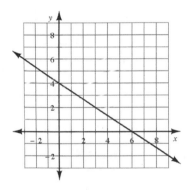

CL 8-123. Factor and use the Zero Product Property to find the roots of the following quadratic equations.

a. $0 = x^2 - 7x + 12$ b. $0 = 6x^2 - 23x + 20$

c. $0 = x^2 - 9$ d. $0 = x^2 + 12x + 36$

CL 8-124. Use the Quadratic Formula to solve these equations.

a. $0 = x^2 - 7x + 3$ b. $3x^2 + 5x + 1 = 0$

CL 8-125. Use the graph at right to answer the
questions below.

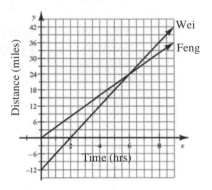

a. One of these lines represents Feng, and
one represents Wai. Write an equation
for each girl's line.

b. The two girls are riding bikes. How
fast does each girl ride?

c. When do Feng and Wai meet? At that
point, how far are they from school?

CL 8-126. Factor each expression below completely.

a. $3x^2 + 21x + 30$

b. $7x^2 - 63$

CL 8-127. Find the coordinates of the y-intercept, x-intercepts, and vertex of $y = x^2 - 2x - 15$.
Show all of the work that you do to find these points.

CL 8-128. Solve for x using the method of your choice.

a. $0 = 2x^2 - 5x - 33$

b. $0 = 3x^2 - 4x - 1$

CL 8-129. Quinn started off with twice as
much candy as Denali, but then
he ate 4 pieces. When Quinn and
Denali put their candy together,
they now have a total of 50
pieces. How many pieces of
candy did Denali start with?

CL 8-130. Check your answers using the table at the end of the closure section. Which
problems do you feel confident about? Which problems were hard? Use the table to
make a list of topics you need help on and a list of topics you need to practice more.

⑤   HOW AM I THINKING?

This course focuses on five different **Ways of Thinking**: reversing thinking, justifying, generalizing, making connections, and applying and extending understanding. These are some of the ways in which you think while trying to make sense of a concept or to solve a problem (even outside of math class). During this chapter, you have probably used each Way of Thinking multiple times without even realizing it!

Choose three of these Ways of Thinking that you remember using while working in this chapter. For each Way of Thinking that you choose, show and explain where you used it and how you used it. Describe why thinking in this way helped you solve a particular problem or understand something new. (For instance, explain why you wanted to **generalize** in this particular case, or why it was useful to see these particular **connections**.) Be sure to include examples to demonstrate your thinking.

Answers and Support for Closure Activity #4
What Have I Learned?

Problem	Solution	Need Help?	More Practice
CL 8-122.	a. $m = -\frac{2}{3}$ b. *y*-intercept: 4 c. $y = -\frac{2}{3}x + 4$ d. $y = \frac{3}{2}x + 7$	Lessons 7.1.3, 7.1.5, 7.2.2, 7.2.3, and 7.3.2 Math Notes boxes	Problems 8-9, 8-31, 8-57, 8-86, 8-99, and 8-121
CL 8-123.	a. $x = 4$ or $x = 3$ b. $x = \frac{5}{2}$ or $x = \frac{4}{3}$ c. $x = -3$ or $x = 3$ d. $x = -6$	Lessons 8.1.4, 8.2.3, and 8.3.2 Math Notes boxes	Problems 8-66, 8-72, 8-77, 8-88, 8-96, and 8-106
CL 8-124.	a. $x = \frac{7 \pm \sqrt{37}}{2}$ ($x \approx 6.54$ or 0.46) b. $x = \frac{-5 \pm \sqrt{13}}{6}$ ($x \approx -0.23$ or -1.43)	Problem 8-92, Lessons 8.3.1 and 8.3.2 Math Notes boxes	Problems 8-94, 8-97, 8-104, and 8-107

Problem	Solution	Need Help?	More Practice
CL 8-125.	a. Feng: $y = 4x$ Wai: $y = 6x - 12$ b. Feng rides at 4 miles per hour; Wai rides at 6 miles per hour. c. Feng and Wai meet after 6 hours. At that point, they are 24 miles from school.	Lessons 7.1.5 and 7.2.2 Math Notes boxes	See Lessons 7.2.2 and 7.2.3
CL 8-126.	a. $3(x + 2)(x + 5)$ b. $7(x + 3)(x - 3)$	Problems 8-13, 8-14, and 8-35; Lesson 8.1.5 Math Notes box	Problems 8-15, 8-16, 8-22, 8-23, 8-24, 8-29, 8-33, 8-36, 8-37, and 8-69
CL 8-127.	y-intercept: -15 x-intercepts: 5 and -3 vertex: $(1, -16)$	Problems 8-43, 8-51, 8-59, 8-60, 8-61, and 8-62	Problems 8-10, 8-54, 8-68, and 8-82
CL 8-128.	a. $x = \frac{11}{2}$ or $x = -3$ b. $x = \frac{4 \pm \sqrt{28}}{6} = \frac{4 \pm 2\sqrt{7}}{6} = \frac{2 \pm \sqrt{7}}{3}$ ($x \approx 1.55$ or $x \approx -0.22$)	Lessons 8.1.4, 8.2.3, 8.3.1, 8.3.2	Problems 8-112 and 8-117
CL 8-129.	Denali has 18 pieces of candy.	Lesson 7.1.4 Math Notes box	Problem 8-116

INEQUALITIES

9

CHAPTER 9   Inequalities

So far in this course you have focused on what you can determine when two expressions are equal. By using what you know about balancing equations, you can now solve linear and quadratic equations for a given variable.

However, what if the two expressions are not equal? If you know that one expression is always larger than the other, what does that tell you about the variable? In this chapter you will learn how to deal with these types of relationships, called *inequalities*, and will develop ways to represent solutions to inequalities both algebraically and graphically.

In addition, you will extend your ability to work with mathematical sentences by learning how to write inequalities from word problems.

In this chapter, you will learn:

➢ How to write an inequality to represent a word problem.

➢ How to solve linear inequalities and represent the solutions on a number line.

➢ How to represent the solutions of linear and nonlinear inequalities with two variables on a graph.

➢ How to graph a system of inequalities.

Guiding Questions

Think about these questions throughout this chapter:

How can I represent it algebraically?

How can I solve it?

What is a solution?

What is the connection?

Chapter Outline

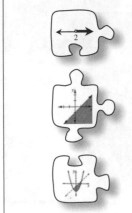	**Section 9.1**	In this section, you will study how to solve linear inequalities and apply this understanding to solving applications.
	Section 9.2	After learning how to represent solutions to one-variable inequalities on a number line, you will study how to represent the solutions of two-variable inequalities on an $x \rightarrow y$ graph.
	Section 9.3	In the final section, you will apply what you know about systems of equations to help find the solutions to a system of inequalities.

     Algebra Connections

9.1.1 What if the quantities are not equal?

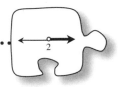

Solving Linear, One-Variable Inequalities

In this course, you have developed a variety of skills to find solutions to different kinds of equations. Now you will **apply** these equation-solving skills to solve inequalities.

9-1.   As a class, create a "human number line" for each of the following mathematical sentences. You will be assigned a number to represent on the number line. When your number makes the equation or inequality true, stand up to show that your number is a solution. If your number does not make the equation or inequality true, remain seated.

   a. $x \geq -2$ b. $x \leq 1$ c. $x = 3$ d. $x \geq 0$

   e. $x = -2$ f. $-1 \leq x \leq 4$ g. $x^2 \geq 4$ h. $x < -3$

9-2.   Based on your observations from problem 9-1, discuss the following questions with your class. Be sure to **justify** your responses.

   a.   Compare the solutions to an inequality (like $x \geq -2$) with that of an equation (like $x = 3$). What is different? What causes this to happen?

   b.   How many solutions does an inequality such as $x \leq 1$ have?

   c.   How is the result of $-1 \leq x \leq 4$ different from the other inequalities? What about the result of $x^2 \geq 4$?

9-3.   Write an inequality that represents the solutions on each number line below.

a.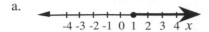

b.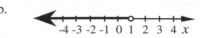

c.

d.

9-4.   SOLUTIONS TO A LINEAR INEQUALITY

With your study team, find at least <u>five</u> x-values that make the inequality below true:

$$2x - 5 \geq 3$$

a.   How many solutions are there?

b.   What is the smallest solution for x? This point is called a **boundary point**.

c.   What is the significance of the boundary point? What is its relationship with the inequality $2x - 5 \geq 3$?

d.   Write an inequality that represents the solutions for x. On a number line, highlight the solutions for x. Be ready to share your number line with the class.

9-5.   SOLVING LINEAR INEQUALITIES WITH ONE VARIABLE

Analyze the process for solving an inequality, such as $3 - 2x < 1$, by addressing the questions below.

a.   The key point to start with is the **boundary point**. How can you quickly solve for this point? Once you have determined your strategy, find the boundary point for $3 - 2x < 1$.

b.   Decide if the boundary point is part of the solution to the inequality. If it <u>is</u> part of the solution, indicate this on a number line with a solid point. If it is <u>not</u> a solution, show this by using an **unfilled circle** as a boundary.

c.   Finally, to determine on which side of the boundary the solutions lie, choose a point to test in the inequality. If the point <u>is</u> a solution, then all points on that side of the boundary are part of the solution. If the point is <u>not</u> a solution, what does that tell you about the solutions? Write your solutions to $3 - 2x < 1$ as an inequality and represent the solutions on a number line.

9-6.   With your study team, find all of the solutions to the inequality $3x + 1 < 7$. Decide how to represent these solutions on a number line and be prepared to **justify** your decisions to the class.

Algebra Connections

MᴇᴛHODS AND Mᴇᴀɴɪɴɢs

MATH NOTES

Inequality Symbols

Just as the symbol "=" is used to represent that two quantities are equal in mathematics, the **inequality symbols** at right are used when describing the relationships between quantities that are not necessarily equal.

$<$ less than
$\leq$ less than or equal to
$>$ greater than
$\geq$ greater than or equal to

When graphing an inequality on a number line, such as $x > 4$, a solid point indicates that the value is a solution of the inequality. However, an unfilled circle indicates that the value is not part of the solution.

9-7.   Solve the problem below by writing and solving an equation. A Guess and Check table may help you write the equation. Be sure to define your variable.

There are a total of 122 countries in Africa, Europe, and North America (as of 2003). Europe has twice as many countries as North America, and Africa has seven more than Europe. How many countries are in each of these three continents? Write an equation and solve it to answer this question.

9-8.   Solve each of the following inequalities for the given variable. Represent your solutions on a number line.

a. $2(3p+1) > -4$ b. $9k-2 < 3k+10$ c. $5-h \geq 4$

9-9.   Solve the following quadratic equations. Check your solutions, if possible.

  a. $2k^2 + k - 6 = 0$ b. $m^2 = 9$

  c. $w(2w + 8) = 24$ d. $3n^2 - 4n = 5$

9-10.   Identify the statements below as sometimes true, always true, or never true.

<	less than
≤	less than or equal to
>	greater than
≥	greater than or equal to

  a. $-4 \le 9$ b. $x < 1$

  c. $-5 > -2$ d. $3x + 5 = 2$ e. $61 = 61$ f. $-6 < -6$

9-11.   Assuming that x does not equal zero, what is $\frac{x}{x}$? Explain how you know.

9-12.   Robbie builds model rockets. One day he sets up a rocket, backs away from the launch pad, and then shoots the rocket off into the air. The rocket's path is represented by the equation $y = -10x^2 + 130x - 400$, where y is the height in meters off the ground and x is the horizontal distance in meters from Robbie.

  a.   Use either the Zero Product Property or the Quadratic Formula to find the x-intercepts of the path of Robbie's rocket. What do the x-intercepts tell you?

  b.   When Robbie's rocket lands, how far is it from the launch pad?

9-13.   For each parabola graphed below, visually estimate the x-intercepts. Then use the Quadratic Formula to confirm your estimates.

  a. $y = x^2 - 5x + 3$ b. $y = x^2 + 2x - 6$

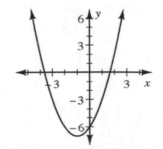

9.1.2 How can I use inequalities?

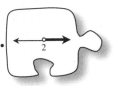

More Solving Inequalities

In Lesson 9.1.1 you learned how to solve inequalities with one variable. Today you will focus on special inequalities and learn how you can use inequalities to solve an application problem.

9-14.   Review what you learned in Lesson 9.1.1 to solve the inequalities below. Represent your solutions both as an inequality and on a number line.

a. $x - 7 < -2$

b. $3m + 2 \leq 8m - 8$

c. $\frac{2}{3}p - 2 > -4$

d. $2 - 3(x - 1) \geq x - 7$

e. $9k - 4 + 1 \leq 2k - 3 + 7k$

f. $3y + 1 < 3y + 1$

9-15.   THE UNITED NATIONS

At the end of this chapter, your team will have the exciting responsibility of representing a country at a special meeting of the United Nations (U.N.). The U.N. needs your help preparing for future large-scale disasters. You will need to help find a solution that not only works best for the country you represent, but that also accommodates the needs of each of the other countries. To prepare you for this task, this chapter will present daily problems to familiarize you with the important issues and concerns of other countries.

Start by writing and solving an equation (or system of equations) that represents the problem below. Be sure to define any variables you use.

Turkey has a population of 66 million people and is made up almost entirely of two ethnic groups: Turks and Kurds. There are four times more Turks than Kurds. Write an equation and solve it to find out how many Kurds live in Turkey.

9-16.   In 1912, Japan gave the United States several thousand flowering cherry trees as a symbol of friendship. Similarly, the nation of Cameroon plans to give flowering Satta trees to other countries this year. When asked how to decide which Satta trees make good gifts, Cameroon's chief arborist explained:

"We plant Satta trees when they are 6 cm tall, and they grow 9 cm every year. The trees only flower when they are taller than 150 cm."

It is very important that the trees Cameroon gives flower this year! It would be considered an insult to receive a tree that did not bloom. Luckily, Cameroon has many groves of Satta trees from which to select its gifts. How old must the trees be so that they will flower within the year?

a.   Discuss with your study team whether an inequality or an equation is appropriate for this situation. Be prepared to share your reasoning.

b.   Write and solve a mathematical sentence to determine how old the trees can be so that they flower this year.

c.   Later, the arborist added:

"I almost forgot to tell you! When the trees become very old, they stop flowering. Make sure you choose trees that are no more than 240 cm tall!"

Discuss with your team how you can use this additional information to make sure you choose trees that will flower. Be prepared to share your answer with the class.

Algebra Connections

9-17. Solve the inequalities below for the given variables. Represent your solutions on a number line.

a. $3(2k-1) < 9$

b. $\frac{2p}{5} \le 6$

c. $-2 + 8n > 2$

d. $7t - 4 \ge 2t - 4$

9-18. Use your graphing shortcuts to graph $y = -2x + 3$. Identify the x- and y-intercepts.

9-19. Find the equation of the line with slope $-\frac{3}{5}$ passing through the point (–6, 2).

9-20. Find each quotient below. Verify your work.

a. $(2p^2 - 7p - 30) \div (p - 6)$

b. $(3x^2 - 5x + 4) \div (x - 1)$

c. $(4m^3 - 4m^2 - 5m) \div (2m + 3)$

9-21. Solve the quadratic equation below. Check your solutions with a calculator.

$$3x^2 + 2.5x = 12.5$$

9-22. Factor the expressions below completely, if possible.

a. $4x^2 - 20x + 25$

b. $x^2 + 11x - 2$

c. $3x^2 - 12x$

d. $10x^2 - 35x - 20$

9.2.1 What if the inequality has two variables?

Graphing Two-Variable Inequalities

In Section 9.1, you learned how to use an inequality with one variable to help solve a word problem. You also discovered that a one-variable inequality can have zero, one, or more solutions and that these solutions can be represented on a number line. But what if an inequality has two variables? What is a solution to a two-variable inequality? And how could these solutions be represented graphically?

9-23. **EXAMINING THE SOLUTIONS OF A LINEAR EQUATION**

Find your graph of $y = -2x + 3$ from problem 9-18. Compare your graph with the poster graph provided by your teacher.

a. Is the point $(-1, 5)$ a solution to the equation $y = -2x + 3$? How can you tell by looking at the graph? How can you tell by using the equation?

b. Is the point $(2, -1)$ a solution? What about the point $(0, 0)$? **Justify** each conclusion with both the graph and the equation.

c. What determines if a point lies on the line? What is the difference between the points on the line and the points not on the line?

9-24. **GRAPHING A LINEAR INEQUALITY**

In problem 9-23, you found that the points on the line are the *only* points that make the equation $y = -2x + 3$ true. But what if you want to graph the solutions for the inequality $y \geq -2x + 3$? How will that graph differ from the graph of $y = -2x + 3$? Consider this question as you follow the steps below.

a. Your team will be given a list of points to test in the inequality $y \geq -2x + 3$. For each point that makes the inequality true, place a sticky dot on that point on the class graph.

b. Now examine the solutions shown on the graph. With your team, discuss the questions below. Be ready to share your discoveries with the class.

   • Are there any points on the graph that you suspect are solutions but do not have a sticker?

   • Are there any stickers that you think may be misplaced? If so, verify these points so that you can have a complete graph of the solutions.

   • What about the points on the line? Are they all solutions to the inequality $y \geq -2x + 3$? Why or why not?

   • How many solutions are there?

   • Why aren't any of the solutions located below the line?

9-25.   What else can you learn about solutions of linear inequalities? Think about this as you answer the questions below with your team.

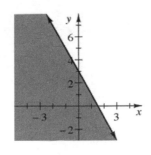

a.   What if the graph were shaded like the one at right? What inequality would correspond with this graph?

b.   Heidi asks, "What if I changed the inequality to be $y < -2x + 3$? Now what would the graph look like?" Discuss this with your teammates and decide the best way to represent the solutions to the inequality $y < -2x + 3$. Be prepared to share your graph with the class.

9-26.   Graph the inequalities below on graph paper. For each inequality:

- Graph the boundary as either a solid or a dashed line.

- Shade the region that makes the inequality true.

a. $y > -\frac{1}{3}x - 1$ b. $y \le 4x + 2$

c. $y < \frac{5}{2}x + 3$ d. $2x - y \le 5$

9-27.   In your Learning Log, explain how to graph a linear inequality. Be sure to address the questions below. Title this entry "Graphing Linear Inequalities" and include today's date.

- How can you determine if the line is part of the solution?

- How can you determine which side of the line the solution belongs to?

- What point(s) is (are) easiest to test?

- How many points do you need to test?

9-28.   Represent the solutions to the inequalities below on a number line.

a. $3x - 2 < 10$ b. $5x - 1 - 3x \geq 4x + 5$

c. $2(x + 2) > 10 - x$ d. $4(x - 3) + 5 \geq -7$

9-29.   Algeria has decided to take out an advertisement in the
U.N newspaper, *Liberty Daily*. The newspaper charges
a base fee of $1200 for an ad. There is an additional fee
of $300 for every inch in height. If Algeria is willing to
spend any amount up to (and including) $2700, what
choices does the country have for the height of the ad?

9-30.   In order to quickly get people between terminals in the Minneapolis Airport, long
conveyor belts were installed. Assume that if someone stood still on a conveyor
belt, that person would travel 2 feet per second.

a.   Since Jung is in a hurry, he decided to walk on the conveyor belt (in the same
direction he would travel standing still). If his terminal is 300 feet away and he
wants to get there in 60 seconds, how fast does he need to walk with respect to
the conveyor belt? (Assume he can ride the conveyor belt the entire distance.)

b.   Jacob, who is four years old, decided it would be fun to walk on the conveyor
belt in the "wrong" direction (i.e., in the direction opposite to that he would
travel if standing still). If he walks for 18 seconds at a rate of 1 foot per
second, how far will he travel? In what direction does he travel? Explain.

9-31.   Line m has intercepts $(-7, 0)$ and $(0, -2)$.

a.   Find the equation of line m.

b.   Is the point $(49, -16)$ also on line m? How do you know?

c.   Write the equation of a line that is perpendicular to line m and passes through
the point $(6, -1)$.

9-32.   Thui made the following hypotheses: $2n - 1 < 5$ and $n + 1 \leq 2n$. Which of the
following conclusions can she make?

a. $1 \leq n \leq 3$ b. $1 \leq n < 3$ c. $1 < n \leq 3$ d. $1 < n < 3$

9-33.   **Multiple Choice:** Which of the expressions below is a factor of $6m^2 + 7m - 5$?

a. $2m + 1$ b. $m + 5$ c. $2m - 5$ d. $3m + 5$

9.2.2 What if the inequality is not linear?

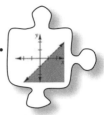

Graphing Linear and Non-Linear Inequalities

In Lesson 9.2.1, you discovered that the solutions of a linear inequality with two variables can be represented by a shaded region on one side of the line. But how can the graph of an inequality help solve a problem? And what happens when the inequality is not linear? Consider these questions as you complete the following problems with your study team.

9-34. Review what you learned about graphing inequalities in Lesson 9.2.1 by graphing the inequality below on graph paper.

$$y \geq -\tfrac{5}{3}x - 3$$

a. What is the minimum number of points you need to test in order to know which side of the line the solution falls on?

b. Orville thinks that using the point $(0, 0)$ to test this inequality is a great idea. Why is using this point so convenient?

c. Anita decided to use the point $(-3, 2)$ to test the inequality. Test the inequality with her point. Does this point help her decide which side to shade? Why or why not?

9-35. FOREIGN AID

One of the purposes of the United Nations is to have nations work together to help each other. Recently, the members of the U. N. decided to give grants to poor countries to help reduce poverty. However, the United Nations only has the resources to help those countries in the greatest need. Therefore, it was decided that only countries in which the number of people in poverty is **more than** one-half of its total population would receive foreign aid.

a. Write an inequality that represents the criteria to receive foreign aid. Let x represent the population and y represent the number of people in poverty.

b. On the Lesson 9.2.2 Resource Page provided by your teacher (also available at www.cpm.org), find the graph that shows the number of people in poverty per the population for each of the countries being considered for foreign aid. Carefully graph your inequality from part (a) on this data graph. Which countries should receive foreign aid?

9-36. What if an inequality is non-linear? Decide with your team how to graph the inequality $y < x^2 - 4x + 3$ on graph paper. Your graphing shortcuts can help.

9-37. With your team, graph the following inequalities on graph paper.

a. $y < -\frac{2}{3}x + 4$ b. $y \geq x^2$ c. $x < 2$

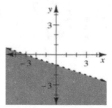

9-38. Write the inequality for the solution graphed at right. Be prepared to explain how you found your rule.

Solving One-Variable Inequalities

To solve a one-variable inequality, first treat the problem as if it were an equality. The solution to the equality is called the **boundary point**. For example, $x = 12$ is the boundary point for the inequality $10 - 2(x - 3) \geq -8$, as shown below.

Problem: $10 - 2(x - 3) \geq -8$

$$10 - 2(x - 3) = -8$$
$$10 - 2x + 6 = -8$$
$$-2x + 16 = -8$$
$$-2x = -24$$
$$x = 12$$

First change the problem to an equality and solve for x:

Since the original inequality is true when $x = 12$, place your boundary point on the number line as a solid point. Then test one value on either side in the *original* inequality to determine which set of numbers makes the inequality true. Therefore, the solution is $x \leq 12$.

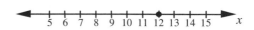

Test : $x = 8$	Test : $x = 15$
$10 - 2(8 - 3) \geq -8$	$10 - 2(15 - 3) \geq -8$
$10 - 2(5) \geq -8$	$10 - 2(12) \geq -8$
$0 \geq -8$	$-14 \geq 17$
TRUE!	FALSE!

When the inequality is < or >, the boundary point is *not* included in the answer. On a number line, this would be indicated with an open circle at the boundary point.

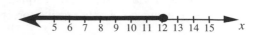

9-39.   **Multiple Choice:** Which of the expressions below is a factor of $6x^2 + 7x - 20$?

    a. $3x - 4$ b. $2x - 5$ c. $3x + 4$ d. $4x - 3$

9-40.   **Multiple Choice:** Which of the following expressions is the product of $(4y - 3x)(2y + x)$?

    a. $8y^2 - 2xy - 3x^2$ b. $6y^2 - 2xy - 2x^2$

    c. $8y^2 + 10xy - 3x^2$ d. $6y^2 - 2x$

9-41.   WHAT'S THE DIFFERENCE?

Examine the following situations in which you need to find the difference between two amounts.

    a.   Rocio has \$298 saved in the bank, while Thomas has \$314. What is the difference between their bank balances? How did you get your answer?

    b.   The temperature in Minneapolis on January 10 ranged between –23° and 19° Fahrenheit. What was the difference between the high and low temperatures for this date? How did you get your answer?

    c.   Urban High School has 1850 students, while Metro High School has 1490 students. What is the difference of their student populations?

    d.   Explain why these differences in (a) through (c) are all positive.

9-42.   Solve the following equations and inequalities for x. Check your solution(s), if possible.

    a. $\frac{3}{x} = 9$ b. $\sqrt{x} = 4$ c. $x^2 = 25$ d. $2(x - 3) > 4$

9-43.   During a race, Bernie ran 9 meters every 4 seconds, while Barnaby ran 2 meters every second and got a 10-meter head start. If the race was 70 meters long, did Bernie ever catch up with Barnaby? If so, when? **Justify** your answer.

9-44.   Determine the number of times the graph of $y = 5x^2 + 7x - 6$ intersects the x-axis using *two different methods*. The answers from each method should match.

9.2.3 What's the difference?

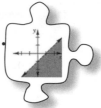

Introduction to Absolute Value

In the past few lessons, you learned what inequalities are and learned how to graph linear and non-linear inequalities with two variables. Today you will learn a new operation and will learn how you can use it to create new and interesting inequality graphs.

9-45.   ABSOLUTE-VALUE OPERATION

Your teacher will present you with information about an operation called **absolute value**. As your teacher finds the absolute values of numbers such as –11 and 4, record the results on your paper. Look for a pattern!

a.   Study the relationship between the number entered in the parentheses and the results shown. Write a statement describing this operation.

```
abs(-11)
                    11
abs(4)
                     4
abs(-100)
                   100
```

b.   Why would you ever need an absolute value?

9-46.   While some graphing calculators, like the one shown in problem 9-45, display the absolute value as "abs(–100) = 100," the written notation is $|-100| = 100$. This notation consists of two vertical lines on each side of the input value.

a.   The expression $|-3| + 1$ can be translated as, "*Change –3 to a positive value and then add 1.*" Translate the expression $|-5+1| - 3$ into words and then find its value.

b.   Evaluate these expressions:

   i. $|-100| - 98$ *ii.* $5|2-8|$

   iii. $|-13| + |0|$ *iv.* $14 - |-10+3|$

c.   Now create your own expression using the absolute value that has a result of 10. Be creative and be ready to share your expression with the class.

9-47.   Mr. Guo is thinking of a number. When he takes the absolute value of his number, he gets 15. What could his number be? Is there more than one possible answer?

9-48.   Riley wants to know what an absolute value might look like on a graph.

a.   Set up a table and graph $y = |x|$.

b.   Describe for Riley what the graph looks like. Be as detailed as you can.

Algebra Connections

9-49.   Dorinae is confused. She is making a table for $y = |x + 1|$. She is trying to find y when $x = -3$, but she is not sure if she should find the absolute value first, or if she should first add 1. Explain to Dorinae what she should do first. **Justify** your reasoning.

9-50.   Graph the inequality $y < |2x - 1|$. Be ready to share your graph with the class.

METHODS AND MEANINGS

MATH NOTES

Definition of Absolute Value

An **absolute value**, represented by two vertical bars, | |, determines the positive value of a number. Numerically, it represents a distance on a number line between a number and zero. Since a distance is always positive, the absolute value is *always* either a positive value or zero. The absolute value of a number is *never* negative.

For example, the number –3 is 3 units away from 0, as shown on the number line at right. Therefore, the absolute value of –3 is 3. This is written $|-3| = 3$.

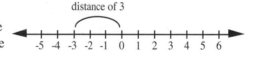
distance of 3

Likewise, the number 5 is 5 units away from 0. The absolute value of 5 is 5, written $|5| = 5$.

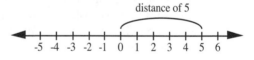
distance of 5

Review & Preview

9-51.   Brazil's rain forests currently cover about 1,400,000 square miles, but are becoming smaller every year because of deforestation. Realizing that the rain forests are a great resource, Brazil has decided to control how quickly the forests are cleared.

In 50 years Brazil would like the rain forests to cover more than 1,200,000 square miles. If x represents the forest area that is cleared each year, write and solve an inequality that would help determine acceptable values of x.

9-52. Calculate the value of each expression below. You may want to refer to the Math Notes box for this lesson for help.

a. $\left|-4\right|-3$ b. $\left|6-11+3\right|$ c. $-9-\left|-2\right|$ d. $5\left|6\right|-2$

9-53. Clifford thinks that $x = 7$ is a solution to $3(x-2) \leq 4$. Is he correct? Show why or why not.

9-54. Graph the inequalities below on graph paper.

a. $y \leq -x + 5$ b. $y > \frac{2}{3}x - 1$

9-55. Zachary has $718 in his bank account and automatically withdraws (subtracts) $14 every month to pay for his computer service. Christian has $212 in his bank account and deposits (adds) $32 each month from his newspaper-delivery tips. Assuming they make no other deposits or withdrawals, when will Zachary and Christian have the same amount of money in their bank accounts?

9-56. Stacey is the star of the basketball team. She makes many baskets during each game and could break the record for the most baskets made in one season at her high school. The data for the first five games of this season is below.

Game Number	Total Number of Baskets
1	6
2	11
3	18
4	25
5	31

a. Plot a graph with these data points.

b. Draw a trend line for this data using two carefully selected points that best represent the data.

c. Use the equation of your line to predict how many baskets Stacey will make by the end of the season if the season has 15 games.

Algebra Connections

9.3.1 How can I represent it?

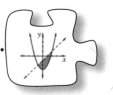

Systems of Inequalities

In Chapter 6 you learned that the solution to a system of equations is a point that makes both equations true. But what about the solution of a system of two inequalities? How can you represent these solutions on a graph? How many solutions can a system of inequalities have?

Consider these questions as you learn how to graph a system of inequalities.

9-57.   Find your graphs for problem 9-54.

a.   Compare your solution graphs for $y \le -x+5$ and $y > \frac{2}{3}x-1$ with those of your teammates. Correct any errors. Be sure to focus on whether the boundary line should be included in each graph.

b.   What would the graph of the system of inequalities look like? Consider the system of inequalities below. Which points are solutions to this system (that is, which points make *both* inequalities true)?

$$y \le -x+5$$
$$y > \frac{2}{3}x-1$$

c.   If you have not done so already, verify your solution region from part (b) algebraically by substituting the coordinates of a point from your solution region into each inequality.

d.   How can you be sure that this region is the only set of points that makes both inequalities true?

9-58.   Draw a graph of the region satisfying both inequalities at right. Start by graphing the boundary lines and then test points to find the region that makes both inequalities true.

$$y < x+2$$
$$y \le 10 - \frac{3}{4}x$$

9-59.   HOW MANY REGIONS?

When graphing the system of inequalities
below, Reyna started with the boundary graph
of each inequality shown at right.

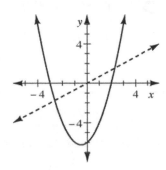

$$y \le x^2 + x - 6$$
$$y > \tfrac{2}{3}x$$

a.   Why is the line dashed while the parabola is
not?

b.   Find a copy of Reyna's graph on the Lesson 9.3.1B
Resource Page provided by your teacher. How many possible solution regions
are there? Carefully count each region with your teammates.

c.   Pick a point in each region and test it in the system of inequalities. Shade any
regions that contain solutions to both inequalities. How many regions make up
the solution to this system?

d.   Why is (0, 0) not a good point to use to test for this solution?

9-60.   How does changing the inequality affect the solution graph? Notice that each
system of inequalities below uses the same boundary graphs as Reyna's graph
from problem 9-59. However, notice that this time the inequalities are slightly
altered.

With your teammates, devise a method to determine which region (or regions) are
solutions for each system. Shade the appropriate regions on your resource page.

a. $y \ge x^2 + x - 6$ b. $y \ge x^2 + x - 6$ c. $y \le x^2 + x - 6$
$y > \tfrac{2}{3}x$ $y < \tfrac{2}{3}x$ $y < \tfrac{2}{3}x$

9-61.　The United Nations asked every nation to write a system of inequalities that best approximates its country's shape (the U.N. thinks this will help find each country's area). Honduras sent in its inequalities by fax, but some of the information is unreadable. With your study team, determine the missing parts of the inequalities and rewrite them on your paper.

 $x + 3$　$y \geq \frac{1}{2}x -$

2　$y \quad -\frac{2}{3}x + 4$

$y \quad -\frac{2}{3}x - 1$

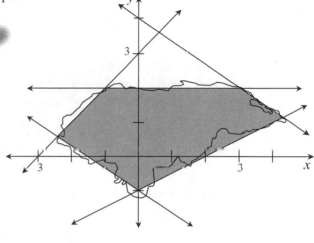

METHODS AND MEANINGS

MATH NOTES

Graphing Inequalities with Two Variables

To graph an inequality with two variables, first graph the boundary line or curve. If the inequality does not include an equality (that is, if it is > or < rather than ≥ or ≤), then the graph of the boundary is dashed to indicate that it is not included in the solution. Otherwise, the boundary is a solid line or curve.

Once the boundary is graphed, choose a point that does not lie on the boundary to test in the inequality. If that point makes the inequality true, then the entire region in which that point lies is a solution. Examine the two examples below.

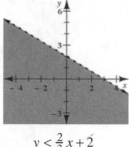

$$y < \frac{2}{3}x + 2$$

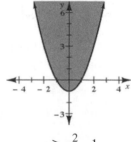

$$y \geq x^2 - 1$$

9-62.   Match each graph below with the correct inequality.

a. $y > -x + 2$ b. $y < 2x - 3$ c. $y \geq \frac{1}{2}x$ d. $y \leq -\frac{2}{3}x + 2$

1) 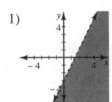   2) 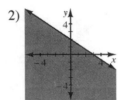   3) 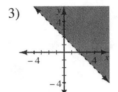   4)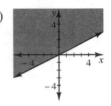

9-63.   Solve each inequality below. Represent the solutions on number lines.

a. $7x - 2 < 3 + 2x$ b. $\frac{1}{3}x \geq 2$

c. $3(2m - 1) - 5m \leq -1$ d. $2k + 3 \leq 2k + 1$

9-64.   Which of the following expressions are equal to 1? (Note: More than one expression may be equal to 1!)

a. $\frac{114}{114}$ b. $\frac{2}{3} \cdot \frac{3}{2}$ c. $\frac{m+4}{m+4}$ d. $\frac{p^2}{p \cdot p}$

9-65.   Factor the following quadratics completely.

a. $5x^3 + 13x^2 - 6x$ b. $6t^2 - 26t + 8$ c. $6x^2 - 24$

9-66.   When a family with two adults and three children bought tickets for a movie, they paid a total of $27.75. The next family in line, with two children and three adults, paid $32.25 for the same movie. Find the adult and child ticket prices by writing a system of equations with two variables.

9-67.   **Multiple Choice:** Which of the points below is a solution of $y < |x - 3|$?

a.   (2, 1)   b.   (−4, 5)   c.   (−2, 8)   d.   (0, 3)

9.3.2 How can I apply it?

More Systems of Inequalities

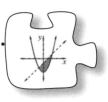

9-68.   Review what you learned about systems of inequalities in Lesson 9.3.1 by graphing the system of inequalities at right on graph paper. Carefully shade the region of points that make *both* inequalities true.

$$y \le |x| + 4$$
$$-x + 4y \ge 4$$

9-69.   SEARCH AND RESCUE

"I'm completely lost… water everywhere I can see… both engines have failed… Wait! I see land. I'm going to try to land. I think it's…"

Those were the last words heard from Harold in his hot-air balloon. The last time the balloon showed up on radar, it was near the Solomon Islands in the Pacific Ocean.

Your Task: Your team must determine where to send the search-and-rescue teams! Use the following reports along with the map on the Lesson 9.3.2 Resource Page (also available at www.cpm.org) and look carefully for information that will help you draw boundary lines. Write a system of inequalities to give to the search-and-rescue team. Be sure to identify the probable landing site on the map.

Basic facts of the case:

The balloon departed from the airport at the very northern tip of the Philippines. The flight was supposed to follow a straight path *directly* to an airport in French Polynesia.

The balloon's last known location was at (–1000, 1000) near the Solomon Islands.

Pilot's report from a nearby airplane:

"We were on our way from Australia, when we saw a hot-air balloon sinking rapidly. I am certain that it crashed south of our flight path. When we left Australia, we traveled 2000 km north for every 3000 km east that we flew."

Phone call received today:

"I was a passenger on a flight that flew directly from French Polynesia to Indonesia. I was looking out my window when I saw the balloon going down to the north of where we were flying."

9-70.   Notice that each system of inequalities below contains the same boundary lines. On graph paper, graph the boundaries for the system on one set of axes. Then, for each pair of inequalities, work with your teammates to decide which region is the solution, if a solution exists. Be ready to share your conclusions with the class.

a. $y \le \frac{2}{3}x + 3$

$y \ge \frac{2}{3}x$

b. $y \le \frac{2}{3}x + 3$

$y \le \frac{2}{3}x$

c. $y \ge \frac{2}{3}x + 3$

$y \le \frac{2}{3}x$

9-71.   In your Learning Log, describe your method for graphing systems of inequalities for a student who has missed class for the last couple of days. Be sure to include examples and important details. Title this entry "Graphing Systems of Inequalities" and include today's date.

9-72.   Graph and shade the solution for the inequality below.

$$y \le x^2 + 2x - 8$$

9-73.   Graph and shade the solution for the system of inequalities below.

$$y \ge \frac{3}{4}x - 2$$
$$y < -\frac{1}{2}x + 3$$

9-74.   Write the inequality that represents the x-values highlighted on each number line below.

a.

b.

c.

d.

9-75.   Determine if the following statements are true or false.

a. $|-6| < 4$ b. $|-3+5| > 2.5$ c. $4 \ge |0|$ d. $|-4+3| > 1$

9-76.   **Multiple Choice:** Which equation below is perpendicular to the line $y = \frac{1}{3}x + 7$?

   a. $x + 3y = 4$ b. $x - 3y = 4$ c. $3x + y = 4$ d. $3x - y = 4$

9-77.   For the Spring Festival, the Math Club is
selling rulers for $1 and compasses for
$2.50.

   a.   While the club would like to sell as
          many items as they can to raise
          funds, they need to make at least
          $15.00 to break even. Write an
          inequality to represent this
          situation. Let r = the number of
          rulers sold and c = the number of
          compasses sold.

   b.   School rules state that the club can sell a maximum of 25 items for the festival.
          Write an inequality for this constraint (limitation).

   c.   Graph the inequalities from parts (a) and (b) on the same set of axes so that
          compasses are represented on the x-axis and rulers are represented on the
          y-axis. Find the region of points that are solutions to each of them. Can this
          region fall below the x-axis or to the left of the y-axis? Why or why not?

   d.   What do the points in the solution region represent?

9.3.3 How can I use inequalities to solve problems?

Applying Inequalities to Solve Problems

Today you will pull together all of the mathematics you have studied in this chapter and **apply** it
to solve an application problem.

9-78.   UNITED NATIONS TO THE RESCUE

As a representative of your country, you have been sent the following letter and given an important task:

Dear Representative to the United Nations:

A critical matter has come to the attention of the United Nations. In the past, when a catastrophe struck a part of the world, the U. N. gathered supplies to give to people in need. Unfortunately, because the U. N. had to collect supplies from each country at the time of the catastrophe, it was always quite a few days before the supplies could be sent to the areas that needed them the most.

A recommendation has come before the U. N. to create a supply of food and medicine packages for future emergencies. Each food package will be able to feed several hundred people, while each medicine package will supply one first-aid station. I am asking each country to donate the same number of packages so each country shares the burden equally.

I am asking each country to determine how many food and medicine packages they are able to give. You will present your findings at today's United Nations meeting. Please be certain to use the information that your country's Budget Committee has prepared to help you decide how many packages you can afford.

Best of luck, and may our efforts make our world a better place!

Sincerely,
The Secretary General of the United Nations

After consulting with your country's Budget Committee, your teacher will supply you with some information that will help decide how many food and medicine packets your country can afford.

Your Task: To communicate your country's budget constraints, write an inequality expressing how many food and medicine packages your country is able to give. Let *x* equal the number of food packages and *y* equal the number of medicine packages.

On the Lesson 9.3.3B Resource Page provided by your teacher (also available at www.cpm.org), graph the solution region representing the number of medicine and food packets that can be donated by your country. Be prepared to share your graph with the other countries of the United Nations.

9-79.   As a member of the United Nations, you must consider each of the following proposals. In each case, assume that the United Nations would like to receive as many emergency supplies as possible, while still having each nation give equally.

   a.   One proposal is that each country gives 185 medicine packages. How many food packages should the United Nations require from each country in this case? Explain how you made your decision.

   b.   Another proposal is to get the largest number of medicine packages possible. What is the largest number of medicine packages that each country can offer? How did you find your answer?

9-80.   EXTENSION

A last-minute proposal suggests balancing the number of food and medicine supplies. For instance, if a country gives 150 food packages, then they would also give 150 medicine packages. How many food and medicine packages should the United Nations require from each country in this case? Explain how you determined your solution.

9-81.   While setting up a mathematical sentence to solve a problem, Paulina and Aliya came up with the equations below. Since the equations did not look alike, the girls turned to you for help.

$$Paulina: \quad 4x + 2y = 6$$

$$Aliya: \quad 12x + 6y = 18$$

   a.   Are these equations equivalent? That is, will the graph of each line be the same? Explain how you know.

   b.   Find another equation that is equivalent to both of these. How did you find your equation?

9-82.   The town you live in has decided to limit the amount of trash thrown out each month. Your town, which has 3280 homes, has asked each household to keep track of how many pounds of trash they produce during a month. In addition, the town council has found that other sources of trash, such as local businesses, combine to create 1500 lbs of trash each month. If the town has a goal of creating **less than** 50,000 lbs of trash, how much trash should a household be limited to? Write an inequality for this situation and solve it.

9-83.   Solve the following inequalities for the given variable and represent the solutions on a number line.

a. $2 < 2m - 8$

b. $\frac{1}{3}x - 1 \le -3$

c. $5(2x - 8) + 24 > 3(4 + 2x)$

d. $5 + 2k < k - 2 + k$

9-84.   Graph the system of inequalities below.

$$y \ge x(x - 4)$$
$$y < x$$

a.   Carefully shade the solution region.

b.   Is $(0, 0)$ a solution to this system? How can you tell?

9-85.   Solve the quadratic equation below *twice*, once using the Zero Product Property and once using the Quadratic Formula. Verify that the solutions from both methods are the same.

$$2x^2 - 19x + 9 = 0$$

9-86.   Read the following problem. Then decide which system of equations below can represent this situation.

Multiple Choice: The length of a rectangle is 4 units longer than twice its width. If the area is 126 square units, find the length and width.

a. $w = 2l + 4$
$wl = 126$

b. $l = 2w + 4$
$l + w = 126$

c. $w = 2l + 4$
$l + w = 126$

d. $l = 2w + 4$
$wl = 126$

Chapter 9 Closure   What have I learned?

Reflection and Synthesis

The activities below offer you a chance to reflect on what you have learned during this chapter. As you work, look for concepts that you feel very comfortable with, ideas that you would like to learn more about, and topics you need more help with. Look for **connections** between ideas as well as **connections** with material you learned previously.

① TEAM BRAINSTORM

With your team, brainstorm a list for each of the following topics. Be as detailed as you can. How long can you make your list? Challenge yourselves. Be prepared to share your team's ideas with the class.

Topics: What have you studied in this chapter? What ideas and words were important in what you learned? Remember to be as detailed as you can.

Ways of Thinking: What Ways of Thinking did you use in this chapter? When did you use them?

Connections: What topics, ideas, and words that you learned *before* this chapter are **connected** to the new ideas in this chapter? Again, make your list as long as you can.

② MAKING CONNECTIONS

The following is a list of the vocabulary used in this chapter. The words that appear in bold are new to this chapter. Make sure that you are familiar with all of these words and know what they mean. Refer to the glossary or index for any words that you do not yet understand.

absolute value	**boundary**	coordinates
equation	graph	**inequality**
number line	**region**	solution
system of inequalities		

Make a concept map showing all of the **connections** you can find among the key words and ideas listed above. To show a **connection** between two words, draw a line between them and explain the **connection**, as shown in the example on the following page. A word can be **connected** to any other word as long as there is a **justified connection**. For each key word or idea, provide a sketch that illustrates the idea (see the example on the following page).

Continues on next page →

②   *Continued from previous page.*

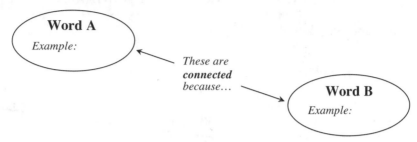

Your teacher may provide you with vocabulary cards to help you get started. If you use the cards to plan your concept map, be sure either to re-draw your concept map on your paper or to glue the vocabulary cards to a poster with all of the **connections** explained for others to see and understand.

While you are making your map, your team may think of related words or ideas that are not listed here. Be sure to include these ideas on your concept map.

③   SUMMARIZING MY UNDERSTANDING

This section gives you the opportunity to show what you know about certain math topics or ideas. Your teacher will give you directions for exactly how to do this.

④   WHAT HAVE I LEARNED?

This section will help you evaluate which types of problems you have seen with which you feel comfortable and those with which you need more help. This section appears at the end of every chapter to help you check your understanding. Even if your teacher does not assign this section, it is a good idea to try the problems and find out for yourself what you know and what you need to work on.

Solve each problem as completely as you can. The table at the end of the closure section has answers to these problems. It also tells you where you can find additional help and practice on problems like these.

CL 9-87.   Write an inequality that represents the graph at right.

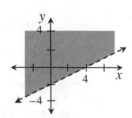

CL 9-88.   Find the equation of the line that passes through the points $(-3, 13)$ and $(4, -1)$.

CL 9-89. Is the point (0, 4) a solution to the system of inequalities at right? **Justify** your answer.

$$y \leq -3x + 4$$
$$y > x^2 + 3x - 2$$

CL 9-90. Factor these quadratic expressions completely, if possible.

a. $x^2 + x - 30$

b. $-3x^3 + 23x^2 - 14x$

c. $2x^2 - 5x + 4$

d. $6x^3 + 10x^2 - 24x$

CL 9-91. Solve each inequality below for the given variable. Then represent each solution on a number line.

a. $4x - 3 \geq 9$

b. $3(t + 4) < 5$

c. $\frac{2y}{7} < 8$

d. $5x + 4 > -3(x - 8)$

CL 9-92. Brian was holding a ballroom dance. He wanted to make sure girls would come, so he charged boys \$5 to get in but girls only \$3. The 45 people who came paid a total of \$175. How many girls came to the dance?

CL 9-93. Solve these quadratic equations using any method.

a. $0 = 3x^2 + 4x - 7$

b. $x^2 - 3x + 18 = 0$

CL 9-94. Write equations for lines (a) through (e) shown in the graph at right.

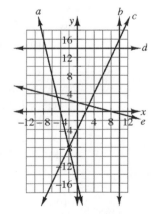

CL 9-95. Graph the system of inequalities below on graph paper.

$$y < x^2$$
$$y \geq x + 2$$

CL 9-96. Lew says to his granddaughter Audrey, "Even if you tripled your age and added 9, you still wouldn't be as old as I am." Lew is 60 years old. Write and solve an inequality to determine the possible ages Audrey could be.

CL 9-97. Graph the solutions of $y \geq |x + 2|$ on graph paper.

CL 9-98. The hare leaps 500 centimeters every 20 seconds. The tortoise crawls 250 centimeters every 50 seconds, but gets a 1000-centimeter head start. Use any method you know to determine how long it takes the hare to catch up to the tortoise.

CL 9-99. Check your answers using the table at the end of the closure section. Which problems do you feel confident about? Which problems were hard? Use the table to make a list of topics you need help on and a list of topics you need to practice more.

⑤ HOW AM I THINKING?

This course focuses on five different **Ways of Thinking**: reversing thinking, justifying, generalizing, making connections, and applying and extending understanding. These are some of the ways in which you think while trying to make sense of a concept or to solve a problem (even outside of math class). During this chapter, you have probably used each Way of Thinking multiple times without even realizing it!

Review each of the Ways of Thinking that are described in the closure sections of Chapters 1 through 5. Then choose three of these Ways of Thinking that you remember using while working in this chapter. For each Way of Thinking that you choose, show and explain where you used it and how you used it. Describe why thinking in this way helped you solve a particular problem or understand something new. (For instance, explain why you wanted to **generalize** in this particular case, or why it was useful to see particular **connections**.) Be sure to include examples to demonstrate your thinking.

Answers and Support for Closure Activity #4
What Have I Learned?

Problem	Solution	Need Help?	More Practice
CL 9-87.	$y > \frac{1}{2}x - 2$	Lesson 9.3.1 Math Notes box	Problems 9-38 and 9-62
CL 9-88.	$y = -2x + 7$	Lesson 7.3.3 and Lesson 7.3.4 Math Notes box	Problems 9-19 and 9-31
CL 9-89.	Yes; the point (0, 4) lies on the graph $x^2 + 3x - 2 < y \le -3x + 4$. Therefore, it is a solution to the system of inequalities. 	Problems 9-57 and 9-59	Problems 9-58, 9-60, 9-68, 9-70, 9-73, and 9-84
CL 9-90.	a. $(x+6)(x-5)$ b. $x(-3x+2)(x-7)$ c. not factorable d. $2x(x+3)(3x-4)$	Problems 8-13, 8-14, and 8-35; Lesson 8.1.4 Math Notes box	Problems 9-22, 9-33, 9-39, and 9-65
CL 9-91.	a. $x \ge 3$ b. $t < -\frac{7}{3}$ c. $y < 28$ d. $x > 2.5$	Lesson 9.2.2 Math Notes box	Problems 9-6, 9-8, 9-14, 9-17, 9-28, 9-63, and 9-83
CL 9-92.	25 girls came to the dance.	Lesson 7.1.4 Math Notes box	Problems 9-7, 9-30, 9-66, and 9-86

Problem	Solution	Need Help?	More Practice
CL 9-93.	a. $x = 1$ or $x = -\frac{7}{3}$ b. no solution	Lessons 8.1.4, 8.2.3, 8.3.1, and 8.3.2	Problems 9-9, 9-21, and 9-85
CL 9-94.	a. $y = -4x - 16$ b. $x = 10$ c. $y = 2x - 4$ d. $y = 14$ e. $y = -\frac{1}{4}x + 2$	Lesson 7.2.2 Math Notes box	Problems 9-18, 9-19, and 9-31
CL 9-95.		Problems 9-57 and 9-59	Problems 9-58, 9-60, 9-68, 9-70, 9-73, and 9-84
CL 9-96.	Audrey is less than 17 years old.	Lessons 9.1.1 and 9.2.2 Math Notes boxes	Problems 9-29, 9-51, 9-77, and 9-82
CL 9-97.		Lessons 9.2.3 and 9.3.1 Math Notes boxes	Problems 9-25, 9-26, 9-50, 9-54, 9-62, 9-62, and 9-72
CL 9-98.	The hare catches up to the tortoise after 50 seconds.	Lesson 7.1.4 Math Notes box	Problems 9-43 and 9-55

10

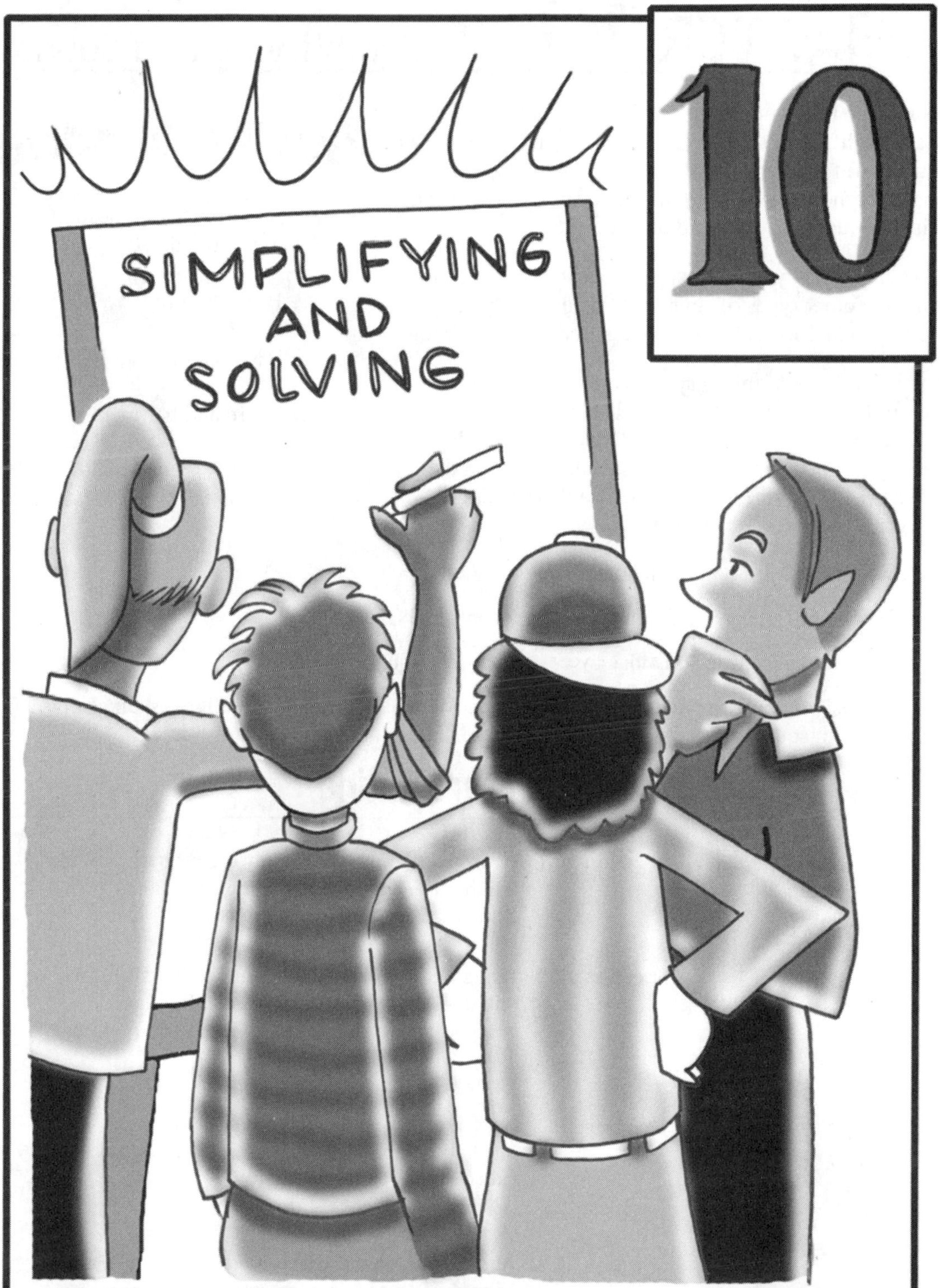

CHAPTER 10 Simplifying and Solving

Since the beginning of this course, you have studied several different types of equations and have developed successful methods to solve them. For example, you have learned how to solve linear equations, systems of linear equations, and quadratic equations.

In Chapter 10, you will **extend** your solving skills to include other types of equations, including equations with square roots, absolute values, and messy fractions.

Another focus of this chapter is on learning how to simplify algebraic fractions (called "rational expressions") and expressions with exponents. By using the special properties of the number 1 and the meaning of exponents, you will be able to simplify large, complicated expressions.

In this chapter, you will learn how to:

➢ Simplify expressions involving exponents and fractions.

➢ Solve quadratic equations by completing the square.

➢ Use multiple methods to solve new types of equations and inequalities, such as those with square roots, rational expressions, and absolute values.

Guiding Questions

Think about these questions throughout this chapter:

How can I rewrite it?

How can I solve it?

Is there another method?

What is special about the number 1?

Chapter Outline

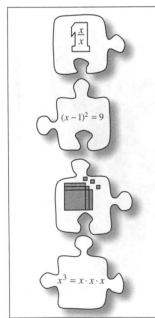

Section 10.1 In this section, you will study the properties of the number 1 and use them to simplify rational expressions and solve equations with fractions.

Section 10.2 Using the skills you learned in Section 10.1, you will develop new ways to solve unfamiliar, complicated equations involving square roots and absolute values.

Section 10.3 In this section, you will learn how to rewrite quadratics in perfect square form using a process called "completing the square."

Section 10.4 At the end of this chapter, you will use the meaning of an exponent to develop strategies to simplify exponential expressions.

Algebra Connections

10.1.1 How can I simplify?

Simplifying Expressions

In Chapter 8, you used the special qualities of the number zero to develop a powerful way to solve factorable quadratics. In Section 10.1, you will focus on another important number: the number 1. What is special about 1? What can you do with the number 1 that you cannot do with any other number? You will use your understanding of the number 1 to simplify algebraic fractions, which are also known as **rational expressions**.

10-1.   What do you know about the number 1? Brainstorm with your team and be ready to report your ideas to the class. Create examples to help show what you mean.

10-2.   Mr. Wonder claims that anything divided by itself equals 1 (as long as you do not divide by zero).

  a.   He states that $\frac{16x}{16x} = 1$ if x is not zero. What is his hypothesis and conclusion?

  b.   Is Mr. Wonder correct? That is, is his statement true? **Justify** your conclusion.

  c.   Why can't x be zero?

  d.   Next he considers $\frac{x-3}{x-3}$. Does this equal 1? What value of x must be excluded in this fraction?

  e.   Create your own rational expression (algebraic fraction) that equals 1. **Justify** that it equals 1.

  f.   Mr. Wonder also says that when you multiply any number by 1, the number stays the same. For example, he says that the product below equals $\frac{x}{y}$. Is he correct?

$$1\frac{\frac{z}{z}} \cdot \frac{x}{y} = \frac{x}{y}$$

10-3.   Use what you know about the number 1 to simplify each expression below, if possible. State any values of the variables that would make the denominator zero.

  a. $\frac{x^2}{x^2}$

  b. $\frac{x}{x} \cdot \frac{x}{x} \cdot \frac{x}{3}$

  c. $\frac{x-2}{x-2} \cdot \frac{x+5}{x-1}$

  d. $\frac{9}{x} \cdot \frac{x}{9}$

  e. $\frac{h \cdot h \cdot k}{h}$

  f. $\frac{(2m-5)(m+6)}{(m+6)(3m+1)}$

  g. $\frac{6(n-2)^2}{3(n-2)}$

  h. $\frac{3-2x}{(4x-1)(3-2x)}$

10-4.　Mr. Wonder now tries to simplify $\frac{4x}{x}$ and $\frac{4+x}{x}$.

a.　Mr. Wonder thinks that since $\frac{x}{x} = 1$, then $\frac{4x}{x} = 4$.
Is he correct? Substitute three values of x to **justify**
your answer.

b.　He also wonders if $\frac{4+x}{x} = 5$. Is this simplification correct?
Substitute three values of x to **justify** your answer. Remember
that $\frac{4+x}{x}$ is the same as $(4 + x) \div x$.

c.　Compare the results of parts (a) and (b). When can a rational expression be
simplified in this manner?

d.　Which of the following expressions below is simplified correctly? Explain
how you know.

　　i.　$\frac{x^2 + x + 3}{x+3} = x^2$ 　　　　　　　　ii.　$\frac{(x+2)(x+3)}{x+3} = x+2$

10-5.　In problem 10-4, you may have noticed that the numerator and denominator of an
algebraic fraction must both be written as a product before any terms create a 1.
Examine the expressions below. Factor the numerator and denominator of each
fraction, if necessary. That is, rewrite each one as a product. Then look for "ones"
and simplify. For each expression, assume the denominator is not zero.

a.　$\frac{x^2+6x+9}{x^2-9}$ 　　　b.　$\frac{2x^2-x-10}{3x^2+7x+2}$ 　　　c.　$\frac{28x^2-x-15}{28x^2-x-15}$ 　　　d.　$\frac{x^2+4x}{2x+8}$

10-6.　In your Learning Log, explain how to simplify rational expressions
such as those in problem 10-5. Be sure to include an example. Title
this entry "Simplifying Rational Expressions" and include today's date.

MATH NOTES

LOOKING DEEPER

Multiplicative Identity Property

When any number is multiplied by 1, its value stays the same.

For example:

$142 \cdot 1 = 142$ 　　　　　$1 \cdot k^2 = k^2$ 　　　　　$\frac{4}{4} \cdot \frac{2}{3} = \frac{2}{3}$

Algebra Connections

10-7. How many solutions does each equation below have?

   a. $4x + 3 = 3x + 3$ b. $3(x - 4) - x = 5 + 2x$

   c. $(5x - 2)(x + 4) = 0$ d. $x^2 - 4x + 4 = 0$

10-8. While David was solving the equation $100x + 300 = 500$, he wondered if he could first change the equation to $x + 3 = 5$. What do you think?

   a.   Solve both equations and verify that they have the same solution.

   b.   What could you do to the equation $100x + 300 = 500$ to change it into $x + 3 = 5$?

10-9. Solve each of the following inequalities for the given variable. Represent your solutions on a number line.

   a. $5 + 3x < 5$ b. $-3x \geq 8 - x$

10-10. For each rational expression below, state any values of the variables that would make the denominator zero. Then complete each part.

   a.   Use the fact that $(x + 4)^2 = (x + 4)(x + 4)$ to rewrite $\frac{(x+4)^2}{(x+4)(x-2)}$. Then look for "ones" and simplify.

   b.   Use the strategy you used in part (a) to simplify the expression $\frac{8(x+2)^3(x-3)^3}{4(x+2)^2(x-3)^5}$.

10-11. In Lesson 10.1.2 you will focus on multiplying and dividing rational expressions. Recall what you learned about multiplying and dividing fractions in a previous course as you answer the questions below. To help you, the following examples have been provided.

$$\frac{9}{16} \cdot \frac{4}{6} = \frac{36}{96} = \frac{3}{8}$$

$$\frac{5}{6} \div \frac{20}{12} = \frac{5}{6} \cdot \frac{12}{20} = \frac{60}{120} = \frac{1}{2}$$

   a.   Without a calculator, multiply $\frac{2}{3} \cdot \frac{9}{14}$ and reduce the result. Then use a calculator to check your answer. Describe your method for multiplying fractions.

   b.   Without a calculator, divide $\frac{3}{5} \div \frac{12}{25}$ and reduce the result. Then use a calculator to check your answer. Describe your method for dividing fractions.

10-12. **Multiple Choice:** Which of the points below is a solution to $y < |x - 3|$?

   a.   (2, 1)   b.   (–4, 5)   c.   (–2, 8)   d.   (0, 3)

10.1.2 How can I rewrite it?

Multiplying and Dividing Rational Expressions

In a previous course you learned how to multiply and divide fractions. But what if the fractions have variables in them? (That is, what if they are rational expressions?) Is the process the same? Today you will learn how to multiply and divide rational expressions and will continue to practice simplifying rational expressions.

10-13. Review what you learned yesterday as you simplify the rational expression at right. What are the excluded values of x? (That is, what values can x <u>not</u> be?)

$$\frac{3x^2+11x-4}{2x^2+11x+12}$$

10-14. With your team, review your responses to homework problem 10-11. Verify that everyone obtained the same answers and be prepared to share with the class how you multiplied and divided the fractions below.

$$\frac{2}{3} \cdot \frac{9}{14} \qquad\qquad \frac{3}{5} \div \frac{12}{25}$$

10-15. Use your understanding of multiplying and dividing fractions to rewrite the expressions below. Then look for "ones" and simplify. For each rational expression, also state any values of the variables that would make the denominator zero.

a. $\dfrac{4x+3}{x-5} \cdot \dfrac{x-5}{x+3}$

b. $\dfrac{x+2}{9x-1} \div \dfrac{2x+1}{9x-1}$

c. $\dfrac{2m+3}{3m-2} \cdot \dfrac{7+4m}{3+2m}$

d. $\dfrac{(y-2)^3}{3y} \cdot \dfrac{y+5}{(y+2)(y-2)}$

e. $\dfrac{15x^3}{3y} \div \dfrac{10x^2y}{4y^2}$

f. $\dfrac{(5x-2)(3x+1)}{(2x-3)^2} \div \dfrac{(5x-2)(x-4)}{(x-4)(2x-3)}$

10-16. **PUTTING IT ALL TOGETHER**

Multiply or divide the expressions below. Leave your answers as simplified as possible. For each rational expression, assume the denominator is not zero.

a. $\dfrac{20}{22} \cdot \dfrac{14}{35}$

b. $\dfrac{12}{40} \div \dfrac{15}{6}$

c. $\dfrac{5x-15}{3x^2+10x-8} \div \dfrac{x^2+x-12}{3x^2-8x+4}$

d. $\dfrac{12x-18}{x^2-2x-15} \cdot \dfrac{x^2-x-12}{3x^2-9x-12}$

e. $\dfrac{5x^2+34x-7}{10x} \cdot \dfrac{5x}{x^2+4x-21}$

f. $\dfrac{2x^2+x-10}{x^2+2x-8} \div \dfrac{4x^2+20x+25}{x+4}$

10-17. In your Learning Log, explain how to multiply and divide rational expressions. Include an example of each. Title this entry "Multiplying and Dividing Rational Expressions" and include today's date.

Algebra Connections

MATH NOTES

METHODS AND MEANINGS

Rewriting Rational Expressions

To simplify a rational expression, both the numerator and denominator must be written in factored form. Then look for factors that make 1 and simplify. Study Examples 1 and 2 below.

Example 1: $\frac{x^2+5x+4}{x^2+x-12}=\frac{(x+4)(x+1)}{(x+4)(x-3)}=1\cdot\frac{x+1}{x-3}=\frac{x+1}{x-3}$ for $x \neq -4$ or 3

Example 2: $\frac{2x-7}{2x^2+3x-35}=\frac{(2x-7)(1)}{(2x-7)(x+5)}=1\cdot\frac{1}{x+5}=\frac{1}{x+5}$ for $x \neq -5$ or $\frac{7}{2}$

Just as you can multiply and divide fractions, you can multiply and divide rational expressions.

Example 3: Multiply $\frac{x^2+6x}{(x+6)^2}\cdot\frac{x^2+7x+6}{x^2-1}$ and simplify for $x \neq -6$ or 1.

After factoring, this expression becomes: $\frac{x(x+6)}{(x+6)(x+6)}\cdot\frac{(x+1)(x+6)}{(x+1)(x-1)}$

After multiplying, reorder the factors: $\frac{(x+6)}{(x+6)}\cdot\frac{(x+6)}{(x+6)}\cdot\frac{x}{(x-1)}\cdot\frac{(x+1)}{(x+1)}$

Since $\frac{(x+6)}{(x+6)}=1$ and $\frac{(x+1)}{(x+1)}=1$, simplify: $1\cdot1\cdot\frac{x}{(x-1)}\cdot1 \Rightarrow \frac{x}{(x-1)}$

Example 4: Divide $\frac{x^2-4x-5}{x^2-4x+4}\div\frac{x^2-2x-15}{x^2+4x-12}$ and simplify for $x \neq 2, 5, -3$, or -6.

First, change to a multiplication expression: $\frac{x^2-4x-5}{x^2-4x+4}\cdot\frac{x^2+4x-12}{x^2-2x-15}$

Then factor each expression: $\frac{(x-5)(x+1)}{(x-2)(x-2)}\cdot\frac{(x-2)(x+6)}{(x-5)(x+3)}$

After multiplying, reorder the factors: $\frac{(x-5)}{(x-5)}\cdot\frac{(x-2)}{(x-2)}\cdot\frac{(x+1)}{(x-2)}\cdot\frac{(x+6)}{(x+3)}$

Since $\frac{(x-5)}{(x-5)}=1$ and $\frac{(x-2)}{(x-2)}=1$, simplify to get: $\frac{(x+1)(x+6)}{(x-2)(x+3)} \Rightarrow \frac{x^2+7x+6}{x^2+x-6}$

Note: From this point forward in the course, you may assume that all values of x that would make a denominator zero are excluded.

10-18.   Now David wants to solve the equation $4000x - 8000 = 16,000$.

   a.   What easier equation could he solve instead that would give him the same
         solution? (In other words, what equivalent equation has easier numbers to
         work with?)

   b.   **Justify** that your equation in part (a) is equivalent to $4000x - 8000 = 16,000$
         by showing that they have the same solution.

   c.   David's last equation to solve is $\frac{x}{100} + \frac{3}{100} = \frac{8}{100}$. Write and solve an equivalent
         equation with easier numbers that would give him the same answer.

10-19.   Find the slope and y-intercept of each line below.

   a. $y = -\frac{6}{5}x - 7$ b. $3x - 2y = 10$

   c.   The line that goes through the points $(5, -2)$ and $(8, 4)$.

10-20.   Solve the systems of equations below using any method.

   a. $3x - 3 = y$ b. $3x - 2y = 30$
         $6x - 5y = 12$ $2x + 3y = -19$

10-21.   Simplify the expressions below.

   a. $\frac{x^2 - 8x + 16}{3x^2 - 10x - 8}$ for $x \neq -\frac{2}{3}$ or 4 b. $\frac{10x + 25}{2x^2 - x - 15}$ for $x \neq -\frac{5}{2}$ or 3

   c. $\frac{(k-4)(2k+1)}{5(2k+1)} \div \frac{(k-3)(k-4)}{10(k-3)}$ for $k \neq 3, 4,$ or $-\frac{1}{2}$

10-22.   Solve the equations below. Check your solution(s).

   a. $\frac{m}{6} = \frac{m+1}{5}$ b. $\frac{3x-5}{2} = \frac{4x+1}{4}$ c. $\frac{8}{k} = \frac{14}{k+3}$ d. $\frac{x}{9} = 10$

10-23.   A piece of metal at 20°C is warmed at a steady rate of 2 degrees per minute. At the
          same time, another piece of metal at 240°C is cooled at a steady rate of 3 degrees per
          minute. After how many minutes is the temperature of each piece of metal the
          same? Explain how you found your answer.

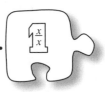

10.1.3 How can I solve it?

Solving by Rewriting

Lessons 10.1.1 and 10.1.2 focused on how to multiply, divide, and simplify rational expressions. How can you use these skills to solve problems?

10-24.   Review what you learned in Lessons 10.1.1 and 10.1.2 by multiplying or dividing the expressions below. Simplify your results.

a. $\frac{x-7}{9(2x-1)} \div \frac{(x+5)(x-7)}{6x(x+5)}$

b. $\frac{6x^2-x-1}{3x^2+25x+8} \cdot \frac{x^2+4x-32}{2x^2+7x-4}$

10-25.   Cassie wants to solve the quadratic equation $x^2+1.5x-2.5=0$. "I think I need to use the Quadratic Formula because of the decimals," she told Claudia. Suddenly, Claudia blurted out, "No, Cassie! I think there is another way. Can't you first rewrite this equation so it has no decimals?"

a.   What is Claudia talking about? Explain what she means. Then rewrite the equation so that it has no decimals.

b.   Now solve the new equation (the one without decimals). Check your solution(s).

10-26.   SOLVING BY REWRITING

Rewriting $x^2+1.5x-2.5=0$ in problem 10-25 gave you a new, **equivalent** equation that was much easier to solve. If needed, refer to the Math Notes box for this lesson for more information about equivalent equations.

How can each equation below be rewritten so that it is easier to solve? With your team, find an equivalent equation for each equation below. Be sure your equivalent equation has no fractions or decimals and has numbers that are reasonably small. Strive to find the *simplest* equation. Then solve the new equation and check your answer(s).

a. $32(3x)-32(5)=32(7)$

b. $9000x^2-6000x-15000=0$

c. $\frac{1}{3}+\frac{x}{3}=\frac{10}{3}$

d. $2x^2+4x-2.5=0$

10-27.   Examine the equation below.

$$\frac{x}{6} - \frac{5}{8} = 4$$

   a.   Multiply each term by 6. What happened? Do any fractions remain?

   b.   If you have not already done so, decide how you can change your result from part (a) so that no fractions remain. Then solve the resulting equation.

   c.   Multiplying $\frac{x}{6} - \frac{5}{8} = 4$ by 6 did not eliminate all the fractions. What could you have multiplied by to get rid of all the fractions? Explain how you got your answer and write the equivalent equation that has no fractions.

   d.   Solve the resulting equation from part (c) and check your solution in the original equation.

10-28.   Now you are going to **reverse** the process. Your teacher will give your team a simple equation that you need to "complicate." Change the equation to make it seem harder (although you know it is still equivalent to the easy equation).

   a.   Verify that your new equation is equivalent to the one assigned by your teacher.

   b.   Share your new equation with the class by posting it on the overhead projector or chalkboard.

   c.   Copy down the equations generated by your class on another piece of paper. You will need these equations for homework problem 10-29.

 METHODS AND **M**EANINGS

MATH NOTES

Equivalent Equations

   Two equations are **equivalent** if they have all the same solutions. There are many ways to change one equation into a different, equivalent equation. Common ways include: *adding* the same number to both sides, *subtracting* the same number from both sides, *multiplying* both sides by the same number, *dividing* both sides by the same (non-zero) number, and *rewriting* one or both sides of the equation.

   For example, the equations below are all equivalent to $2x + 1 = 3$:

$$20x + 10 = 30 \qquad\qquad 2(x + 0.5) = 3$$

$$\frac{2x}{3} + \frac{1}{3} = 1 \qquad\qquad 0.002x + 0.001 = 0.003$$

10-29.   Solve the equations generated by your class in problem 10-28. Be sure to check each solution and show all work.

10-30.   Multiply or divide the expressions below. Leave your answers as simplified as possible.

a. $\dfrac{(3x-1)(x+1)}{4(2x-5)} \cdot \dfrac{10(2x-5)}{(4x+1)(x+7)}$

b. $\dfrac{(m-3)(m+11)}{(2m+5)(m-3)} \div \dfrac{(4m-3)(m+11)}{(4m-3)(2m+5)}$

c. $\dfrac{2p^2+5p-12}{2p^2-5p+3} \cdot \dfrac{p^2+8p-9}{3p^2+10p-8}$

d. $\dfrac{4x-12}{x^2+3x-10} \div \dfrac{2x^2-13x+21}{2x^2+3x-35}$

10-31.   Find the equation of the line parallel to $y=-\frac{1}{3}x+5$ that goes through the point (9, –1).

10-32.   Write the inequality represented by the graph at right.

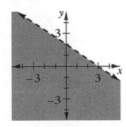

10-33.   Jessica has three fewer candies than twice the number Dante has.

a.   If Dante has d candies, write an expression to represent how many candies Jessica has.

b.   If Jessica has 19 candies, write and solve an equation to find out how many candies Dante has.

10.1.4 How can I solve it?

Fraction Busters

In Lesson 10.1.3, you learned a powerful new method to help solve complicated equations: rewriting the equation first to create a simpler, equivalent equation. Today you will continue to solve new, complicated equations and will focus specifically on equations with fractions. As you solve these new problems, look for ways to **connect** today's work with what you have learned previously.

10-34. Examine the equation below.

$$\frac{5x}{3} + \frac{15}{2} = \frac{5}{2}$$

    a.   Solve the equation by first finding an equivalent equation without fractions. Check your solution(s).

    b.   Often, this method of eliminating fractions from an equation is called the **Fraction Busters Method** because the multiplication of the equation by a common denominator or several of the denominators eliminates ("busts") the fractions. The result is an equation with no fractions.

        By what number (or numbers) did you multiply both sides of the equation in part (a) to eliminate the fractions? How did you choose that number? Is it the smallest number that would eliminate all of the fractions?

10-35. Work with your team to solve each of the equations below by first finding an equivalent equation that contains no fractions. Each problem presents new challenges and situations. Be ready to **justify** how you solved each problem and share why you did what you did with the class. Remember to check each solution.

    a. $\frac{x}{4} - \frac{x}{6} = \frac{2}{3}$ b. $\frac{5}{x} - 2x = 3$

    c. $\frac{-2x+1}{3} - \frac{x+3}{7} = 8$ d. $\frac{x+3}{x-2} + 2 = \frac{x+5}{x-2}$

10-36. Now examine the equation below.

$$\frac{4+p}{p^2+2p-8} + 3 = \frac{4}{p-2}$$

    a.   What values of p are not allowed? Show how you know.

    b.   Use your new skills to rewrite the equation above so that it has no fractions. Then solve the new equation. Check your solution(s). What happened?

Algebra Connections

10-37.   Solve the equations below by first changing each equation to a simpler, equivalent equation. Check your solution(s).

a. $50x^2 + 200x = -150$

b. $\frac{a}{9} + \frac{1}{a} = \frac{2}{3}$

c. $1.2m - 0.2 = 3.8 + m$

d. $\frac{2}{x+5} + \frac{3x}{x^2+2x-15} = \frac{4}{x-3}$

$\mathbf{L}$OOKING DEEPER

Solving Equations with Algebraic Fractions (also known as Fraction Busters)

Example: Solve $\frac{x}{3} + \frac{x}{5} = 2$ for x.

This equation would be much easier to solve if it had no fractions. Therefore, the first goal is to find an equivalent equation that has no fractions.

$$\frac{x}{3} + \frac{x}{5} = 2$$

The lowest common denominator of $\frac{x}{3}$ and $\frac{x}{5}$ is 15.

To eliminate the denominators, multiply both sides of the equation by the common denominator. In this example, the lowest common denominator is 15, so multiplying both sides of the equation by 15 eliminates the fractions. Another approach is to multiply both sides of the equation by one denominator and then by the other.

$$15 \cdot \left(\frac{x}{3} + \frac{x}{5}\right) = 15 \cdot 2$$

$$15 \cdot \frac{x}{3} + 15 \cdot \frac{x}{5} = 15 \cdot 2$$

Either way, the result is an equivalent equation without fractions:

$$5x + 3x = 30$$
$$8x = 30$$

The number used to eliminate the denominators is called a **fraction buster**. Now the equation looks like many you have seen before, and it can be solved in the usual way.

$$x = \frac{30}{8} = \frac{15}{4} = 3.75$$

$$\frac{3.75}{3} + \frac{3.75}{5} = 2$$

Once you have found the solution, remember to check your answer.

$$1.25 + 0.75 = 2$$

10-38. Solve the equations below by first changing each equation to a simpler equivalent equation. Check your solutions.

a. $3000x - 2000 = 10,000$

b. $\frac{x^2}{2} + \frac{3x}{2} - 5 = 0$

c. $\frac{5}{2}x - \frac{1}{3} = 13$

d. $\frac{3}{10} + \frac{2x}{5} = \frac{1}{2}$

10-39. Multiply or divide the expressions below. Express your answers as simply as possible.

a. $\frac{5x^2 - 11x + 2}{x^2 + 8x + 16} \cdot \frac{x^2 + 10x + 24}{10x^2 + 13x - 3}$

b. $\frac{6x + 3}{2x - 3} \div \frac{3x^2 - 12x - 15}{2x^2 - x - 3}$

10-40. To avoid a sand trap, a golfer hits a ball so that its height is represented by the equation $h = -16t^2 + 80t$, where h is the height measured in feet and t is the time measured in seconds.

a. When does the ball land on the ground?

b. What is the maximum height of the ball during its flight?

10-41. Write and solve an equation (or a system of equations) for the following situation. Be sure to define your variables.

Each morning, Jerry delivers the *Times* to one neighborhood and then the *Star* to a different neighborhood. While delivering the *Times*, Jerry delivers 2 papers per minute. However, since the *Star* is so heavy, he can only deliver 1 *Star* paper per minute. If he delivers a total of 91 papers and takes exactly an hour to deliver all papers, how many of each type of paper does he deliver?

10-42. Graph the system of inequalities below on graph paper. Shade the region that represents the solution.

$$y \geq x^2 - 4$$
$$y \leq -x^2 + 4$$

10-43. **Multiple Choice:** $x = 2$ is a solution to which of the equations or inequalities below?

a. $\frac{x-4}{3} = \frac{x}{15}$
b. $(x - 2)^2 < 0$
c. $|3x - 8| \geq -1$
d. $\sqrt{x + 2} = 16$

10.2.1 How can I solve it?

· ·

Multiple Methods for Solving Equations

$(x-1)^2 = 9$

So far in this course you have developed many different methods for solving equations, such as adding things to both sides of the equation or multiplying each term by a number to eliminate fractions. But how would you solve a complicated equation such as the one shown below?

$$(\sqrt{|x+5|} - 6)^2 + 4 = 20$$

By looking at equations in different ways, you will be able to solve some equations much more quickly and easily. These new approaches will also allow you to solve new kinds of equations you have not studied before. As you solve equations in today's lesson, ask your teammates these questions:

How can you see it?

Is there another way?

10-44.   DIFFERENT METHODS TO SOLVE AN EQUATION

By the end of this section you will be able to solve the equation $(\sqrt{|x+5|} - 6)^2 + 4 = 20$. This equation is very complex and will require you to look at solving equations in new ways. To be prepared for other strange and unfamiliar equations, you will first examine all of the solving tools you currently have by solving a comparatively easier equation:

$$4(x+3) = 20$$

Your Task: With your team, solve $4(x+3) = 20$ for x in *at least* two different ways. Explain how you found x in each case and be prepared to share your explanations with the class.

10-45.   SOLVING BY REWRITING

David wants to find x in the equation
$4(x + 3) = 20$. He said, "*I can rewrite
this equation by distributing the 4 on the
left-hand side.*" After distributing, what
should his new equation be? Solve this
equation using David's method.

10-46.   SOLVING BY UNDOING

Juan says, "I see the whole thing a different way." Here is how he explains his
approach to solving $4(x + 3) = 20$, which he calls "undoing": "*Instead of
distributing first, I want to eliminate the 4 from the left side by undoing the
multiplication.*"

a.   What can Juan do to both sides of the equation to remove the 4? Why does this
work?

b.   Solve the equation using Juan's method. Did you get the same result as David?

c.   Why is it appropriate for this method to be called "undoing"?

10-47.   SOLVING BY LOOKING INSIDE

Kenya said, "I solved David's equation in a much quicker way!" She solved the
equation $4(x + 3) = 20$ with an approach that she calls "looking inside." Here is
how she described her thinking: "*I think about everything inside the parentheses as a
group. After all, the parentheses group all that stuff together. I think the contents of
the parentheses must be 5.*"

a.   Why must the expression inside the parentheses equal 5?

b.   Write an equation that states that the contents of the parentheses must equal 5.
Then solve this equation. Did you get the same result as with David's method?

——————   *Further Guidance*   ——————
                section ends here.

10-48.   THE THREE METHODS

    a.   Find the Math Notes box for this lesson and read it with your team.

    b.   Match the names of approaches on the left with the examples on the right.

    1.   Rewriting   i.   "If $3+(4n-4)=12$, then $(4n-4)$ must
                                    equal 9..."
    2.   Looking inside

    3.   Undoing   ii.   "Subtracting is the opposite of adding, so for
                                    the equation $3(x-7)+4=23$, I can start by
                                    subtracting 4 from both sides..."

                             iii.   "This problem might be easier if I turned
                                    $4(2x-3)$ into $8x$ 12..."

10-49.   For each equation below, decide whether it would be best to rewrite, look inside, or
          undo. Then solve the equation, showing your work and writing down the name of
          the approach you used. Check your solutions, if possible.

    a. $\frac{2x-8}{10}=6$ b. $4+(x\div3)=9$

    c. $\sqrt{3x+3}=6$ d. $8-(2x+1)=3$

    e. $\sqrt{x}+4=9$ f. $\frac{x}{3}-\frac{x}{9}=6$

10-50.   Consider the equation $(x-7)^2=9$.

    a.   Solve this equation using *all three* approaches studied in this lesson. Make
          sure each team member solves the equation using all three approaches.

    b.   Did you get the same solution using all three approaches? If not, why not?

    c.   Of the three methods, which do you think was the most efficient method for
          this problem? Why?

METHODS AND MEANINGS

Methods to Solve One-Variable Equations

Here are three different approaches you can take to solve a one-variable equation:

Rewriting: Use algebraic techniques to rewrite the equation. This will often involve using the Distributive Property to get rid of parentheses. Then solve the equation using solution methods you know.

$$5(x-1) = 15$$
$$5x - 5 = 15$$
$$5x = 20$$
$$x = 4$$

Looking inside: Choose a part of the equation that includes the variable and is grouped together by parentheses or another symbol. (Make sure it includes *all* occurrences of the variable!) Ask yourself, "What must this part of the equation equal to make the equation true?" Use that information to write and solve a new, simpler equation.

$$5(x-1) = 15$$
$$5(\ 3\ ) = 15$$
$$x - 1 = 3$$
$$x = 4$$

Undoing: Start by undoing the *last* operation that was done to the variable. This will give you a simpler equation, which you can solve either by undoing again or with some other approach.

$$\frac{5(x-1)}{5} = \frac{15}{5}$$
$$x - 1 = 3$$
$$+1 = +1$$
$$x = 4$$

Review & Preview

10-51.   Read the statements made by Hank and Frank below.

Hank says, "The absolute value of 5 is 5."

Frank says, "The absolute value of –5 is 5."

a.   Is Hank correct? Is Frank correct?

b.   How many different values for x make the equation $|x| = 5$ true?

Algebra Connections

10-52.   Use the results from problem 10-51 to help you find all possible values for x in each of the following equations.

   a. $|x| = 4$ b. $|x| = 100$

   c. $|x| = -3$ d. $|x - 2| = 5$

10-53.   Which of the expressions below are equal to 1? (Note: More than one answer is possible!)

   a. $\frac{2x+3}{3+2x}$ b. $\frac{6x-12}{6(x-2)}$

   c. $\frac{(2x-3)(x+2)}{2x^2+x-6}$ d. $\frac{x}{2} \div \frac{2}{x}$

10-54.   Solve the inequalities below. Write each solution as an inequality.

   a. $8 + 3x > 2$ b. $\frac{2}{3}x - 6 \leq 2$

   c. $-2x - 1 < -3$ d. $\frac{5}{x} \leq \frac{1}{3}$

10-55.   For the equation $\frac{3}{200} + \frac{x}{50} = \frac{7}{100}$:

   a.   Find a simpler equivalent equation (i.e., an equivalent equation with no fractions) and solve for x.

   b.   Which method listed in this lesson's Math Notes box did you use in part (a)?

10-56.   Mr. Nguyen has decided to divide $775 among his three daughters. If the oldest gets twice as much as the youngest, and the middle daughter gets $35 more than the youngest, how much does each child get? Write an equation and solve it. Be sure to identify your variables.

10.2.2 How many solutions?

Determining the Number of Solutions

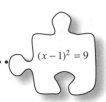
$(x-1)^2 = 9$

So far in this course you have seen many types of equations – some with no solution, some with one solution, others with two solutions, and still others with an infinite number of solutions! Is there any way to predict how many solutions an equation will have without solving it? Today you will focus on this question as you study quadratic equations written in perfect square form and equations with an absolute value. As you work with your team, ask the following questions:

Is there another way?

How do you see it?

Did you find all possible solutions?

10-57.   The quadratic equation below is written in **perfect square form**. It is called this because the term $(x-3)^2$ forms a square when built with tiles. Solve this quadratic equation using one of the methods you studied in Lesson 10.2.1.

$$(x-3)^2 = 12$$

    a.   How many solutions did you find?

    b.   Write your answer in **exact** form. That is, write it in a form that is precise and does not have any rounded decimals.

    c.   Write your answer in **approximate** form. Round your answers to the nearest hundredth (0.01).

10-58.   THE NUMBER OF SOLUTIONS

The equation in problem 10-57 had two solutions. However, from your prior experience you know that some quadratic equations have no solutions and some have only one solution. How can you quickly determine how many solutions a quadratic equation has?

With your team, solve the equations below. Express your answers in both **exact form** and **approximate form**. Look for patterns among those with no solution and those with only one solution. Be ready to report your patterns to the class.

    a. $(x+4)^2 = 20$ b. $(7x-5)^2 = -2$ c. $(2x-3)^2 = 49$

    d. $(5-10x)^2 = 0$ e. $(x+2)^2 = -10$ f. $(x+11)^2 + 5 = 5$

10-59.   Use the patterns you found in problem 10-58 to determine quickly how many solutions each quadratic below has. You do not need to solve the equations.

    a. $(5m-2)^2 + 6 = 0$ b. $(4+2n)^2 = 0$ c. $11 = (7+2x)^2$

10-60.   Consider the equation $|2x-5|=9$.

  a.   How many solutions do you think this equation has? Why?

  b.   Which of the three solution approaches do you think will work best for this equation?

  c.   With your team, solve $|2x-5|=9$. Record your work carefully as you go. Check your solution(s).

10-61.   The equation $|2x-5|=9$ from problem 10-60 had two solutions. Do you think all absolute-value equations must have two solutions? Consider this as you answer the questions below.

  a.   Can an absolute-value equation have no solution? With your team, create an absolute-value equation that has no solution. How can you be sure there is no solution?

  b.   Likewise, create an equation with an absolute value that will have only one solution. **Justify** why it will have only one solution.

10-62.   Is there a **connection** between how to determine the number of solutions of a quadratic in perfect square form and how to determine the number of solutions of an equation with an absolute value? In your Learning Log, describe this connection and explain how you can determine how many solutions both types of equations have. Be sure to include examples for each. Title this entry "Number of Solutions" and include today's date.

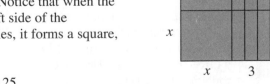

METHODS AND **M**EANINGS

MATH NOTES

Perfect Square Form of a Quadratic

When a quadratic equation is written in the form $(x-a)^2 = b^2$, such as the one below, we say it is in **perfect square form**. Notice that when the quadratic expression on the left side of the equation below is built with tiles, it forms a square, as shown at right.

$$(x+3)^2 = 25$$

10-63. Solve these equations, if possible. Each time, be sure you have found all possible solutions. Check your work and write down the name of the method(s) you used.

a. $(x+4)^2 = 49$

b. $3\sqrt{x+2} = 12$

c. $\frac{2}{x} + \frac{3}{10} = \frac{13}{10}$

d. $5(2x-1)-2 = 13$

10-64. Is $x = -4$ a solution to $\frac{1}{3}(2x+5) > -1$? Explain how you know.

10-65. Multiply or divide the rational expressions below. Leave your answer in simplified form.

a. $\dfrac{(x+4)(2x-1)(x-7)}{(x+8)(2x-1)(3x-4)} \div \dfrac{(4x-3)(x-7)}{(x+8)(3x-4)}$

b. $\dfrac{2m^2+7m-15}{m^2-16} \cdot \dfrac{m^2-6m+8}{2m^2-7m+6}$

10-66. An **exponent** is shorthand for repeated multiplication. For example, $x^3 = x \cdot x \cdot x$. Use the meaning of an exponent to rewrite each of the expressions below.

a. $(3x-1)^2$ b. 7^4 c. m^3 d. w^{10}

10-67. Factor each of the following expressions completely. Be sure to look for any common factors.

a. $4x^2 - 12x$

b. $3y^2 + 6y + 3$

c. $2m^3 + 7m^2 + 3m$

d. $3x^2 + 4x - 4$

10-68. Write and solve an equation to answer the question below. Remember to define any variables you use.

Pierre's Ice Cream Shoppe charges $1.19 for a scoop of ice cream and $0.49 for each topping. Gordon paid $4.55 for a three-scoop sundae. How many toppings did he get?

3 scoop SUNDAE $4.55

10.2.3 Which method is best?

More Solving and an Application

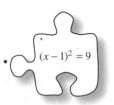

$(x-1)^2 = 9$

Recently you investigated three different approaches to solving one-variable equations: rewriting, looking inside, and undoing. Today you will use those approaches to solve new kinds of equations you have not solved before. You will also use your equation-writing skills to write an inequality for an application. As you work today, ask yourself these questions:

How can I represent it?

What is the best approach for this equation?

Have I found all of the solutions?

10-69. Solve these equations. Each time, be sure you have found all possible solutions. Check your work and write down the name of the method(s) you used.

a. $|x+1| = 5$

b. $(x-13)^3 = 8$

c. $2\sqrt{x-4} = 14$

d. $|4x+20| = 8$

e. $3(x+12)^2 = 27$

f. $6|x-8| = 18$

10-70. RUB A DUB DUB

Ernie is thinking of installing a new hot tub in his backyard. The company he will order it from makes square hot tubs, and the smallest tub he can order is 4 feet by 4 feet. He plans to add a 3-foot-wide deck on two adjacent sides, as shown in the diagram below. If Ernie's backyard (which is also a square) has 169 square feet of space, what are the possible dimensions that his hot tub can be? Write and solve an inequality that represents this situation. Be sure to define your variable.

3 ft

Hot Tub

3 ft

Deck

METHODS AND MEANINGS

Solving Absolute-Value Equations

To solve an equation with an absolute value algebraically, first determine the possible values of the quantity inside the absolute value.

For example, if $|2x+3| = 7$, then the quantity $(2x+3)$ must equal 7 or –7.

With these two values, set up new equations and solve as shown below.

$$|2x+3| = 7$$

$$2x+3 = 7 \quad \text{or} \quad 2x+3 = -7$$
$$2x = 4 \qquad\qquad 2x = -10$$
$$x = 2 \qquad\qquad\quad x = -5$$

Always check your solutions by substituting them into the original equation:

Test $x = 2$: $\qquad |2(2)+3| = 7$ ✓ True

Test $x = -5$: $\qquad |2(-5)+3| = 7$ ✓ True

Review & Preview

10-71. Sketch a graph of the inequality below. Shade the region containing the solutions of the inequality.

$$y > (x-4)(x+3)$$

10-72. Jessie looked at the rule $y = (x-11)^2 + 4$ and stated, "The graph of this rule has no x-intercepts!" How could she know without graphing?

10-73. Solve these equations, if possible. Be sure to find all possible solutions. Check your work and write down the name of the method(s) you used.

a. $9(x-4)^2 = 81$

b. $|x-6| = 2$

c. $5 = 2 + \sqrt{3x}$

d. $2|x+1| = -4$

10-74.   Review what you know about solving inequalities by solving the inequalities below. Show your solutions on a number line.

   a. $6x - 1 < 11$

   b. $\frac{1}{3}x \geq 2$

   c. $9(x - 2) > 18$

   d. $5 - \frac{x}{4} \leq \frac{1}{2}$

10-75.   Multiply or divide the rational expressions below. Leave each answer in simplified form.

   a. $\frac{(x-3)^2}{2x-1} \cdot \frac{2x-1}{(3x-14)(x+6)} \cdot \frac{x+6}{x-3}$

   b. $\frac{4x^2+5x-6}{3x^2+5x-2} \div \frac{4x^2+x-3}{6x^2-5x+1}$

10-76.   Use the meaning of an exponent to rewrite the expression $5x^3y^2$. Review the meaning of an exponent in problem 10-66 if necessary.

10.2.4   How can I solve the inequality?

$(x-1)^2 = 9$

Solving Inequalities with Absolute Value

The three approaches you have for solving equations can also be used to solve inequalities. While the one-variable inequalities you solve today look different than the ones in Chapter 9, the basic process for solving them is similar. As you solve equations and inequalities in today's lesson, ask yourself these questions:

How can I represent it?

What **connection** can I make?

10-77.   Solve the inequality $2x + 7 < 12$. Represent the solution on a number line.

   a.   What is the boundary point? Is it part of the solution? Why or why not?

   b.   In general, how do you find a boundary point? How do you find the solutions of an inequality after you have found the boundary point? Briefly review the process with your team.

10-78.   Now consider the inequality $\left|x-2\right|>3$.

   a.   Can you use the process from problem 10-77 to solve this inequality? How is it different from solving $\left|x-2\right|=3$? Solve the inequality and represent your solution on a number line.

   b.   How was solving $\left|x-2\right|>3$ different from solving $2x+7<12$?

10-79.   Examine the graph of $y=\left|x-2\right|$ and $y=3$ at right.

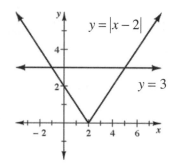

   a.   How does this graph confirm your solution to $\left|x-2\right|>3$ from problem 10-78? Be prepared to explain your thinking.

   b.   How would the solution change for the inequality $\left|x-2\right|\le 3$? Draw this solution on a number line. Explain how the graph at right also confirms this solution.

   c.   Now use the graph to predict the x-values that make $\left|x-2\right|\ge -1$ true. **Justify** your answer.

10-80.   Consider the quadratic inequality $x^2+2x+1<4$.

   a.   Solve for the boundary point(s). How many boundary points are there?

   b.   Place the boundary point(s) on a number line. How many regions do you need to test?

   c.   Test each region and determine which one(s) make the inequality true. Identify the solution region(s) on the number line.

   d.   Confirm your solution by graphing $y=x^2+2x+1$ and $y=4$ on the same set of axes on graph paper. Highlight the portion of the parabola that lies below the line $y=4$. Does this confirm your solution to part (c)?

10-81.   Revisit the graph from problem 10-79. Use it to write an inequality involving $\left|x-2\right|$ that has no solution.

10-82.   In your Learning Log, explain how you can solve an inequality that has an absolute value. You may include an explanation of the graphical process if you choose. Then make up your own example problem and show how that problem is solved. Title this entry "Solving Inequalities with Absolute Value" and include today's date.

10-83.   Examine the rectangle formed by the tiles shown at
          right. Write the area of the rectangle as a product and
          as a sum.

10-84.   Without graphing, determine if the graph of each rule below has zero, one, or two
          x-intercepts. Show all work.

          a. $y = 6x^2 + 7x - 20$ b. $y = x^2 - 8x + 16$

          c. $y = 2x^2 + x + 3$ d. $y = (2x + 1)^2$

10-85.   Find the equation of the line perpendicular to $y = -\frac{2}{3}x - 7$ that goes through the
          point (–6, 9).

10-86.   On graph paper, graph the system of inequalities below. Carefully shade the region
          that represents the solution to both inequalities.

          $$y \leq -\left|x - 2\right| + 3$$
          $$y \geq -1$$

10-87.   Multiply or divide the expressions below. Leave your answer as simplified as
          possible.

          a. $\frac{8x^2 - 12x - 8}{2x^2 - 5x - 3} \cdot \frac{x^2 + 2x - 15}{6x - 12}$ b. $\frac{7x^2 + 5x - 2}{x^2 + 2x - 8} \div \frac{3x^2 - 2x - 5}{3x^2 - 11x + 10}$

10-88.   Solve the equations and inequalities below. Check your solution(s), if possible.

          a. $300x - 1500 = 2400$ b. $\frac{3}{2}x = \frac{5}{6}x + 2$

          c. $x^2 - 25 \leq 0$ d. $\left|3x - 2\right| > 4$

10.2.5 How can I solve this inequality?

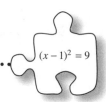

$(x-1)^2 = 9$

Solving Absolute-Value and Quadratic Inequalities

Today you will finish your focus on solving equations and inequalities. By the end of the lesson today, you will have the tools to solve complex equations and inequalities.

10-89.   At right is a graph showing $y = x^2 + x - 6$ and $y = 3x + 2$. Use the graph to find the solutions for $x^2 + x - 6 \geq 3x + 2$. Indicate your answer on a number line.

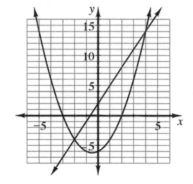

10-90.   Solve the inequalities below, if possible, and represent your solution on a number line.

   a. $|x+2| > 1$ b. $x^2 + x - 12 < 0$

   c. $|2(x-1)| \geq 0$ d. $9x - 4 \leq 6 - x$

   e. $|3x - 11| < -2$ f. $(x-2)^2 > 7$

10-91.   FOG CITY

San Francisco is well known for its fog: very thick, low-lying clouds that hide its hills. One foggy day, Penelope was practicing kicking a football on the football field of her school. Once she kicked the football so high that it disappeared into the fog! If the height h of the ball (in feet) could be represented at time t (in seconds) by the equation $h = -16t^2 + 96t$, and if the fog was 140 feet off the ground, during what times of its flight was the ball not visible? Explain how you got your answer.

10-92.   PULLING IT TOGETHER

Now that you have the skills necessary to solve
many interesting equations and inequalities,
work with your team to solve the equation
below. (This equation was first introduced in
Lesson 10.2.1.) Show your solutions on a
number line and be prepared to share your
solving process with the class.

$$(\sqrt{|x+5|} - 6)^2 + 4 = 20$$

10-93.   Review the meaning of an exponent in problem 10-66. Then use its meaning to
rewrite the expression $(y-2)^3$.

10-94.   How many solutions does the equation $|7-3x|+1=0$ have? Explain how you
know.

10-95.   Solve the equations and inequalities below, if possible.

a. $\sqrt{x-1}+13=13$ b. $6|x|>18$ c. $|3x-2|\le 2$

d. $\frac{4}{5}-\frac{2x}{3}=\frac{3}{10}$ e. $(4x-2)^2 \le 100$ f. $(x-1)^3 = 8$

10-96.   On graph paper, graph a line with slope $-\frac{2}{3}$ that goes through the point $(4,-3)$.

a.   Find the equation of the line.

b.   Is this line perpendicular to the line $6x-4y=8$? Explain how you know.

10-97.   Simplify the rational expressions below as much as possible.

a. $\frac{(x-4)^3(2x-1)}{(2x-1)(x-4)^2}$ b. $\frac{7m^2-22m+3}{3m^2-7m-6}$

c. $\frac{(z+2)^9(4z-1)^7}{(z+2)^{10}(4z-1)^5}$ d. $\frac{(x+2)(x^2-6x+9)}{(x-3)(x^2-4)}$

10-98. **Multiple Choice:** Which of the graphs below shows the solutions for $y < -\frac{2}{5}x + 1$?

a.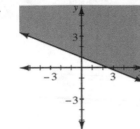

b.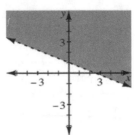

c.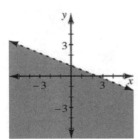

d.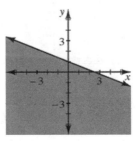

10.3.1 How can I make it a perfect square?

Completing the Square

You have learned many ways to solve quadratic equations so far in this course. Sometimes, using the Quadratic Formula can be complicated and messy, while solving equations in perfect square form (such as $(x+2)^2 = 3$) can be very straightforward. Therefore, it is sometimes convenient to change a quadratic equation from standard form into perfect square form. One method that you will investigate in this lesson is called **completing the square**.

10-99.   Review what you know about solving quadratic equations as you solve the two equations below. Be ready to share your method(s) with the class.

   a. $x^2 + 4x + 1 = 0$

   b. $(x+2)^2 = 3$

10-100.   With your team, and then with the class, discuss the following questions.

   a.   Examine the solutions to $x^2 + 4x + 1 = 0$ and $(x+2)^2 = 3$. What do you notice? What does this tell you about the two equations? Verify your conclusion algebraically.

   b.   Of the methods used in problem 10-99, which do you think was most efficient and straightforward?

10-101.   COMPLETING THE SQUARE

With your team, examine how the two different equations from
problem 10-99 can be represented using tiles on an equation mat,
shown below. Then answer questions (a) and (b) below.

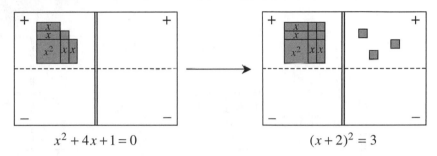

$$x^2 + 4x + 1 = 0 \qquad\qquad (x+2)^2 = 3$$

a.   What "legal" move can be done to the equation $x^2 + 4x + 1 = 0$ that will result
     in the equation $(x+2)^2 = 3$?

b.   Changing a quadratic equation into perfect square form is also known as
     "completing the square." Why is this name appropriate?

10-102.   Use the process from problem 10-101 to change the quadratics below
into perfect square form. Then solve the resulting quadratics. Building
the squares with algebra tiles may be useful. Record your work on the
resource page provided by your teacher.

a.
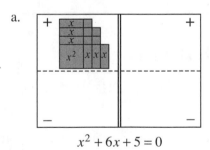

$$x^2 + 6x + 5 = 0$$

b.
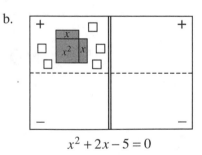

$$x^2 + 2x - 5 = 0$$

10-103.   The problems below introduce different situations that can arise while completing
the square. Carefully choose what to add to both sides of each equation below to
change the quadratics into perfect square form. Then solve the
resulting quadratic. Again, building the equations with algebra tiles
may be useful. Record your work on the resource page provided by
your teacher.

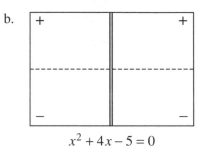

a.

$$x^2 - 6x - 1 = 0$$

b.

$$x^2 + 4x - 5 = 0$$

c.

$$x^2 - 2x - 3 = 1$$

10-104.   Use algebra tiles to change $4x^2 + 12x + 3 = 10$ into perfect square form. Then solve
the resulting quadratic equation.

METHODS AND MEANINGS

Forms of a Quadratic Equation

There are three main forms of a quadratic equation: standard form,
factored form, and perfect square form. Study the examples below.
Assume that $a \neq 0$ and that the meaning of a, b, and c are different for each
form below.

Standard form: Any quadratic written in the form $ax^2 + bx + c = 0$.

Factored form: Any quadratic written in the form $a(x+b)(x+c) = 0$.

Perfect square form: Any quadratic written in the form $a(x+b)^2 = c$.

10-105. Use your understanding of the number 1 to simplify the rational expressions below.

a. $\dfrac{(x-3)(2x+9)(4x-3)}{(2x+9)(5x+1)(x-3)}$

b. $\dfrac{25x^2+20x+4}{25x^2-4}$

c. $\dfrac{16x^2+24x+8}{2x^2-2x-4}$

d. $\dfrac{24xy^2}{36x^2y}$

10-106. Solve the quadratic equation below *twice*: once using the Quadratic Formula and once by completing the square and solving the quadratic in perfect square form. You should get the same result using both methods. What happened?

$$x^2 + 6x + 11 = 0$$

10-107. Solve the inequalities and equations below, if possible. Represent your solution on a number line.

a. $|x| + 3 < 5$

b. $5(2x+1) \geq 30$

c. $\frac{1}{x} - \frac{5}{2} = \frac{3}{2}$

d. $-5 - x > 3 - x$

e. $3\sqrt{4-x} + 1 = 13$

f. $|x+1| \leq 4$

10-108. Verify your solution to part (f) of problem 10-107 by graphing the functions below on the same set of axes. Highlight the portion(s) of the graph for which $|x+1| \leq 4$.

$$y = |x+1|$$
$$y = 4$$

10-109. Write and solve an equation to solve the problem below. State your solution as a sentence.

Shu Min currently has 18 CDs, and her music club sends her three more CDs each month. Her brother, Wei, currently has 22 CDs and buys two more CDs each month with his allowance. Their CD holder can only hold 80 CDs. After how many months will their CD holder be full?

10.3.2 How can I generalize?

More Completing the Square

Today you will learn more about completing the square and will
generalize how to complete the square for any quadratic in standard form.

10-110. Determine the number of solutions for each
quadratic equation below by first completing the
square (using algebra tiles or drawing a diagram).
Then explain how you can quickly determine how
many solutions a quadratic equation has once it is
written in perfect square form.

  a. $x^2 - 6x + 7 = 0$ b. $m^2 + 12m + 37 = 0$

  c. $p^2 + 2p + 1 = 0$ d. $k^2 - 4k + 9 = 0$

10-111. Examine the results of your work in problem 10-110 and look for ways to **generalize**
the process of completing the square. In other words, how can you change a
quadratic into perfect square form without using tiles or drawing a diagram? It may
help to make a table like the one started below. Then answer the questions that
follow.

Standard Form	Perfect Square Form
$x^2 - 6x + 7 = 0$	

  a. Describe any patterns you found when comparing a quadratic written in
  standard form with its corresponding equation in perfect square form.

  b. When a quadratic is changed to perfect square form, how can you predict what
  will be in the parentheses? For example, if you want to change
  $x^2 + 10x - 3 = 0$ into perfect square form, what will be the dimensions of the
  square?

  c. To complete the square, you often need to add some unit tiles to both sides of
  the equation. How can you predict how many tiles will need to be added or
  removed?

10-112. Use your generalized process of completing the square to rewrite and solve each
quadratic equation below.

  a. $w^2 + 28w + 52 = 0$ b. $x^2 + 5x + 4 = 0$

  c. $k^2 - 16k - 17 = 0$ d. $z^2 - 1000z + 60775 = 0$

10-113. What is the slope of the line passing through the points (4, –8) and (–3, 12)?

10-114. Use your generalized process of completing the square to rewrite and solve each quadratic equation below.

a. $x^2 + 4x = -3$

b. $x^2 - 8x + 7 = 0$

c. $x^2 - 24x + 129 = 0$

10-115. Multiply or divide the rational expressions below. Leave your answers in simplified form.

a. $\frac{4x^2+x-14}{3x^2-11x+6} \div \frac{4x-7}{x-3}$

b. $\frac{5x^2-8x-4}{x^2-9x-22} \cdot \frac{x^2-4}{5x^2+22x+8}$

10-116. Solve the following equations and inequalities, if possible. Represent each solution on a number line.

a. $\frac{3}{9} - \frac{x}{3} = \frac{x}{5}$

b. $(3+x)^2 < 9$

c. $8|x+1| \geq 64$

d. $11 - \sqrt{x+3} = 13$

e. $\frac{x}{8} = \frac{2}{x}$

f. $|x-5|+1 > 0$

10-117. On graph paper, graph the inequality $y \leq |x| + 2$.

10-118. Aura currently pays $800 each month to rent her apartment. Due to inflation, however, her rent is increasing by $50 each year. Meanwhile, her monthly take-home pay is $1500 and she predicts that her monthly pay will only increase by $15 each year. Assuming that her rent and take-home pay will continue to grow linearly, will her rent ever equal her take-home pay? If so, when? And how much will rent be that year?

10.4.1 How can I rewrite it?

Simplifying Exponential Expressions

$x^3 = x \cdot x \cdot x$

In Section 10.1, you used the property of the number 1 to simplify rational expressions. Today you will examine how to simplify expressions with exponents. Using patterns, you will develop strategies to simplify expressions when the exponents are too large to expand on paper.

10-119. You have seen that you can rewrite expressions using the number 1. You can also simplify using the meaning of an exponent.

An **exponent** is shorthand for repeated multiplication. For example, $n^4 = n \cdot n \cdot n \cdot n$.

a. Expand each of the expressions below. For example, to expand x^3, you would write: $x \cdot x \cdot x$.

  i. y^7 ii. $5(2m)^3$ iii. $(x^3)^2$ iv. $4x^5 y^2$

b. Simplify each of the expressions below using what you know about exponents and the number 1. Start by expanding the exponents, and then simplify your results.

  i. $\dfrac{x \cdot x \cdot x}{x}$ ii. $\dfrac{x^5}{x^2}$ iii. $x^2 \cdot x^3$ iv. $k^3 \cdot k^5$

  v. $\dfrac{16k^3}{8k^2}$ vi. $m^6 \cdot m$ vii. $x^4 \cdot x^5 \cdot x^3$ viii. $\dfrac{6x^3 y}{2y}$

  challenge: $\dfrac{5x^{50}}{10x^{15}}$

10-120.   Simplify each of the expressions below. Start by expanding the exponents, and then simplify your results. Look for patterns or possible shortcuts that will help you simplify more quickly. Be prepared to **justify** your patterns or shortcuts to the class.

a. $y^5 \cdot y^2$

b. $\frac{w^5}{w^2}$

c. $(x^2)^4$

d. $x^{10} \cdot x^{12}$

e. $\frac{13p^4q^5}{p^2q^2}$

f. $\left(\frac{x^2}{y}\right)^3$

g. $5h \cdot 2h^{24}$

h. $\frac{10m^{30}}{2m^8}$

i. $(3k^{20})^4$

j. $\frac{24hg^2}{3hg^9}$

k. $\left(\frac{m^3}{n^{10}}\right)^4$

l. $w^4 \cdot p \cdot w^3$

10-121.   Work with your team to write four exponent problems, each having a simplification of x^{12}. At least one problem must involve multiplication, one must involve grouping, and one must involve division. Be creative!

10-122.   Gerardo is simplifying expressions with very large exponents. He arrives at each of the results below. For each result, decide if he is correct and **justify** your answer using the meaning of exponents.

a. $\frac{x^{150}}{x^{50}} \Rightarrow x^3$

b. $y^{20} \cdot y^{41} \Rightarrow y^{61}$

c. $(2m^2n^{15})^3 \Rightarrow 2m^6n^{45}$

MᴇᴛʜODS AND Mᴇᴀɴɪɴɢs

Completing the Square

Previously in this course, you have learned to solve quadratic equations by graphing, factoring, and using the Quadratic Formula. Another way to solve a quadratic equation is by **completing the square**. See the example below.

Example: Solve for x by completing the square: $x^2 + 6x + 7 = 14$

First, use algebra tiles or a generic rectangle to determine if $x^2 + 6x + 7$ is already a perfect square.

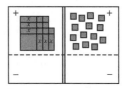

$x^2 + 6x + 7 = 14$

Using algebra tiles (shown at right), you can see that there are not enough tiles to build a complete square. Therefore, two unit tiles must be added to both sides of the equation to complete the square.

Add 2 unit tiles to complete the square.

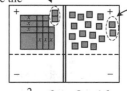

Notice that the square has side length $x + 3$. Any quadratic of the form $x^2 + bx + c$ will be converted to a square of side length $x + \frac{b}{2}$.

$x^2 + 6x + 9 = 16$

Now rewrite the expressions on each side of the equation so that the equation is in perfect square form. Then solve this equation by undoing the square and subtracting 3 from both sides.

$(x + 3)^2 = 16$
$x + 3 = \pm 4$
$x = -3 \pm 4$
$x = 1 \text{ or } -7$

As always, be sure to check your solutions in the original equation.

$(1)^2 + 6(1) + 7 = 14$
$(-7)^2 + 6(-7) + 7 = 14$

10-123. Use what you have learned about exponents to rewrite each of the expressions below.

a. $\dfrac{h^9}{h^{11}}$

b. $x^3 \cdot x^4$

c. $(3k^5)^2$

d. $n^7 \cdot n$

e. $\dfrac{16x^4 y^3}{2x^4}$

f. $4xy^3 \cdot 7x^2 y^3$

10-124. Lacey and Haley are simplifying expressions.

a. Haley simplified $x^3 \cdot x^2$ and gets x^5. Lacey simplified $x^3 + x^2$ and got the same result! However, their teacher told them that only one simplification is correct. Who simplified correctly and how do you know?

b. Haley simplifies $3^5 \cdot 4^5$ and gets the result 12^{10}, but Lacey is not sure. Is Haley correct? Be sure to **justify** your answer.

10-125. On your paper, draw the algebra tiles to represent the equation $x^2 + 2x = 8$ on an equation mat.

a. How many tiles do you need to add or remove from each side of the equation to complete the square?

b. Write the equation in perfect square form.

10-126. Find a rule that represents the number of tiles in the tile pattern at right.

Figure 0   Figure 1   Figure 2

10-127. Solve the equations and inequalities below. If necessary, write your solutions in approximate form.

a. $900x - 200 = 500x + 600$

b. $3k^2 - 15k + 14 = 0$

c. $|x - 4| < 6$

d. $\frac{7}{3} + \frac{x}{2} = \frac{6x-1}{6}$

10.4.2 How can I rewrite it?

Zero and Negative Exponents

$x^3 = x \cdot x \cdot x$

In Lesson 10.4.1, you used the meaning of an exponent to rewrite expressions such as $y^4 \cdot y^2$ and $(x^2 y)^3$. Today you will use the patterns you discovered to learn how to interpret expressions with exponents that are negative or zero.

10-128. Review what you learned about exponents in Lesson 10.4.1 to rewrite each expression below as simply as possible. If you see a pattern or know of a shortcut, be sure to share it with your teammates.

a. $x^7 \cdot x^4$

b. $(x^3)^3$

c. $\dfrac{m^{14}}{m^2}$

d. $(x^2 y^2)^4$

e. $\dfrac{x^2 y^{11}}{x^5 y^3}$

f. $\dfrac{2x^{12}}{8x^2}$

10-129. With your study team, summarize the patterns you found in problem 10-128. For each one, simplify the given expression and write an expression that represents its **generalization**. Then, in your own words, explain why the pattern works.

	Expression	Generalization	Why is this true?
a.	$x^{25} \cdot x^{40} = ?$	$x^m \cdot x^n = ?$	
b.	$\dfrac{x^{36}}{x^{13}} = ?$	$\dfrac{x^m}{x^n} = ?$	
c.	$(x^5)^{12} = ?$	$(x^m)^n = ?$	

10-130. Describe everything you know about $\dfrac{x^m}{x^m}$. What is its value? How can you rewrite it using a single exponent? What new conclusions can you draw? Be prepared to explain your findings to the class.

10-131. Problem 10-130 helped you recognize that $x^0 = 1$. Now you will similarly use division to explore the meaning of x^{-1}, x^{-2}, etc. Simplify each of the expressions below *twice*:

- Once by expanding the terms and simplifying.

- Again by using your new pattern for division with exponents.

Be ready to discuss the meaning of negative exponents with the class.

a. $\dfrac{x^4}{x^5}$ b. $\dfrac{x^2}{x^4}$ c. $\dfrac{x^7}{x^{10}}$

10-132. Use your exponent patterns to rewrite each of the expressions below. For example, if the original expression has a negative exponent, then rewrite the expression so that it has no negative exponents – and vice versa. Also, if the expression contains multiplication or division, then use your exponent rules to simplify the expression.

a. k^{-5} b. m^0 c. $x^{-2} \cdot x^5$ d. $\dfrac{1}{p^2}$

e. $\dfrac{y^{-2}}{y^{-3}}$ f. $(x^{-2})^3$ g. $(a^2b)^{-1}$ h. $\dfrac{1}{x^{-1}}$

10-133. EXPONENT CONCENTRATION

Split your team into two pairs and decide which is Team A and which is Team B. Your teacher will distribute a set of cards for a game described below.

- Arrange the cards face down in a rectangular grid.

- Team A selects and turns over two cards.

- If Team A thinks the values on the cards are equivalent, they must **justify** this claim to Team B. If everyone in Team B agrees, Team A takes the pair. If the values are not equivalent, Team A returns both cards to their original position (face down). This is the end of the turn for Team A.

- Team B repeats the process.

- Teams alternate until no cards remain face down. The team with the most matches wins.

10-134. In your Learning Log, describe the meaning of zero and negative exponents. That is, explain how to interpret x^0 and x^{-1}. Title this entry "Zero and Negative Exponents" and include today's date.

MATH NOTES

LOOKING DEEPER

Inductive and Deductive Reasoning

When you make a conclusion based on a pattern, you are using **inductive reasoning**. So far in this course, you have used inductive reasoning repeatedly to **generalize** patterns. For example, in Lesson 10.4.1 and in this lesson, you used patterns to generalize the facts that $x^m x^n = x^{m+n}$ and $(x^m)^n = x^{mn}$.

However, you can also make a conclusion based on facts, using logic. This is called **deductive reasoning**. You used deductive reasoning during this lesson when you determined that $x^{-1} = \frac{1}{x}$. See the logical deduction below.

Statement	Reason
Since $\frac{x^4}{x^5} = x^{-1}$,	This is true because $\frac{x^m}{x^n} = x^{m-n}$.
And since $\frac{x^4}{x^5} = \frac{x \cdot x \cdot x \cdot x}{x \cdot x \cdot x \cdot x \cdot x} = \frac{1}{x}$,	This is true because $\frac{x}{x} = 1$.
Therefore, $x^{-1} = \frac{1}{x}$.	$\frac{x^4}{x^5}$ equals both x^{-1} and $\frac{1}{x}$, so $x^{-1} = \frac{1}{x}$. (This is called the Transitive Property of Equality.)

Review & Preview

10-135. Which of the expressions below are equivalent to $16x^8$? Make sure you find *all* the correct answers!

a. $(16x^4)^2$

b. $8x^2 \cdot 2x^6$

c. $(2x^2)^4$

d. $(4x^4)^2$

e. $(2x^4)^4$

f. $(\frac{1}{16}x^{-8})^{-1}$

Algebra Connections

10-136. Write the inequality represented by the graph at right.

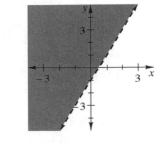

10-137. Examine the tile pattern below. Based on the information provided for Figures 1 through 4, answer the questions below.

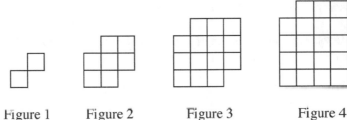

Figure 1   Figure 2   Figure 3   Figure 4

a. Represent the number of tiles with a table and a rule.

b. Find the number of tiles in Figure 5. Explain how you found your answer.

c. If you haven't stated so already, explain if you used inductive reasoning (for example, by using either the tile pattern or the pattern in the table) or deductive reasoning (such as by using the rule).

10-138. Chad is entering a rocket competition. He needs to program his rocket so that when it is launched from the ground, it lands 20 feet away. In order to qualify, it must be 100 feet off the ground at its highest point. What equation should he program into his rocket launcher to win? Let x represent the distance from the launch pad in feet and y represent the height of the rocket in feet. Draw a sketch of the rocket's path.

10-139. Solve the quadratic equation below *twice*, once using the Quadratic Formula and once by completing the square. Which was easier?

$$x^2 - 10x + 21 = -4$$

10-140. Simplify the rational expressions below.

a. $\dfrac{x^2 - 8x + 16}{3x^2 - 10x - 8}$

b. $\dfrac{10x + 25}{2x^2 - x - 15}$

c. $\dfrac{9x^4 y^3 z}{3x^4 y^3 z}$

10.4.3 How can I rewrite it?

Fractional Exponents and Scientific Notation

So far you have discovered ways to deal with exponents when multiplying and dividing. You have also found ways to interpret expressions when the exponent is zero or negative. But what if the exponent is a fraction? And how can exponents help you rewrite numbers?

Today you will develop an understanding for fractional exponents and learn about scientific notation, a way to use exponents to rewrite very large or very small numbers.

10-141. **FRACTIONAL EXPONENTS**

What happens when an exponent is a fraction? Consider this as you answer the questions below.

a. Calculate $9^{1/2}$ with your scientific calculator. What is the result? Also use your calculator to find $49^{1/2}$ and $100^{1/2}$. What effect does having $\frac{1}{2}$ in the exponent appear to have?

b. Based on your observation in part (a), predict the value of $4^{1/2}$ and $(7^{1/2})^2$. Then confirm your prediction with your calculator.

c. Was the reasoning you used in part (a) an example of inductive or deductive reasoning? Refer to the Lesson 10.4.2 Math Notes box to help you decide.

10-142. Danielle wants to understand why $9^{1/2}$ is the same as $\sqrt{9}$. Since exponents represent repeated multiplication, Danielle decided to rewrite the number 9 as $3 \cdot 3$. She then reasoned that $9^{1/2}$ is asking for 1 of the 2 repeated factors with a product of 9.

a. Using Danielle's logic, find $16^{1/2}$. Confirm your answer with your calculator.

b. What is the value of $8^{1/3}$? $125^{1/3}$? How can you use the same reasoning to find these values? Confirm your answers with your calculator.

c. What about $27^{2/3}$? $32^{3/5}$? $25^{3/2}$? Use your calculator to find each of these values. Then apply Danielle's logic to make sense of what each of these expressions mean. Share any insight with your team members.

d. Another name for $x^{1/3}$ is "cube root." This can be written $\sqrt[3]{x}$. What would be the notation for $x^{1/5}$? What should it be called?

10-143. Now that you have many tools to rewrite expressions with exponents, use these tools together to rewrite each of the expressions below. For example, $\sqrt{2^5} = (2^5)^{1/2} = 2^{5/2}$, since taking the square root of a number is the same as raising that number to the one-half power.

a. $(\sqrt{3})^4$

b. $9^{7/2}$

c. $\sqrt[3]{2^5}$

10-144. Match each expression below on the left (letters (a) through (h)) with an equivalent expression on the right (numbers 1 through 8). Assume $x > 0$.

a. $\sqrt{x^3}$

e. $\sqrt[3]{x^2}$

1. x^{-2}

5. $\sqrt{x}$

b. $\frac{x^2}{x^5}$

f. 1

2. x

6. $x^{2/3}$

c. $(\sqrt[3]{x})^5$

g. $x^{-3}x^4$

3. $x^{3/2}$

7. $x^{5/3}$

d. $\frac{1}{x^2}$

h. $(x^{1/4})^2$

4. x^0

8. x^{-3}

10-145. Exponents can also help you represent very large (and very small) numbers. For example, a very large number like the one below can be difficult to write out in complete form (called **standard form**).

$$3,000,000,000,000,000,000,000,000,000,000$$

Instead, you can write this number using **scientific notation**: $3 \cdot 10^{30}$. This shorthand notation is not only easier to write, but it also gives you an immediate sense of how large the number is. Since 10^{30} is 10 multiplied by itself thirty times, then you know that $3 \cdot 10^{30}$ is the number 3 with 30 zeros after it.

Similarly, $1.4 \cdot 10^8$ is 1.4 multiplied by 10 eight times. Thus $1.4 \cdot 10^8 = 140,000,000$.

Scientific notation is also useful for writing small numbers, such as 0.00024. Since $0.00024 = 24 \cdot \frac{1}{10,000}$, you can rewrite the number using scientific notation: $2.4 \cdot 10^{-4}$.

a. Scientists claim that the earth is about $4.6 \cdot 10^9$ years old. Write this number in standard form.

b. The average distance between the Earth and the sun is about 150,000,000,000 meters. Translate this number into scientific notation.

c. It takes light about $3.3 \cdot 10^{-9}$ seconds to travel one meter. Express this number in standard form.

10-146. Scientific notation is not only a convenient way to write very large and very small numbers, but it also makes them easier to put into your calculator.

    a.   For example, multiply $5000 \cdot 20{,}000{,}000{,}000{,}000$ and write the answer in standard form. If these numbers cannot be entered into your calculator, then multiply them by hand on your paper.

    b.   Now multiply these same numbers by first changing each into scientific notation. For example, $5000 = 5 \cdot 10^3$. Express your answer in scientific notation.

    c.   Which method was easier and why?

LOOKING DEEPER

Laws of Exponents

In the expression x^3, x is the **base** and 3 is the **exponent**.

$$x^3 = x \cdot x \cdot x$$

The patterns that you have been using during this section of the book are called the **laws of exponents**. Here are the basic rules with examples:

Law	Examples	
$x^m x^n = x^{m+n}$ for all x	$x^3 x^4 = x^{3+4} = x^7$	$2^5 \cdot 2^{-1} = 2^4$
$\dfrac{x^m}{x^n} = x^{m-n}$ for $x \neq 0$	$x^{10} \div x^4 = x^{10-4} = x^6$	$\dfrac{5^4}{5^7} = 5^{-3}$
$(x^m)^n = x^{mn}$ for all x	$(x^4)^3 = x^{4 \cdot 3} = x^{12}$	$(10^5)^6 = 10^{30}$
$x^0 = 1$ for $x \neq 0$	$\dfrac{y^2}{y^2} = y^0 = 1$	$9^0 = 1$
$x^{-1} = \dfrac{1}{x}$ for $x \neq 0$	$\dfrac{1}{x^2} = \left(\dfrac{1}{x}\right)^2 = (x^{-1})^2 = x^{-2}$	$3^{-1} = \dfrac{1}{3}$
$x^{m/n} = \sqrt[n]{x^m}$ for $x \geq 0$	$\sqrt{k} = k^{1/2}$	$y^{2/3} = \sqrt[3]{y^2}$

10-147. Simplify each of the expressions below. Your final simplification should contain no negative exponents.

    a. $(5x^3)(-3x^{-2})$

    b. $(4p^2 q)^3$

    c. $(x^3 y^{1/2})^6$

10-148. Neil A. Armstrong was the first person ever to walk on the moon. After his historic landing on July 20, 1969, he stepped onto the moon's surface and spoke the famous phrase, "That's one small step for a man, one giant leap for mankind."

His craft, Apollo 11, traveled 238,900 miles from Earth to reach the moon. How many feet was this? Express your answer in both standard form and in scientific notation. Round your decimal to the nearest hundredth. (Note: There are 5280 feet in each mile.)

10-149. Solve each system of equations below. Write your solution(s) in (x, y) form.

a. $8y - 1 = x$
$10y - x = 5$

b. $y = -4x - 2$
$y = x^2 - 3x - 4$

10-150. Write and solve an inequality to represent the situation below. Write your solution as a sentence.

Vinita wants to rent a skateboard and only has $20. She found out that the shop will charge her $8 to rent the skateboard plus $3.75 per hour. She does not know how long she wants to rent it. What are her options?

10-151. A motion detector can record the distance between a moving person and the detector. Examine the graphs below, each of which was generated when a different person walked in front of a motion detector. For each graph, describe the motion of the person. Did they walk quickly? Did they walk slowly? In what direction did they walk? If the motion is not possible, explain why not.

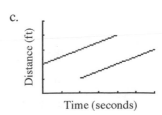

a.
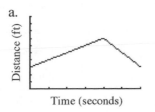
Time (seconds)

b.
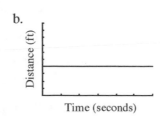
Time (seconds)

c.

Time (seconds)

Chapter 10 Closure   What have I learned?

Reflection and Synthesis

The activities below offer you a chance to reflect on what you have learned during this chapter. As you work, look for concepts that you feel very comfortable with, ideas that you would like to learn more about, and topics you need more help with. Look for **connections** between ideas as well as **connections** with material you learned previously.

①   TEAM BRAINSTORM

With your team, brainstorm a list for each of the following topics. Be as detailed as you can. How long can you make your list? Challenge yourselves. Be prepared to share your team's ideas with the class.

Topics: What have you studied in this chapter? What ideas and words were important in what you learned? Remember to be as detailed as you can.

Ways of Thinking: What Ways of Thinking did you use in this chapter? When did you use them?

Connections: What topics, ideas, and words that you learned *before* this chapter are **connected** to the new ideas in this chapter? Again, make your list as long as you can.

②   MAKING CONNECTIONS

The following is a list of the vocabulary used in this chapter. The words that appear in bold are new to this chapter. Make sure that you are familiar with all of these words and know what they mean. Refer to the glossary or index for any words that you do not yet understand.

absolute value	**base**	boundary point
completing the square	equivalent equations	**exponent**
fraction buster	inequality	**looking inside**
number line	**perfect square form**	quadratic equation
Quadratic Formula	**rational expression**	**rewriting**
scientific notation	simplifying	solution
standard form for quadratics	**undoing**	

Continues on next page →

②   *Continues from previous page.*

Make a concept map showing all of the **connections** you can find among the key words and ideas listed on the previous page. To show a **connection** between two words, draw a line between them and explain the **connection**, as shown in the example below. A word can be **connected** to any other word as long as there is a **justified connection**. For each key word or idea, provide a sketch that illustrates the idea (see the example below).

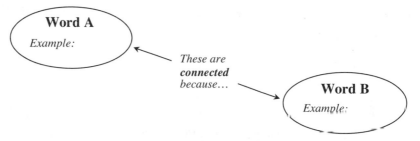

Your teacher may provide you with vocabulary cards to help you get started. If you use the cards to plan your concept map, be sure either to re-draw your concept map on your paper or to glue the vocabulary cards to a poster with all of the **connections** explained for others to see and understand.

While you are making your map, your team may think of related words or ideas that are not listed here. Be sure to include these ideas on your concept map.

③   SUMMARIZING MY UNDERSTANDING

This section gives you an opportunity to show what you know about certain math topics or ideas. Your teacher will give you directions for exactly how to do this.

④   WHAT HAVE I LEARNED?

This section will help you evaluate which types of problems you have seen with which you feel comfortable and those with which you need more help. Even if your teacher does not assign this section, it is a good idea to try these problems and find out for yourself what you know and what you need to work on.

Solve each problem as completely as you can. The table at the end of the closure section has answers to these problems. It also tells you where you can find additional help and practice on problems like these.

CL 10-152. Simplify the following expressions.

     a. $\dfrac{x^2 y^3}{xy^2}$ b. $\dfrac{(x+2)^2(x-4)}{(x+2)(x-4)}$ c. $\dfrac{x^2-x-6}{x-3}$

     d. $\dfrac{5x^2-2xy+7}{5x^2-2xy+7}$ e. $\dfrac{x^2-5x+4}{x^2-x-12}$ f. $\dfrac{x^2-25}{x^2+10x+25} \div \dfrac{x-5}{x+3}$

CL 10-153. Solve the equations below using any method. How many solutions does each problem have?

a. $\frac{6x-5}{2x+1} + \frac{2x-7}{2x+1} = 2$

b. $\sqrt{x-5} + 10 = 15$

c. $|x-7| = 22$

d. $(3x+7)^2 = 144$

CL 10-154. Solve each inequality algebraically. Then represent your solution on a number line.

a. $5x - 7 \geq 2x + 5$

b. $6x - 29 > 4x + 12$

c. $x^2 \leq -4x + 5$

d. $|2x - 7| > 31$

CL 10-155. Solve the quadratic equation below three times: once by completing the square, once by factoring and using the Zero Product Property, and once by using the Quadratic Formula. Make sure you get the same answer using each method!

$$x^2 + 14x + 40 = -5$$

CL 10-156. Graph the system of inequalities at right and shade its solutions.

$$y \geq \tfrac{2}{3}x - 7$$
$$y < -x + 4$$

CL 10-157. Mario and Antoine are each in the middle of reading *War and Peace*. However, they just heard that something exciting happens on page 475. Even though each boy is at a different place in the book, they each agreed to read as fast as they can and to see who can get to page 475 first. Assume they each read at a constant, but different, rate.

a. After 2 hours of reading, Mario is on page 350 and Antoine is on page 425. Who will get to page 475 first? Can you tell? **Justify** your answer.

b. After 6 hours of reading, Mario is on page 450 and Antoine is on page 465. Who will get to page 475 first? Can you tell? **Justify** your answer.

c. What page was Mario on when they started the race? What page was Antoine on when they started?

d. At what rate does Mario read? At what rate does Antoine read?

e. *War and Peace* is 1400 pages long. After how many hours will each boy finish the book?

CL 10-158. For the equation $y = \tfrac{5}{3}x + 7$, find:

a. The equation of the line that is parallel to the given line and passes through the point (3, 2).

b. The equation of the line that is perpendicular to the given line and passes through the point (10, 4).

CL 10-159. Rewrite each of these expressions. Your answer should have no parentheses and no negative exponents.

    a. $4(2x^{-3}y^5)^4$

    b. $\dfrac{10x^3y^{-4}}{25x^5y^2}$

    c. $(9x^4y)^{1/2}$

    d. $\dfrac{m^2}{m^{-8}} \cdot \dfrac{3m^5}{m^9}$

CL 10-160. Check your answers to each problem above using the table at the end of the closure section. Which problems did you feel confident about? Which problems were hard? Use the table to make a list of topics you need help on and a list of topics you need to practice more.

⑤   HOW AM I THINKING?

This course focuses on five different **Ways of Thinking**: reversing thinking, justifying, generalizing, making connections, and applying and extending understanding. These are some of the ways in which you think while trying to make sense of a concept or to solve a problem (even outside of math class). During this chapter, you have probably used each Way of Thinking multiple times without even realizing it!

Review each of the Ways of Thinking with your class. Then choose three of these Ways of Thinking that you remember using while working in this chapter. For each Way of Thinking that you choose, show and explain where you used it and how you used it. Describe why thinking in this way helped you solve a particular problem or understand something new. (For instance, explain why you wanted to **generalize** in this particular case, or why it was useful to see these particular **connections**.) Be sure to include examples to demonstrate your thinking.

Answers and Support for Closure Activity #4
What Have I Learned?

Problem	Solution		Need Help?	More Practice
CL 10-152.	a. xy c. $x+2$ e. $\frac{x-1}{x+3}$	b. $x+2$ d. 1 f. $\frac{x+3}{x+5}$	Lessons 10.1.2 and 10.4.3 Math Notes boxes	Problems 10-3, 10-5, 10-16, 10-21, 10-97, 10-105, 10-123, and 10-128
CL 10-153.	a. $x=3.5$ c. $x=29$ or -15	b. $x=30$ d. $x=\frac{5}{3}$ or $-\frac{19}{3}$	Lessons 10.1.4, 10.2.1, and 10.2.2 Math Notes boxes	Problems 10-22, 10-49, 10-63, 10-69, 10-73, and 10-94

Problem	Solution		Need Help?	More Practice

CL 10-154.
  a. $x \geq 4$

  b. $x > 20.5$

  c. $-5 \leq x \leq 1$

  d. $x > 19$ or $x < -12$

Need Help? Lesson 9.2.2 Math Notes box, Lesson 10.2.4

More Practice: Problems 10-9, 10-74, 10-77, 10-78, 10-80, 10-90, 10-95, 10-107, and 10-116

CL 10-155. $x = -5$ or -9

Need Help? Lessons 8.1.4, 8.2.3, 8.3.1, 8.3.2, and 10.2.4 Math Notes boxes

More Practice: Problems 10-106, 10-112, 10-114, and 10-139

CL 10-156.

Need Help? Problems 9-57 and 9-57

More Practice: Problems 10-42 and 10-86

CL 10-157.
  a. Cannot be determined because we do not know which pages Mario and Antoine were on before they started racing and we do not know the rates they are reading.
  b. Mario and Antoine will get to page 475 at the same time. Each will arrive after another hour.
  c. Mario: page 300, Antoine: page 405
  d. Mario: 25 pages per hour, Antoine: 10 pages per hour
  e. Mario: 44 hours, Antoine: 99.5 hours

Need Help? Lesson 7.1.4 Math Notes box

More Practice: Problems 10-23 and 10-118

CL 10-158.
  a. $y = \frac{5}{3}x - 3$ b. $y = -\frac{3}{5}x + 10$

Need Help? Lesson 7.3.2 Math Notes box

More Practice: Problems 10-19, 10-31, 10-96, and 10-113

CL 10-159.
  a. $\dfrac{64y^{20}}{x^{12}}$ b. $\dfrac{2}{5x^2y^6}$
  c. $3x^2y^{1/2}$ d. $3m^6$

Need Help? Lesson 10.4.3 Math Notes box

More Practice: Problems 10-123, 10-128, 10-135, and 10-147

11

FUNCTIONS AND RELATIONS

CHAPTER 11   Functions and Relations

So far in this course you have studied linear and quadratic functions extensively. In this chapter, you will explore new nonlinear functions and will learn how to describe a function completely. You will get to know the shapes and behaviors of many different functions and will be able to distinguish them by their graphs and rules. Many of the functions will look familiar because their rules relate closely to equations that you have already learned how to solve.

In this chapter, you will learn:

> How to find the domain and range of a function.

> How to recognize symmetry in a graph.

> How to determine if a relation is a function by looking at its table or graph.

> How to predict the shape of a graph by its rule.

> How to recognize the possible rule of a function by examining its graph.

> How different parameters in an equation affect the placement and direction of a graph.

Guiding Questions

Think about these questions throughout this chapter:

What does the graph look like?

Is there a pattern?

How does it grow?

Is it a function?

How can I describe it?

Chapter Outline

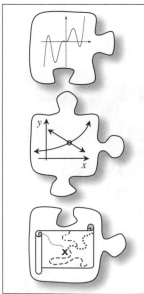

Section 11.1 This section is devoted to learning about special qualities of relations. You will start with an investigation of a parabola. Then you will learn about new ways to describe this relation and other relations better. Finally, you will investigate a variety of functions in order to describe them completely.

Section 11.2 This section clarifies the difference between intercepts and intersections. You will also predict the possible number of intersections in any system of multiple functions.

Section 11.3 This section brings closure to relations and functions with a treasure hunt focused on multiple representations of relations.

11.1.1   How can I describe a graph?

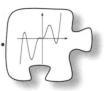

Describing a Graph

What does it mean to describe the graph of a rule completely? Today you will graph and investigate a new graph: $y = \sqrt{x}$.

11-1.   **DESCRIBING A GRAPH**

Your teacher will assign your team one of the rules below. On graph paper, graph your rule for x-values between -3 and 9. When your team is convinced that your graph is correct, discuss all the ways you can describe this graph. Then write as many summary statements about the graph as you can, such as, *"We noticed that as x gets larger, ..."*

$$y = \sqrt{x}$$

$$y = \sqrt{x} + 1$$

$$y = \sqrt{x+2} - 1$$

$$y = \sqrt{x-1} + 3$$

$$y = -\sqrt{x}$$

$$y = -\sqrt{x} - 2$$

11-2.   **PRESENT YOUR FINDINGS**

With your team, create a poster that contains not only the graph of your rule but also all of your observations and summary statements from problem 11-1. Be thorough and complete. Remember that a main goal of this activity is to determine what items a "complete description" of a graph must contain, so be sure to include everything you can. Be prepared to present your poster to the class. Remember to give reasons for all statements that you make.

11-3.   As a class, examine the posters that were presented by the teams. Create a list of all the ways to describe a graph. Then, next to each description, create a question that will prompt you to look for this quality in the graphs of other rules you encounter.

Once your list is complete, copy the questions into your Learning Log. Title this entry "Graph-Investigation Questions" and include today's date.

11-4.   Find the dimensions of the generic rectangle shown at right
          and write its area as a sum and a product.

$-6x$	4
$9x^2$	$-6x$

11-5.   After noon, the number of people in Mal-Wart grows
          steadily until 6:00 PM. If the equation $y = 228 + 58x$
          represents the number of people in the store x hours
          after noon:

          a.   How many people were in the store at noon?

          b.   At what rate is the number of shoppers growing?

          c.   When were there 402 shoppers in the store?

11-6.   Find the following absolute values.

          a. $\left|0.75\right|$ b. $\left|-99\right|$ c. $\left|4 - 2 \cdot 3\right|$ d. $\left|\pi\right|$

11-7.   Jacob discovered that the x-intercepts of a certain parabola are $(3, 0)$ and $(-1, 0)$, but
          now he needs to find the vertex. Can you get him started? What do you know about
          the vertex? Draw a sketch of this parabola to help you.

11-8.   When a family with two adults and three children bought tickets for
          an amusement park, they paid a total of $56.50. The next family in
          line, with four children and one adult, paid $49.50. Find the adult
          and child ticket prices by writing and solving a system of equations.

11-9.   Find the slope (m) and y-intercept (b) for each line below.

          a. $2x + 7y = 14$ b. $y = 6 - \frac{x}{3}$

          c. $y = \frac{10x - 2}{2}$ d. $y = 3x$

11-10.   Solve the following inequalities for x.

          a. $4x - 1 \geq 7$ b. $3 - 2x < x + 6$

          c. $2(x - 5) \leq 8$ d. $\frac{1}{2}x > 5$

11-11.   Using your knowledge of exponents, rewrite each expression below so that there are no negative exponents or parentheses remaining.

a. $\dfrac{4x^{18}}{2x^{22}}$

b. $(s^4tu^2)(s^7t^{-1})$

c. $(3w^{-2})^4$

d. $(m^{-1/2})(\sqrt{m})$

11-12.   Match each graph below with the correct inequality.

a. $y > -x + 2$ b. $y < 2x - 3$ c. $y \geq \frac{1}{2}x$ d. $y \leq -\frac{2}{3}x + 2$

1)   2)   3)   4)

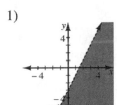
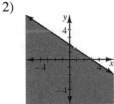
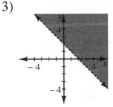
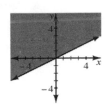

11-13.   Add, subtract, multiply, or divide the following rational expressions. Simplify your answers if possible.

a. $\dfrac{12x^2 + 4x - 1}{36x^2 - 12x + 1} \cdot \dfrac{x^2 - 64}{2x^2 + 17x + 8}$

b. $\dfrac{2x^2 - 10x}{x^2 - 4} \div \dfrac{x^2 - 5x}{x^2 - 4x - 12}$

11-14.   For the parabola $y = 2x^2 - 7x + 3$:

a.   Give the coordinates of the y-intercept.

b.   Give the coordinates of the two x-intercepts. Explain how you found them.

11-15.   Look for patterns in the statements at right.

a.   Describe all the patterns you see. Be sure to look for patterns in both columns, as well as within each equation.

b.   According to the patterns you found, what would be $64^{1/2}$ and $128^{1/2}$? **Justify** your answers.

c.   When answering part (b), did you use inductive reasoning or deductive reasoning? Explain.

$2^{1/2} = \sqrt{2}$

$4^{1/2} = 2$

$8^{1/2} = 2\sqrt{2}$

$16^{1/2} = 4$

$32^{1/2} = 4\sqrt{2}$

11.1.2 What's the relationship?

Relation Machines

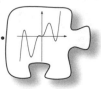

In the next few lessons you will add to your list of what you can ask about a graph of a rule. Throughout this course, you have used rules that relate two variables (like $y = -2x^2 + 11x + 1$) to make graphs and find information. Today you will look more closely at how rules that relate two variables help establish a relationship between the variables. You will also learn a new notation to help represent these relationships.

11-16.   ARE WE RELATED?

Examine the table of input (x) and output (y) values below. Is there a relationship between the input and output values? If so, state the relationship.

x	−3	−2	−1	0	1	2	3
y	8	3	0	−1	0	3	8

11-17.   RELATION MACHINES

Each equation that relates inputs to outputs is called a **relation**. This is easy to remember because the equation helps you know how all the y-values (outputs) on your graph are **related** to their corresponding x-values (inputs).

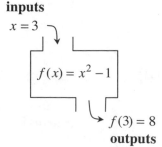

A relation works like a machine, as shown in the diagram below. A relation is given a name that can be a letter, such as f or g. The notation $f(x)$ represents the output when x is processed by the machine. (Note: $f(x)$ is read, "f of x.") When x is put into the machine, $f(x)$, the value of a function for a specific x-value, comes out.

Numbers are put into the relation machine (in this case, $f(x) = x^2 - 1$) one at a time, and then the relation performs the operation(s) on each input to determine each output. For example, when $x = 3$ is put into the relation $f(x) = x^2 - 1$, the relation squares it and then subtracts 1 to get the output, which is 8. The notation $f(3) = 8$ shows that the relation named f connects the input (3) with the output (8).

inputs

$x = 3$

$f(x) = x^2 - 1$

$f(3) = 8$

outputs

a.   Find the output for $f(x) = x^2 - 1$ when the input is $x = 4$; that is, find $f(4)$.

b.   Likewise, find $f(-1)$ and $f(10)$.

c.   If the output of this relation is 24, what was the input? That is, if $f(x) = 24$, then what is x? Is there more than one possible input?

11-18. Find the relationship between x and $f(x)$ in the table below and complete the rule of the relation.

x	9	1	100	4	49		0	25	20
$f(x)$		1			7	4		5	

Relation: $f(x) =$ _____

11-19. Find the corresponding outputs or inputs for the following relations. If there is no possible output for the given input, explain why not.

a.
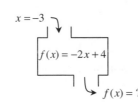

b.
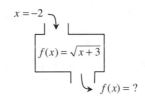

c.
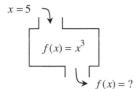

d.
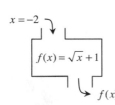

e.
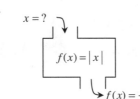

f.
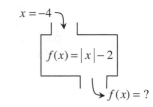

g.

$x = ?$

$f(x) = |x|$

$f(x) = -3$

h.

$x = -4$

$f(x) = |x - 2|$

$f(x) = ?$

i.

$x = -4$

$f(x) = |x| - 2$

$f(x) = ?$

11-20. Examine the relation defined at right. Notice that $g(1) = -1$; that is, when x is 1, the output (y or $g(1)$) is -1.

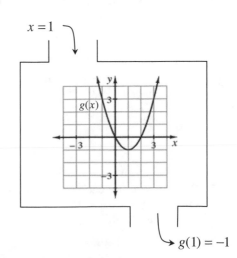

a. What is the output of the relation when the input is 2? That is, find $g(2)$.

b. Likewise, what are $g(-1)$ and $g(0)$?

c. What is the input of this relation when the output is 1? In other words, find x when $g(x) = 1$. Is there more than one possible solution?

11-21. If $f(x) = x^2$, then $f(4) = 4^2 = 16$. Find:

a. $f(1)$ b. $f(-3)$ c. $f(t)$

11-22. Find the equation of the line with slope $m = -\frac{4}{3}$ that passes through the point $(12, -4)$.

11-23. Marley thinks that the two lines below are perpendicular, but Bob thinks they are not. Who is correct and how do you know?

$$2x - 7y = 16$$
$$7x + 2y = 3$$

11-24. Ten minutes after he left his home, Gerald was 40 miles from his grandmother's house. Then, 22 minutes after he left, he was 34 miles from her house. If he was traveling toward his grandmother's home at a constant rate and reached her house after 90 minutes, how far away from her house does he live?

11-25. Use your method for multiplying and dividing fractions to simplify the expressions below.

a. $\dfrac{x+2}{x-1} \cdot \dfrac{x-1}{x-6}$

b. $\dfrac{(4x-3)(x+2)}{(x-5)(x-3)} \div \dfrac{(x-1)(x+2)}{(x-1)(x-3)}$

c. $\dfrac{(x-6)^2}{(2x+1)(x-6)} \cdot \dfrac{x(2x+1)(x+7)}{(x-1)(x+7)}$

d. $\dfrac{(x+3)(2x-5)}{(3x-4)(x-7)} \div \dfrac{(2x-5)}{(3x-4)}$

e. $\dfrac{3x-1}{x+4} \div \dfrac{x-5}{x+4}$

f. $\dfrac{x-3}{x+4} \cdot \dfrac{3x-10}{x+11} \cdot \dfrac{x+4}{3x-10}$

11-26. Rewrite each expression below without negative or zero exponents.

a. 4^{-1} b. 7^0 c. 5^{-2} d. x^{-2}

11.1.3 Can I predict the output?

Functions

You have studied relations and have learned that each relation defines a relationship between the input and output values. But what happens when your relation gives you unpredictable results? That is, what happens when you cannot predict the output for a given input? Today you will study this situation and will be introduced to a special type of relation called a *function*.

11-27.   THE COLA MACHINE

The cola machine at your school offers several types of soda. There are two buttons for your favorite drink, *Blast*, while the other drinks (*Slurp, Lemon Twister,* and *Diet Slurp*) each have one button.

a.   Explain how the cola machine is a relation.

b.   Describe the input and output of this soda machine.

c.   While buying a soda, Ms. Whitney pushed the button for *Lemon Twister* and got a can of *Lemon Twister*. Later she went back to the same machine, but this time pushing the *Lemon Twister* button got her a can of *Blast*. Is the machine functioning consistently? Why or why not?

d.   When Brandi pushed the top button for *Blast* she received a can of *Blast*. Her friend, Miguel, decided to be different and pushed the second button for *Blast*. He, too, received a can of *Blast*. Is the machine functioning consistently? Why or why not?

e.   When Loutfi pushed a button for *Slurp*, he received a can of *Lemon Twister*! Later, Tayeisha also pushed the *Slurp* button and received a can of *Lemon Twister*. Still later, Tayeisha noticed that everyone else who pushed the *Slurp* button received a *Lemon Twister*. Is the machine functioning consistently? Explain why or why not.

f.   When a relation is functioning consistently and predictably, we call that relation a **function**. What is the main difference between a relation that is a function and a relation that is not a function?

11-28.   Using your own words, write a definition of a function. Be prepared to share your definition with the class.

11-29.   Examine each of the relations below. Compare the inputs and outputs of each relation and decide if the relation is a function. Explain your reasoning. Use your definition of a function (from problem 11-28) to help you **justify** your conclusion.

a.
Button Number	1	1	2	4	2	3
Type of Candy	Stix	Stix	M&Ns	M&Ns	Duds	Duds

b.
x	7	-2	0	4	9	-3	6
$f(x)$	6	-3	4	2	10	-3	0

c.
x	3	-1	2	0	1	2	9
$g(x)$	4	-5	9	7	4	-8	2

d.
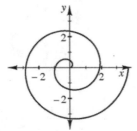

e.
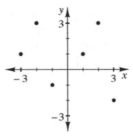

f.
x	$h(x)$
–8	11
4	3
11	–8
6	3
–8	11

g.
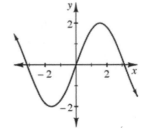

11-30.   Jade noticed that the line graphed at right is a function. "Hey – I think *all* lines are functions!" she exclaimed. Is she correct? Support your claim with a diagram.

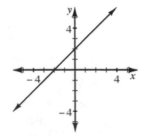

11-31.   In your Learning Log, describe what it means for a relationship to be a **function**. Think of another type of machine that you use on a regular basis and describe how it also operates as a function. Title this entry "Functions" and include today's date.

Algebra Connections

11-32.   If $g(x) = \sqrt{x-7}$, find $g(8)$, $g(32)$, and $g(80)$.

11-33.   Solve the system of equations below using any method. Be sure to check your solution.

$$5u + 6v = 2$$
$$u - 2v = 10$$

11-34.   Solve each equation below. Check each solution.

   a. $6 - (3 + x) = 10$

   b. $100(x + 3) = 200$

   c. $\frac{1}{3}x + 4 = x - 2$

   d. $\frac{4}{5} = \frac{x+2}{45}$

11-35.   Solve for x. Use any method. Check your solutions by testing them in the original equation.

   a. $|x - 3| = 5$

   b. $5|x| = 35$

   c. $|x + 1| = 2$

   d. $|x + 3| - 6 = -4$

11-36.   Rewrite each of the expressions below with no parentheses and no fractions. Negative exponents are acceptable in your answer.

   a. $(5a^{-2}b^3)^8 \cdot (5ab^{-2})^{-6}$

   b. $\frac{15x^{-5}y^2}{(3x^2)^2 \cdot y^{-3}}$

11-37.   **Multiple Choice:** Which line below is parallel to $y = -\frac{2}{3}x + 5$?

   a. $2x - 3y = 6$

   b. $2x + 3y = 6$

   c. $3x - 2y = 6$

   d. $3x + 2y = 6$

11.1.4 What can go in? What can come out?

Domain and Range

So far you have described relations using intercepts and symmetry. You also have noticed that sometimes relations are functions. Today you will finish your focus on relations by describing the inputs and outputs of relations.

11-38.   Examine the graph of the relation $h(x)$ at right. Use it to estimate:

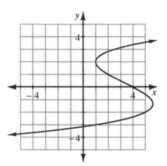

   a. $h(4)$

   b. $h(1)$

   c. $h(-4)$

   d.   Is this relation a function? Why or why not?

11-39.   Examine the relation shown at right.

   a.   Find $f(-3)$, $f(0)$, and $f(2)$.

   b.   Find $f(3)$. What happened?

   c.   Are there any other numbers that cannot be evaluated by this relation? In other words, are there any other values that cannot be x? Explain how you know.

   $x = ?$

   $$f(x) = \frac{6}{x-3}$$

   $f(x) = ?$

   d.   The set (collection) of numbers that can be used for x in a relation is called the **domain** of the relation. The domain is a description or list of all the possible x-values for the relation. Describe the domain of $f(x) = \frac{6}{x-3}$.

11-40.   Now examine $g(x)$ graphed at right.

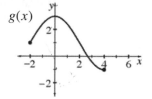

    a.   Is $g(x)$ a function? How can you tell?

    b.   Which x-values have points on the graph? That is, what is the domain of $g(x)$?

    c.   What are the possible outputs for $g(x)$? This is called the **range** of the relation.

    d.   Ricky thinks the range of $g(x)$ is: –1, 0, 1, 2, and 3. Is he correct? Why or why not?

11-41.   FINDING DOMAIN AND RANGE

The domain and range are good descriptors of a relation because they help you know what numbers can go into and come out of a relation. The domain and range can also help you set up useful axes when graphing and help you describe special points on a graph (such as a missing point or the lowest point).

Work with your team to describe in words the domain and range of each relation below.

a.

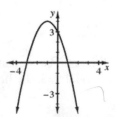

b.

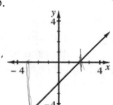

c.

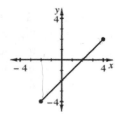

d.

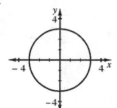

e.

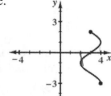

f.

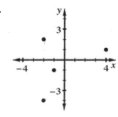

11-42.   Chiu loves tables! He has decided to make the table below for a relation $f(x)$ to help him find its domain and range.

x	-3	-2	-1	0	1	2	3
$f(x)$	5	0	-3	-4	-3	0	5

a.   From his table, can you tell what the domain of $f(x)$ is? Why or why not?

b.   From the table, can you tell the range of $f(x)$? Why or why not?

c.   Is using a table an effective way to determine the domain and range of a relation?

11-43.   Daniel is thinking about the relation shown at right.

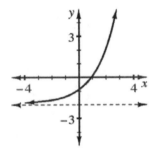

a.   He noticed that the curve continues to the left and to the right. What is the domain of this relation?

b.   He found out that the dotted line represents a boundary that the graph gets closer to but never touches or crosses. (Another name for this dotted line is **asymptote**.) How should Daniel describe the range?

11-44.   TEAM CHALLENGE

Sketch the graph of a relation that has a domain of all the numbers greater than or equal to –2 and a range of all the numbers less than or equal to 3. Is there more than one possible answer?

Algebra Connections

METHODS AND MEANINGS

Relations and Functions

A **relation** establishes a correspondence between its inputs and outputs (in math language called "sets"). For equations, it establishes the relationship between two variables and determines one variable when given the other. Some examples of relations are:

$$y = x^2, \ y = \frac{x}{x+3}, \ y = -2x + 5$$

Since the value of y usually depends on x, y is often referred to as the **dependent variable**, while x is called the **independent variable**.

The set of possible inputs of a relation is called the **domain**, while the set of all possible outputs of a relation is called the **range**. For example, notice that all the points on the graph at right have x-values that are greater than or equal to -3. The arrows on the graph indicate that the graph will continue to expand to the right. Thus, the entire domain is the set of numbers that are greater than or equal to -3. Likewise, since each y-value has a corresponding point on the graph, then the range is the set of all numbers. This is also referred to as the set of **all real numbers**. In the future, this course will refer to these as "all numbers."

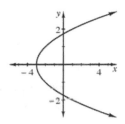

A **relation** is called a **function** if there exists <u>no more than one</u> output for each input. If a relation has two or more outputs for a single input value, it is not a function. For example, the relation graphed above is not a function because there are two y-values for each x-value greater than -3.

Functions are often given names, most commonly "f," "g," or "h." The notation $f(x)$ represents the output of a function, named "f" when x is the input. It is read "f of x." The notation $f(2)$, read "f of 2," represents the output of function f when $x = 2$. In the example at right, $f(2) = 10$.

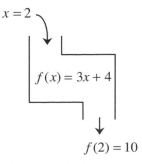

The equations $y = 3x + 4$ and $f(x) = 3x + 4$ represent the <u>same function</u>. Notice that this notation is interchangeable; that is, $y = f(x)$.

11-45.   Which of the relations below are functions? If a relation is not a function, give a reason to support your conclusion.

a.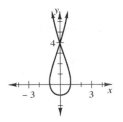

b.

x	y
−3	19
5	19
19	0
0	−3

c.

x	7	−2	0	7	4
y	10	0	10	3	0

d.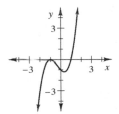

11-46.   Find the *x*- and *y*-intercepts for the graphs of the relations in problem 11-45.

11-47.   Marisol and Mimi walked the same distance from their school to a shopping mall. Marisol walked 2 miles per hour, while Mimi left 1 hour later and walked 3 miles per hour. If they reached the mall at the same time, how far from the mall is their school?

11-48.   A line passes through the points A(−3, −2) and B(2, 1). Does it also pass through the point C(5, 3)? **Justify** your conclusion.

11-49.   Solve each equation below for the indicated variable.

a. $3x - 2y = 18$ for x

b. $3x - 2y = 18$ for y

c. $rt = d$ for r

d. $C = 2\pi r$ for r

11-50.   Simplify each expression below.

a. $\dfrac{3x^2 + 8x + 5}{x^2 - 5x - 6} \cdot \dfrac{2x - 5}{3x + 5}$

b. $\dfrac{x^2 + x - 12}{x^2 - x - 6} \div \dfrac{x - 5}{x^2 - 3x - 10}$

11.1.5 How can I describe this relation?

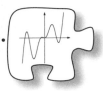

Investigating a New Relation

You are now familiar with the graphs of lines, parabolas, and square roots. What other types of relations can you study? Today you will use the questions your class generated in Lesson 11.1.1 to investigate several new relations. Your team will then report its findings to the class. Pay close attention to presentations! As you listen to the presentations of your classmates, you will learn about several new and interesting relations.

11-51.   NEW RELATIONS

Your teacher will assign your team a new relation from the list below. On graph paper, carefully graph your new relation. Be sure to include enough values in your table to show any unusual behavior of your graph. Then use your list of questions about relations to investigate your particular relation.

Write clear summary statements that describe your relation. Create a team poster for your relation with a graph and any observations and statements your team made. Be ready to present your poster to the class.

(1) $f(x) = \frac{1}{x}$ (2) $f(x) = x^3$

(3) $f(x) = \frac{1}{x^2}$ (4) $f(x) = 0.5^x$

(5) $f(x) = 2^x$ (6) $f(x) = \sqrt{16 - x^2}$

11-52.   On the resource page provided by your teacher, find a box for each of the relations listed in problem 11-51. As you listen to the presentations, take notes on each relation. Be sure to sketch a graph of the relation as well as list any special points or features. Remember to date this entry and place the resource page in your Learning Log.

11-53.   MATCH-A-GRAPH

Match each rule (a) through (f) with its corresponding graph below.

a. $f(x) = \sqrt{x-3}$ b. $f(x) = \frac{1}{x} + 1$

c. $f(x) = x^3 - 2$ d. $f(x) = \sqrt{4-(x+2)^2}$

e. $f(x) = \frac{3}{x^2}$ f. $f(x) = 2^{x-2}$

1)
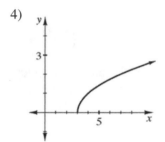

2)
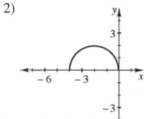

3)
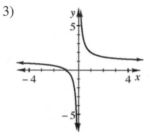

4)
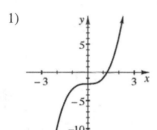

5)
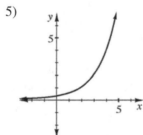

6)
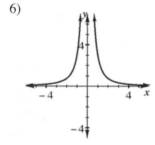

11-54.   For each relation graphed in problem 11-53, name the domain and the range.

11-55.   On the same set of axes, graph $y = |x|$ and $y = |x| + 2$. What is the same about these two graphs? What is different?

11-56.   Simplify the rational expression below. What values can x not be?

$$\frac{3x^2 + 11x - 20}{2x^2 + 11x + 5}$$

11-57.   Find the corresponding inputs or outputs for the following relations. If there is no
          solution, explain why not. Be careful: In some cases, there may be no solution or
          more than one possible solution.

a. $x = 8$

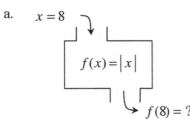

b. $x = ?$

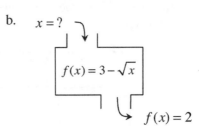

c. $k = -6$

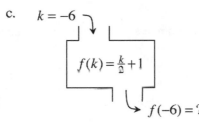

d. $x = 3$

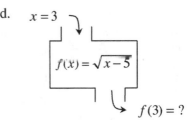

11-58.   Find the equation of a line that is perpendicular to $y = -\frac{1}{5}x + 11$ but goes through
          the point (6, 8).

11-59.   Solve each equation below for the given variable. Be sure to check your solution.

a. $6x - 11 = 3x + 16$

b. $-2(5 - 3x) + 5 = 9 + 3x$

c. $\frac{6}{k-2} = 10$

d. $\frac{4}{3x-1} = \frac{2}{x+3}$

11-60.   Simplify using only positive exponents.

a. $(3x^2 y)(5x)$

b. $(x^2 y^3)(\sqrt{xy})$

c. $\frac{x^3}{x^{-2}}$

d. $(2x^{-1})^3$

11-61.   Find the inputs for the following relations with the given outputs. If there is no
          possible input for the given output, explain why not.

a. $x = ?$

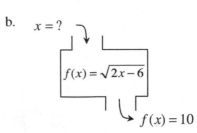

b. $x = ?$

11-62.   One way to represent the solutions shown on
the number line at right is $-3 \le x < 1$. For
each number line below, write a similar
mathematical sentence to describe the
solutions for x.

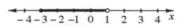

a.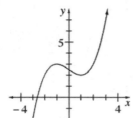

b.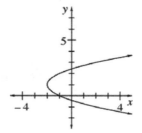

c.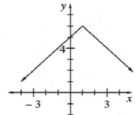

d.

11-63.   Which graphs below have a domain of all numbers? Which have a range of all
numbers?

a.   b.   c.

11-64.   Solve each of the following equations or systems.

a. $x^2 - 1 = 15$ b. $y = 3x - 2$
$y = 4x + 3$

c. $x^2 - 2x - 8 = 0$ d. $2x^2 = -x + 7$

11-65.   Graph and shade the solution for the system of inequalities below.

$$y \le 4 + \tfrac{3}{4}x$$
$$y > -\tfrac{1}{2}x + 1$$

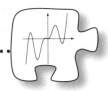
Transformation of a Function

11-66. PROMOTION OPPORTUNITY

You and your co-workers at Functions of America have received the following note from your boss. Read the letter and complete the task that follows.

To My Faithful Employees,

I have been pleased to read in the "Relations Daily" about the high customer-service satisfaction ratings of this company. Now I want to expand to control the function-rental industry.

Before Functions of America can begin renting out our expensive graphs, I need an equation attached to each one. That way, when a graph is returned to the company, employees will be able to verify that it is the same function that was originally rented to the customer. Also, if the graph of the function was damaged or switched for a less sophisticated graph, we will then be able to prosecute the customer to the full extent of the law.

Employees will be given a designated time to explore their new and innovative function with a partner. Please be ready to report on how the numbers in a rule change its graph.

At the end of the day, every employee will be challenged to identify the equation of a function correctly by observing only its graph. Doing so will earn you a management position. I wish all of you the best of luck.

> *Sincerely,*
> *Freda Function, CEO, Functions of America*

Your Task: Your teacher will assign your team one of the functions below. Explore the graph of your function as *a, h,* and *k* change values. Choose positive, negative, and zero values for *a, h,* and *k* to uncover all possible patterns. Reflect on the relationships you find between the graph and its equation. Discuss your observations with your study team and record your results on paper.

(1) $f(x) = a(x-h)^3 + k$ (2) $f(x) = a(x-h)^2 + k$ (3) $f(x) = a\sqrt{x-h} + k$

(4) $f(x) = a|x-h| + k$ (5) $f(x) = \frac{a}{x-h} + k$ (6) $f(x) = 2^{a(x-h)} + k$

Problem continues on next page →

11-66.   *Problem continued from previous page.*

Discussion Points

What is the goal of this investigation?

What is the best way to choose values of a, h, and k to see a pattern?

Further Guidance

11-67.   When you asked for clarification, your boss sent you the following note:

> *Dear Employees,*
>
> *Thank you for your questions. I am sorry I was so vague. In your report, I would like you to tell me:*
>
> 1. *How does the equation affect how "skinny" or "wide" the graph is?*
>
> 2. *What changes in the equation move the graph up or down? Left or right?*
>
> 3. *Is there a way to change the equation so that the function turns "upside down"?*
>
> *Use your graphing technology to test different values of a, h, and k to discover the answers to the questions above. Examine only one letter at a time so that you can find patterns quickly. For example, if you want to see what the value of a does to the graph of a function, then change a while you keep h and k the same.*
>
> *Good luck!*
> *Ms. Function*

————————   *Further Guidance*   ————————
                         section ends here.

11-68.   PROMOTION CHALLENGE

Here is your opportunity to impress your boss. Find the equation for each relation graphed below. Remember the observations you made in problem 11-66 and pay close attention to details.

a.   b.

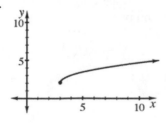   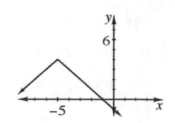

11-69.   EXTENSION

How do the domain and range of a function change when it moves? To answer this question, examine what happens as the square-root function $f(x) = \sqrt{x}$ is moved ("translated").

a.   Describe the domain and range of $f(x) = \sqrt{x}$.

b.   Now describe the domain and range of $g(x) = \sqrt{x+2} - 3$.

c.   Are the domain and range for $f(x)$ and $g(x)$ above the same? If not, how are they different?

11-70.   Match each rule below with its corresponding graph. Can you do this without making any tables?

a. $y = |x - 1|$ b. $y = |x| + 3$ c. $y = |x - 1| + 3$

1)   2)   3)

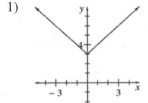   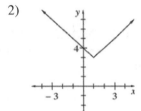   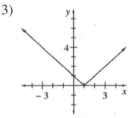

11-71.   Graph the rule $y = -x^2 + 4x$ and label its intercepts and vertex.

11-72.   If $f(x) = 7 + |x|$ and $g(x) = x^3 - 5$, then find:

a. $f(-5)$ b. $g(4)$ c. $f(0)$

d. $f(2)$ e. $g(-2)$ f. $g(0)$

11-73.   Solve for x in each equation below.

a. $2x = 8$ b. $2x + 2 = 10$

c. $6x + 2 - 4x = 10$ d. $2(3x+1) - 4x = 10$

e.   Check your solutions for the equations above. What do you notice?

11-74.　For the function $y = \frac{1}{2}x + 3$, calculate the y-values that complete the table below.

IN (x)	-3	-2	-1	0	1	2	3
OUT (y)							

a.　For this function, what is y when $x = 5$?

b.　For this function, what is x when $y = -11$?

c.　For each answer for parts (a) and (b), did you use inductive or deductive reasoning? Explain.

11-75.　Solve the following inequalities for x. Graph your solutions on a number line.

a.　$3x - 5 \le 7 + 2x$

b.　$|x| - 3 < 7$

c.　$5(2 - x) + 6 > 16$

d.　$|x + 2| > 3$

11.2.1　Intercept or intersect?

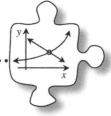

Intercepts and Intersections

Now that you know about many kinds of functions, you will look more closely at intercepts and intersections. What is the difference between an intercept and a point of intersection? Think about this as you develop algebraic methods to find points where two functions cross. In the next few lessons you will have chances to practice your quadratic-solving skills as well as your newer solving skills from Chapter 10.

11-76.　Examine the graphs of the parabola $y = x^2 - 3x - 10$ and the line $y = -2x + 2$ at right.

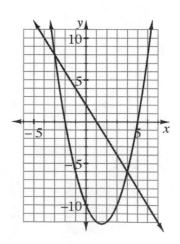

a.　Name all x- and y-intercepts for the parabola.

b.　Name all x- and y-intercepts for the line.

c.　Where do the graphs intersect each other?

d.　The words "intersect" and "intercept" look and sound a lot alike, but what do they mean? How are they alike? How are they different?

11-77. Intercepts and intersections are similar, but they are not exactly the same. How can you tell which one you are looking for? Read the situations below and decide if the graphical solution would best be represented as an **intercept** or an **intersection**. Be prepared to defend your decision. Note: You do not need to solve the problem!

a. A 5-gram candle on a birthday cake is lit. Two minutes after it is lit, the candle weighs 4.2 grams. How long will the candle burn?

b. A local bowling alley charges you $4 to rent shoes and $3.50 for each game you play. Another alley charges you $7 to rent shoes and $2 for each game you play. How many games would you need to play in order for both alleys to charge you the same amount?

c. Two months after Aliya's birthday, she had $450, while her sister Claudia had $630. Five months after her birthday, Aliya had $800, while Claudia had $920. How much did each person have on Aliya's birthday?

11-78. Using a graph to find the intersection of two curves can be challenging when the rules are complicated or when the point of intersection ends up off the graph. Therefore, it helps to know another way to find the intersection without using a graph.

a. Name the algebraic methods you already know to solve linear systems.

b. Use one of the methods you listed in part (a) to solve for the intersection of $y = x^2 - 3x - 10$ and $y = -2x + 2$. Be sure to collaborate with your teammates and check your results along the way. Does the graph in problem 11-76 confirm your results?

11-79. Solve the system of equations below for x and y. Write your solution(s) in the form (x, y). Then graph the system on the same set of axes and confirm your solution.

$$y = \frac{1}{x}$$
$$y = 2x + 1$$

11-80. In your Learning Log, explain the difference between intercepts and intersections. Include a sketch or graph to help your explanation. Title this entry "Intercepts and Intersections" and include today's date.

11-81.   Find the output for the relation with the given input. $x = 1$
          If there is no possible output for the given input,
          explain why not.

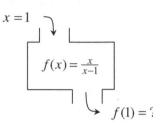

$$f(x) = \frac{x}{x-1}$$

$$f(1) = ?$$

11-82.   Examine the two lines
          graphed at right. Will these
          two lines intersect? Find the
          equation of each line and test
          your prediction.

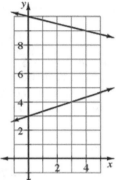

11-83.   For each line in problem 11-82,
          find the x- and y-intercepts.

11-84.   Which of the equations below is equivalent to $4(3x-1)+3x = 9x+5$? More than
          one may be equivalent. **Justify** your answer.

          a. $12x-4+3x = 9x+5$ b. $12x-1+3x = 9x+5$

          c. $11x = 14x$ d. $15x-4 = 9x+5$

11-85.   Paula graphed a line and found that $f(-2) = 5$ and $f(0) = 2$. Graph this line and
          find its equation.

11-86.   Which of the relations below are functions? **Justify** your answer.

          a.   b.   c.

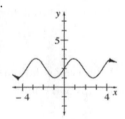   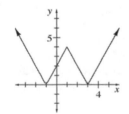   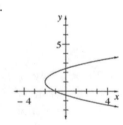

11-87.   For each graph in problem 11-86 above, name the domain and range.

11-88.   Examine the graphs in problem 11-86 again. Which, if any, have symmetry? Copy
          each graph on your paper and show any lines of symmetry.

11.2.2 How many points of intersection?

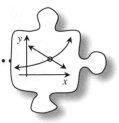

Pulling It All Together

In Lesson 11.2.1, you developed a method for finding the points of intersection of a line and a parabola. Today you will study different possibilities for lines and parabolas intersecting or not intersecting.

11-89.   As you have seen, sometimes a parabola and a line never intersect. However, if a parabola and a line do intersect, how many different intersection points can they have? How many intersections can two parabolas have? Do two parabolas *always* intersect?

On graph paper, sketch a graph that fits each description below. Not every graph is possible. As you graph, consider the questions above.

a.   A line and a parabola that intersect twice.

b.   A line and a parabola that intersect once.

c.   A line and a parabola that intersect more than twice.

d.   Two parabolas that intersect twice.

e.   Two parabolas that have an infinite number of intersections.

f.   Two parabolas that never intersect.

g.   Two parabolas that only intersect once.

11-90.   HOW MANY INTERSECTIONS?

When given a graph of two parabolas or a line and a parabola, it is usually easy to determine how many points of intersection they have. But how can you tell algebraically?

Your Task: Each team will be assigned one of the systems below. With your team:

- Use any algebraic solving method to find the point(s) of intersection for your team's system, if any exist. Examine your algebraic solution and decide what it indicates about the graph of the system. (That is, do the parabolas intersect once? Do they never intersect?)

- Once you have solved your team's system, have your teacher come to your team and listen to you explain your results. Use a graphing calculator (or sketch a graph using your graphing shortcuts) to verify your conclusion.

- If time allows, design a poster that shows the algebraic solution of your system as well as a sketch of the graph.

Systems:

a. $y = x^2$
      $y = 2x - 1$

b. $y = x^2 - 5x + 6$
      $y = -x^2$

c. $y = x^2 - 4x + 5$
      $y = -x^2 + 4x - 1$

d. $y = x^2 - x - 2$
      $y = x^2 + 2x + 1$

e. $y = x^2 - x - 2$
      $y = x - 6$

f. $y = 2x^2 + 3x - 9$
      $y = x - 5$

11-91.   ALGEBRA COMES TO THE RESCUE!

Darrel is so excited! When he called his local radio station during a contest, he was the 9th caller! The talk-show host, Maribel, explained that Darrel would win a brand-new graphing calculator if he answers this question correctly:

"How many times do the parabola $y = 2x^2 - 5x$
and the line $y = \frac{2}{3}x - 4$ intersect?"

a.   Quickly, Darrel used his graphing calculator to graph the system – but then his calculator broke! Help him by graphing the system on your grapher. Time is running out… What should he tell Maribel?

b.   Maribel paused and then asked, *"Are you **absolutely sure** that is your final answer?"* Help Darrel confirm his answer by solving the system algebraically. What is the correct answer?

Algebra Connections

11-92. Solve each quadratic equation below using any method you choose. Check your solutions.

a. $(5x-1)(x+3)=0$

b. $4x^2+10x-6=0$

c. $0.5x^2-3x+4.5=0$

d. $x^2+5x=14$

11-93. Use your graphing shortcuts to graph $f(x)=x^2-6x+5$.

a. What is the vertex?

b. Describe the domain and range of this relation.

11-94. Solve the following problem and write your solution as a sentence.

Mr. Ripley's fruit stand sells watermelons for $5 and apples for $2. Last weekend, he sold 40 pieces of fruit (all apples and watermelons) for $107. How many watermelons did he sell?

11-95. Find all points where the graphs of $y=x^2-3x+2$ and $y=2x+8$ intersect.

11-96. **Multiple Choice:** Which of the lines below is parallel to the line $5x-3y=11$?

a. $5x-3y=4$

b. $5x+3y=-2$

c. $3x-5y=11$

d. $3x+5y=-1$

11-97. **Multiple Choice:** Which expression below is the result of dividing $4x^2+8x-5$ by $2x+5$?

a. $2x-5$ b. $2x-1$ c. $2x+1$ d. $x+5$

11.3.1 Can I find it?

Relation Treasure Hunt

Now that you have many ways to describe a relation, you can use these ways to distinguish between different relations that are given in different representations.

11-98.   TREASURE HUNT

Today your teacher will give you several descriptive clues about different relations. (This information is also available online at www.cpm.org.) For each clue, work with your team (or a partner) to find all the possible matches among the relations posted around the classroom or provided on the resource page. Remember that more than one relation may match each clue. Once you have decided which relation(s) match a given clue, defend your decision to your teacher and receive the next clue. Be sure to record your matches on paper.

Your goal is to find the match (or more than one match) for each of **eight** clues. Once you and your team (or partner) have finished, only one relation will be left unmatched. That relation is the treasure!

11-99.   For each relation graphed below, describe the domain (input) and range (output). Then state whether it is a function. If it is not a function, give a reason to support your claim.

a.
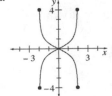

b.
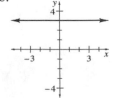

c.
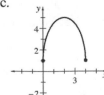

d.
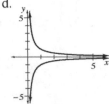

11-100. Reflect on the reasoning you have used during Chapter 11.

    a.   Give an example of a situation in which you used inductive reasoning. Why did you use inductive reasoning in that situation? Explain.

    b.   Give an example of a situation in which you used deductive reasoning. Why did you use inductive reasoning in that situation? Explain.

11-101. What number is not part of the domain of $f(x) = \frac{3}{x+5}$? How can you tell?

11-102. Find the equation of the line perpendicular to $5x - 2y = 13$ that passes through the point (60, –20).

11-103. Find all of the points at which the parabolas below intersect. Write your solution(s) in (x, y) form.

$$y = x^2 + 5x - 4$$
$$y = x^2 + x - 12$$

11-104. The diagram at right shows one way to represent the fraction $\frac{1}{7}$.

    a.   Draw a similar diagram to represent $\frac{3}{7}$.

    b.   What is $\frac{1}{7} + \frac{3}{7}$? Use your diagram to **justify** your answer.

    c.   Use a new diagram to add $\frac{3}{5} + \frac{4}{5}$.

11-105. Rewrite each of the expressions below. Avoid leaving negative exponents in your solution.

    a. $\left(\frac{2x}{y^2}\right)^2$
              b. $\left(6x^3\right)\left(3x^{-1}y\right)$
              c. $\frac{(xy)^{-1}}{(x^2y^3)^{-1}}$

Chapter 11 Closure   What have I learned?

Reflection and Synthesis

The activities below offer you a chance to reflect on what you have learned during this chapter. As you work, look for concepts that you feel very comfortable with, ideas that you would like to learn more about, and topics you need more help with. Look for **connections** between ideas as well as **connections** with material you learned previously.

①   TEAM BRAINSTORM

With your team, brainstorm a list for each of the following topics. Be as detailed as you can. How long can you make your list? Challenge yourselves. Be prepared to share your team's ideas with the class.

Topics:	What have you studied in this chapter? What ideas and words were important in what you learned? Remember to be as detailed as you can.
Ways of Thinking:	What Ways of Thinking did you use in this chapter? When did you use them?
Connections:	What topics, ideas, and words that you learned *before* this chapter are **connected** to the new ideas in this chapter? Again, make your list as long as you can.

② MAKING CONNECTIONS

The following is a list of the vocabulary used in this chapter. The words that appear in bold are new to this chapter. Make sure that you are familiar with all of these words and know what they mean. Refer to the glossary or index for any words that you do not yet understand.

domain	**function**	graph
input	intersection	output
range	**relation**	rule
solution	x-intercept	$x \rightarrow y$ table
y-intercept		

Make a concept map showing all of the **connections** you can find among the key words and ideas listed above. To show a **connection** between two words, draw a line between them and explain the **connection**, as shown in the example below. A word can be **connected** to any other word as long as there is a **justified connection**. For each key word or idea, provide a sketch that illustrates the idea (see the example below).

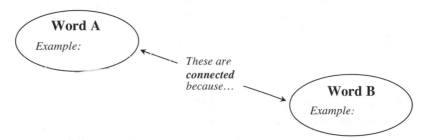

Your teacher may provide you with vocabulary cards to help you get started. If you use the cards to plan your concept map, be sure either to re-draw your concept map on your paper or to glue the vocabulary cards to a poster with all of the **connections** explained for others to see and understand.

While you are making your map, your team may think of related words or ideas that are not listed above. Be sure to include these ideas on your concept map.

③ SUMMARIZING MY UNDERSTANDING

This section gives you an opportunity to show what you know about one or more topics or ideas. Your teacher will give you directions for exactly how to do this.

WHAT HAVE I LEARNED?

This section will help you evaluate which types of problems you have seen with which you feel comfortable and those with which you need more help. Even if your teacher does not assign this section, it is a good idea to try these problems and find out for yourself what you know and what you need to work on.

Solve each problem as completely as you can. The table at the end of the closure section has answers to these problems. It also tells you where you can find additional help and practice on problems like these.

CL 11-106. For each of the representations below, decide if the relation represented is a function. **Justify** your answer.

a.

x	y
4	8
7	8
45	7
52	-6
7	9
13	0

b.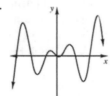

c.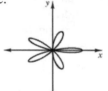

d. $2x + 3y = 4$

CL 11-107. Examine the relation $h(x)$ defined at right. Then estimate the values below.

a. $h(1)$

b. $h(3)$

c. x when $h(x) = 0$

d. $h(-1)$

e. $h(-4)$

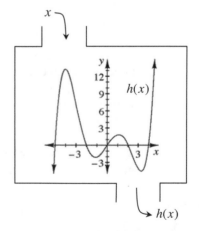

CL 11-108. Consider the parabola $y = 2x^2 + 6x - 20$.

a. Find this parabola's x- and y-intercepts.

b. Find where this parabola intersects the line $y = 3x + 1$.

CL 11-109. Solve for the given variable, if possible. Be sure to check your solution.

   a. $\frac{3x}{5} - x = \frac{1}{2}(18 - 2x)$ b. $\sqrt{3y+8} = 5$

   c. $|2m-7| = 16$ d. $(-x+8)^2 \geq 16$

   e. $\frac{3x-2}{x+5} = \frac{14}{16}$ f. $12 > |3x+15|$

CL 11-110. For each system of equations below, find all points of intersection.

   a. $2x + 3y = 7$ b. $y = 2x^2 - 12x + 18$ c. $y = 2x - 4.5$
         $-3x - 5y = -13$ $y = x^2 + 4x - 10$ $18 = 8x - 4y$

CL 11-111. Simplify the expressions below. Each answer should have no parentheses or negative exponents.

   a. $\dfrac{(x+3)^3}{3x^2 - 11x - 70} \div \dfrac{x^2 + 6x + 9}{x-7}$ b. $\dfrac{(24a^{12}b^0c^{-3})(4a^{-3}c^2)}{(6a^4b^3)^2}$

CL 11-112. Check your answers using the table at the end of the closure section. Which problems do you feel confident about? Which problems were hard? Use the table to make a list of topics you need help on and a list of topics you need to practice more.

⑤   HOW AM I THINKING?

This course focuses on five different **Ways of Thinking**: reversing thinking, justifying, generalizing, making connections, and applying and extending understanding. These are some of the ways in which you think while trying to make sense of a concept or to solve a problem (even outside of math class). During this chapter, you have probably used each Way of Thinking multiple times without even realizing it!

Review each of the Ways of Thinking with your class. Then choose three of these Ways of Thinking that you remember using while working in this chapter. For each Way of Thinking that you choose, show and explain where you used it and how you used it. Describe why thinking in this way helped you solve a particular problem or understand something new. (For instance, explain why you wanted to **generalize** in this particular case, or why it was useful to see these particular **connections**.) Be sure to include examples to demonstrate your thinking.

Answers and Support for Closure Activity #4
What Have I Learned?

Problem	Solution	Need Help?	More Practice
CL 11-106.	a. not a function b. function c. not a function d. function	Lessons 11.1.3 and 11.1.4, Lesson 11.1.4 Math Notes box	Problems 11-29, 11-38(d), 11-40(a), 11-45, 11-86, and 11-100
CL 11-107.	a. 2 b. -4 c. $-5, -2, 0, 2, 4$ d. -2 e. 13	Lesson 11.1.2, Lesson 11.1.4 Math Notes box	Problems 11-20 and 11-38
CL 11-108.	a. x-intercepts $(2, 0)$ and $(-5, 0)$, y-intercept $(0, -20)$ b. approximately $(2.6, 8.8)$ and $(-4.1, -11.2)$	Lessons 11.2.1 and 11.2.2	Problems 11-14, 11-71, 11-76, 11-78(b), 11-90, and 11-95
CL 11-109.	a. 15 b. $y = \frac{17}{3}$ c. $m = \frac{23}{2}, \ -\frac{9}{2}$ d. $x \le 4$ or $x \ge 12$ e. 3 f. $-9 < x < -1$	Lessons 9.2.2, 10.1.3, 10.1.4, 10.2.1, and 10.2.3 Math Notes boxes	Problems 11-10, 11-35, 11-59, and 11-75
CL 11-110.	a. $(-4, 5)$ b. $(2, 2)$ and $(14, 242)$ c. Infinite solutions because the two lines coincide.	Lessons 11.2.1 and 11.2.2	Problems 11-33, 11-64(b), 11-78, 11-79, 11-90, 11-95, and 11-103
CL 11-111.	a. $\frac{x+3}{3x+10}$ b. $\frac{8a}{3b^6c}$	Lessons 10.1.2 and 10.4.3 Math Notes boxes	Problems 11-13, 11-15, 11-25, 11-36, 11-50, and 11-105

12

Algebraic Extensions

CHAPTER 12　Algebraic Extensions

As the title of this chapter suggests, during this chapter you will revisit and build upon many of the topics you have studied so far in this course. For example, you already have learned how to simplify, multiply, and divide rational expressions. In this chapter, you will develop a method to add and subtract them as well.

You will also revisit quadratics and will apply your techniques for problem solving to solve new kinds of word problems.

Finally, you will pull together the knowledge and tools you have gained throughout this course to solve a series of meaningful and challenging problems.

In this chapter, you will learn:

> How to add and subtract rational expressions.

> How to factor a difference of squares or a perfect square trinomial quickly without using a generic rectangle.

> How to solve word problems involving rates of work and mixtures of quantities.

> How to derive the Quadratic Formula by completing the square.

> How to provide thorough mathematical justification for predictions and solutions.

Guiding Questions

Think about these questions throughout this chapter:

Is there a shortcut?

How can I rewrite it?

What's the connection?

Is there another way?

Chapter Outline

Section 12.1 You will expand your ability to rewrite expressions by learning new ways to factor special quadratics and to add and subtract rational expressions.

Section 12.2 You will learn how to solve word problems about making mixtures and working together.

$x = \frac{-b \pm \sqrt{b^2 - 4ac}}{2a}$

Section 12.3 You will learn how to derive the Quadratic Formula.

Section 12.4 You will apply the mathematics you have learned throughout this course to analyze a challenging tile pattern, make a prediction about a burning candle, analyze an interesting inequality, and find the maximum area of a pen for a cow.

12.1.1 Is there a shortcut?

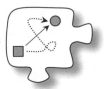

Factoring Shortcuts

Are there any types of quadratics that you can factor quickly without using a generic rectangle? If so, what do these quadratics look like and how can you recognize them? Today your team will examine the factored forms of many different quadratics and look for patterns and shortcuts for factoring certain types of quadratics.

12-1.　　SPECIAL QUADRATICS

Your team will be assigned several of the quadratics below to factor (if possible). Look for similarities and differences among the expressions below and their corresponding factored forms. Be prepared to share your factors with the class. Then work as a class to sort the quadratics into groups based on the patterns you find in their factored forms.

a.　$x^2 - 49$ 　　　　b.　$x^2 + 2x - 24$ 　　　　c.　$x^2 - 10x + 25$

d.　$9x^2 + 12x + 4$ 　　e.　$5x^2 - 4x - 1$ 　　　f.　$4x^2 - 25$

g.　$x^2 - 6x + 9$ 　　　h.　$x^2 - 36$ 　　　　i.　$7x^2 - 20x - 3$

j.　$4x^2 + 20x + 25$ 　　k.　$x^2 + 4$ 　　　　l.　$9x^2 - 1$

12-2.　　Which of the following quadratics fit the patterns you found in problem 12-1? Factor each of the following expressions using your new shortcuts, if possible.

a.　$25x^2 - 1$ 　　　　b.　$x^2 - 5x - 36$ 　　　c.　$x^2 + 8x + 16$

d.　$9x^2 - 12x + 4$ 　　e.　$9x^2 + 4$ 　　　　f.　$9x^2 - 100$

12-3.　　Special quadratics, like $9x^2 - 100$ in part (f) of problem 12-2, can be factored quickly once you discover the pattern. But why do the patterns you found in problem 12-1 work?

a.　A quadratic in the form $a^2x^2 - b^2$ is called a **difference of squares**. Use a generic rectangle to prove that $a^2x^2 - b^2 = (ax - b)(ax + b)$. Be ready to share your work with the class.

b.　A quadratic in the form $a^2x^2 + 2abx + b^2$ is called a **perfect square trinomial**. Use a generic rectangle to prove that $a^2x^2 + 2abx + b^2 = (ax + b)^2$. Be ready to share your work with the class.

12-4.   In your Learning Log, describe how to factor a difference of squares and a perfect square trinomial. Be sure to include an example of each type. Title this entry "Factoring Shortcuts" and include today's date.

12-5.   Use your factoring shortcuts to simplify the following expressions.

a. $\dfrac{x^2-9}{x^2-6x+9}$

b. $\dfrac{2x+5}{4x^2-25} \cdot \dfrac{2x-5}{x+7}$

c. $\dfrac{x^2+x-20}{x^2-16} \cdot \dfrac{x^2+9x+20}{x^2+10x+25}$

d. $\dfrac{x^2+12x+36}{x^2-25} \div \dfrac{x+6}{x+5}$

12-6.   Solve the following equations for x.

a. $4x - 6y = 20$

b. $\frac{1}{2}(x-6) = 9$

c. $\frac{4}{3x} + \frac{6}{x} = 9$

d. $3 + \sqrt{5-x} = 5$

12-7.   Simplify each expression below. Your answer should contain no parentheses and no negative exponents.

a. $(-\frac{2}{3}x^5 y^{1/3})^0$

b. $(25^{1/2} x^5)(4x^{-6})$

c. $5t^{-3}$

d. $\left(\dfrac{x^4 y}{x}\right)^3$

12-8.   Examine the graphs of relations $f(x)$ and $g(x)$ at right. Use the graph to approximate the values below (if possible).

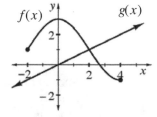

a. $f(0)$ b. $g(4)$ c. $f(5)$

d. $g(0)$ e. $g(2)$ f. $f(2)$

12-9.   Solve the equations and inequalities below by completing the square.

a. $x^2 - 2x - 3 \le 0$

b. $x^2 + 4x = 3$

c. $x^2 + 12x + 39 > 0$

d. $x^2 - 3x - 13.75 = 0$

12-10.   Describe how you add and subtract fractions that have a common denominator.

a.   Add or subtract the fractions below. Draw a diagram to show that your answer is correct.

     i. $\frac{8}{11} - \frac{3}{11}$ *ii.* $\frac{x}{6} + \frac{2}{6}$

b.   What if you are given two fractions to add or subtract and the denominators are not the same? Add the fractions below and check your result on your calculator.

$$\frac{1}{3} + \frac{2}{5}$$

12.1.2 How can I rewrite it?

···

Adding and Subtracting Rational Expressions

So far in this course you have learned a lot about rational expressions. You have learned how to simplify complex algebraic fractions by factoring the numerators and denominators. You have also learned how to multiply and divide rational expressions. What else is there to learn? Today you will develop a method to add and subtract algebraic fractions.

12-11.   With your team, review your responses for homework problem 12-10. Verify that everyone obtained the same answers and be prepared to share how you added fractions with the class.

$$\frac{8}{11} - \frac{3}{11} \qquad\qquad \frac{x}{6} + \frac{2}{6} \qquad\qquad \frac{1}{3} + \frac{2}{5}$$

12-12.   Examine each expression below. For each one:

- Use your understanding of adding fractions to add the algebraic expressions.

- Simplify your solutions, if possible.

a. $\frac{2x}{2x^2+x-21} + \frac{7}{2x^2+x-21}$ b. $\frac{5x}{x^2-2x-3} - \frac{15}{x^2-2x-3}$

c. $\frac{3x+9}{8x^2-50} - \frac{x+4}{8x^2-50}$ d. $\frac{x^2+5x-2}{3x^2+2x-8} + \frac{2x^2-3x-6}{3x^2+2x-8}$

12-13.   What if the algebraic fractions do not have the same denominator? With your team, discuss how to add the fractions below. Be prepared to **justify** your strategy with the class.

a. $\dfrac{x}{3x+1} + \dfrac{2x^2-2}{(x-5)(3x+1)}$

b. $\dfrac{9-3x}{(x+3)(x-3)} + \dfrac{2x}{x+3}$

12-14.   Estacia wants to learn more about excluded values.

a.   Explain to Estacia why x cannot be 4 in the expression $\dfrac{x+2}{x-4}$.

b.   Find the excluded values of x in each of the expressions of problem 12-13.

c.   With your team, create an expression that has the excluded values of $x \neq -6$ and $x \neq \frac{1}{3}$. Be prepared to share your expression to the class.

12-15.   In your Learning Log, explain how to add and subtract rational expressions. Be sure to include an example. Title this entry "Adding and Subtracting Rational Expressions" and include today's date.

12-16.   Use your understanding of adding fractions to add the algebraic expressions below. Then simplify your solutions, if possible.

a. $\dfrac{5m+18}{m+3} + \dfrac{4m+9}{m+3}$

b. $\dfrac{3a^2+a-1}{a^2-2a+1} - \dfrac{2a^2-a+2}{a^2-2a+1}$

12-17.   Solve the equations and inequalities below. Check your solutions, if possible.

a. $\left|5x+8\right| \geq -4$

b. $x^2 + x - 20 < 0$

c. $2x^2 - 6x = -5$

d. $\frac{5}{9} - \frac{x}{3} = \frac{4}{9}$

12-18.   Multiply the expressions below using generic rectangles.

a. $(5m-1)(m+2)$

b. $(6-x)(2+x)$

c. $(5x-y)^2$

d. $3x(2x-5y+4)$

12-19.   Examine the graphs of each relation below. Decide if each is a function. Then
           describe the domain and range of each.

a.

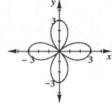

b.

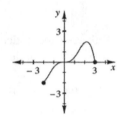

12-20.   Graph the function $g(x) = \frac{x+2}{x-1}$ on graph paper and name all x- and y-intercepts.
           What happens at $x = 1$?

12-21.   If $f(x) = 3x - 9$ and $g(x) = -x^2$, find:

a. $f(-2)$ b. $g(-2)$ c. x if $f(x) = 0$ d. $g(m)$

12.1.3 How can I rewrite it?

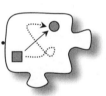

More Adding and Subtracting Rational Expressions

Today you will complete your work with rational expressions. By the end of this lesson you
will know how to add, subtract, multiply, and divide rational expressions.

12-22.   Review what you learned in Lesson 12.1.2 by adding and subtracting the expressions
           below. Leave your solutions as simplified as possible.

a. $\frac{5}{8} + \frac{1}{6}$ b. $\frac{8}{9} - \frac{2}{3}$

c. $\frac{x+5}{x+2} + \frac{2x+1}{x+2}$ d. $\frac{x^2-3}{(x+5)(2x-1)} + \frac{x}{2x-1}$

12-23.   Examine the expression below.

$$\frac{2x-1}{3x^2+13x+4} + \frac{x+3}{x^2-3x-28}$$

a.   With your team, decide how you can alter the expression so that the fractions have a common denominator. Be ready to share your idea with the class.

b.   If you have not already do so, add the fractions. Then simplify the result, if possible.

c.   Repeat the process to subtract the expressions below. Simplify the result, if possible.

$$\frac{2}{x+4} - \frac{4x-x^2}{x^2-16}$$

12-24.   PULLING IT ALL TOGETHER

You now know how to add, subtract, multiply, and divide rational expressions. Pull this all together by simplifying the following expressions.

a. $\frac{x^2-3x-10}{x^2-4x-5} \div \frac{x^2-7x-18}{2x^2-5x-7}$

b. $\frac{2x^2+x}{(2x+1)^2} - \frac{3}{2x+1}$

c. $\frac{15x-20}{x-5} \cdot \frac{x^2-2x-15}{3x^2+5x-12}$

d. $\frac{4}{2x+3} + \frac{x^2-x-2}{2x^2+5x+3}$

e. $\frac{6x-4}{3x^2-17x+10} - \frac{1}{x^2-2x-15}$

f. $\frac{x^2-x-2}{4x^2-7x-2} \div \frac{x^2-2x-3}{3x^2-8x-3}$

METHODS AND **M**EANINGS

MATH NOTES

Adding and Subtracting Rational Expressions

In order to add and subtract fractions, the fractions must have a common denominator. One way to do this is to change each fraction so that the denominator is the **least common multiple** of the denominators. For the example at right, the least common multiple of $(x+3)(x+2)$ and $x+2$ is $(x+3)(x+2)$.

$$\frac{4}{(x+2)(x+3)} + \frac{2x}{x+2}$$

The denominator of the first fraction already is the least common multiple. To get a common denominator in the second fraction, multiply the fraction by $\frac{(x+3)}{(x+3)}$, a form of the number 1.

$$= \frac{4}{(x+2)(x+3)} + \frac{2x}{x+2} \cdot \frac{(x+3)}{(x+3)}$$

Multiply the numerator and denominator of the second term.

$$= \frac{4}{(x+2)(x+3)} + \frac{2x(x+3)}{(x+2)(x+3)}$$

Distribute the numerator, if necessary.

$$= \frac{4}{(x+2)(x+3)} + \frac{2x^2+6x}{(x+2)(x+3)}$$

Add, factor, and simplify the result.

$$= \frac{2x^2+6x+4}{(x+2)(x+3)} = \frac{2(x+1)(x+2)}{(x+2)(x+3)} = \frac{2(x+1)}{(x+3)}$$

12-25.   Add, subtract, multiply, or divide the following rational expressions. Simplify your answers, if possible.

a. $\dfrac{2x}{3x^2+16x+5} + \dfrac{10}{3x^2+16x+5}$

b. $\dfrac{x^2-x-12}{3x^2-11x-4} \cdot \dfrac{3x^2-20x-7}{x^2-9}$

c. $\dfrac{2x^2+8x-10}{2x^2+15x+25} \div \dfrac{4x^2+20x-24}{2x^2+x-10}$

d. $\dfrac{16x-12}{4x^2+5x-6} - \dfrac{3}{x+2}$

12-26. Examine the graph of $f(x)=|x-3|+1$ at right. Use the graph to find the values listed below.

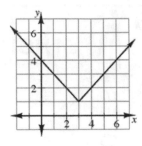

a. $f(3)$ b. $f(0)$

c. $f(4)$ d. $f(-1)$

12-27. Use the graph of $f(x)=|x-3|+1$ in problem 12-26 to solve the equations and inequalities below. It may be helpful to copy the graph onto graph paper first.

a. $|x-3|+1=1$ b. $|x-3|+1\le4$

c. $|x-3|+1=3$ d. $|x-3|+1>2$

12-28. Solve the quadratic below *twice*: once by factoring and using the Zero Product Property and once by completing the square. Verify that the solutions match.

$$x^2+14x+33=0$$

12-29. Match each graph below with its domain.

a. D: All values of x b. D: $x>-2$ c. D: $x\le3$

1) 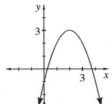 2) 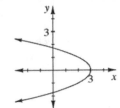 3)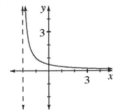

12-30. Graph the two functions below and find all points where they intersect. List all points in the form (x, y).

$$f(x)=x^2-3x-10$$
$$g(x)=-5x-7$$

12.2.1 How can I solve it?

Solving Work Problems

So far in this course you have learned to solve many different types of word problems using a variety of tools. During Section 12.2, you will complete your understanding of solving word problems by focusing on two new types: those that involve rates of work and those that involve a mixture of quantities.

12-31.   MOWING THE LAWN

The National Mall, located in Washington, D.C., is a mile-long rectangular lawn surrounded by several museums and famous monuments. It has been the site of many major historical and political events.

The lawn is cared for by two teams of gardeners. It takes one team (working alone) 10 hours to mow the lawn, while it takes the other team 15 hours to cut the entire lawn area.

Your Task: With your team, determine how long it would take to mow the entire lawn if both teams of gardeners work together. Create a diagram on graph paper to represent the work done by each team. Write and solve an equation for this situation. Be sure to define your variable(s).

Discussion Points

What is the goal of this task?

About how many hours would it take to mow the lawn if they worked together?
Make an estimate. Is it more or less than 10 hours? Why?

Does it matter how big the lawn is?
Why or why not?

How much of the lawn does each team of gardeners mow in one hour?
How can you tell?

Further Guidance

12-32.   To help solve problem 12-31, analyze what each piece of information gives you.

   a.   One team of gardeners can mow the lawn in 10 hours. How much of the lawn can this team mow in one hour? Draw a diagram to represent how much of the lawn this team can mow in one hour.

   b.   The other team of gardeners can mow the lawn in 15 hours. How much of the lawn can this second team mow in one hour? Draw a diagram to represent how much of the lawn this team can mow in one hour.

   c.   When the two teams of gardeners work together, how much of the lawn is mowed per hour? Explain how you got your answer.

   d.   How long will it take for both teams of gardeners to mow the entire lawn? Explain how you got your answer.

   e.   Write and solve an equation to represent this situation. Be sure to define your variables.

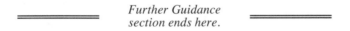

Further Guidance
section ends here.

12-33.   Hong can staple the programs for graduation in 30 minutes. However, since Eva has an electric stapler, it only takes her 10 minutes. If they work together, how long will it take to staple the programs? Be ready to share your work with the class.

12-34.   It takes Frederick 8 minutes to wash his dad's truck. When he works with his sister, it takes them only 6 minutes. How long would it take his sister to wash the truck alone? Write and solve an equation for this situation.

12-35.   Ellie estimates that it would take 3 students 2 hours to hang 50 streamers for the prom. If she has 5 students hang streamers for 3 hours, how many streamers could be hung? Explain how you found your answer.

12-36.   Solve the quadratic equation below *twice*, once by completing the square and once by using the Quadratic Formula. Leave all solutions in exact form. Verify that your solutions from each method match.

$$x^2 + 11 = 8x$$

12-37.   Susan can paint her living room in 2 hours. Her friend, Jaime, estimates it would take him 3 hours to paint the same room. If they work together, how long will it take them to paint Susan's living room?

12-38.   Write and solve an equation (or system of equations) for the situation below. Define your variable(s) and write your solution as a sentence.

Jessica has 147 coins that are all dimes and quarters. The number of quarters is 6 fewer than twice the number of dimes. What is the value of her coins?

12-39.   Which of the following expressions are equivalent to $12x^6$? (Note: More than one answer is possible!)

a. $3(2x^3)^2$ b. $(6x^8)(2x^{-2})$

c. $(144x^{12})^{1/2}$ d. $\dfrac{60x^{10}y}{5x^4y}$

12-40.   Find the equation of $f(x)$ graphed at right.

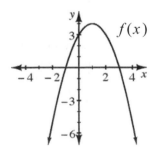

12-41.   Solve each equation or inequality below, if possible. Check your solution.

a. $-(x-3)(x+1) = 4$

b. $10|x-3| > 40$

c. $(x-5)^3 = 8$

12.2.2 How can I solve it?

Solving Percent Mixture Problems

Today you will continue to develop ways to apply your problem-solving techniques to solve word problems as you examine a new type of problem: percent mixture problems.

12-42. GET OUT THE VOTE

In an election for school president, 40% of 7th graders and 90% of 8th graders voted for John. If 1000 students voted in the election, and if John ended up with 72% of the votes, how many students are in each grade at John's school? Assume that John's school only contains 7th and 8th grades. Explain how you found your answer.

12-43. This year, the math club decided to make candy gifts for graduates. They will mix Choco-nuts, which cost $1 per ounce, with Munchies, which cost $2 per ounce. They would like their candy bags to weigh 4 ounces and cost $5.40. How much of each type of candy should be used per bag?

12-44. Antoine works in the paint department at his local hardware store. He is trying to create a new color of paint using two different colors in stock: powder blue, which is made with 2% blue (the rest is white), and spring blue, which is 10% blue (the rest is white). He wants to end up with one gallon of paint made with 4% blue. How much of each color should he use?

12-45. In your Learning Log, describe what you know about solving percent mixture problems. Explain in your own words how to set up an equation or use Guess and Check to help solve this type of problem. Be sure to include an example. Title this entry "Percent Mixture Problems" and include today's date.

12-46. How much coffee costing $6 a pound should be mixed with 3 pounds of coffee costing $4 per pound to create a mixture costing $4.75 per pound?

12-47.   If $g(x) = \sqrt{x-3} + 1$, find the values below. If there is no solution, **justify** your conclusion.

a. $g(7)$ b. $g(4)$ c. $g(8)$ d. $g(2)$

12-48.   Graph the function $f(x) = |x-3| - 1$ and label all of its special points.

12-49.   Add, subtract, multiply, or divide the expressions below. Leave your answer as simplified as possible.

a. $\frac{4x^2-13x+3}{5x^2+23x-10} \cdot \frac{5x-2}{x^2+6x-27} \cdot \frac{x^2+5x-36}{4x-1}$ b. $\frac{x^2-9}{x^2+6x+9} \div \frac{x^2-x-6}{x^2+4}$

c. $6 + \frac{3}{x+1}$ d. $\frac{5}{x} - \frac{10}{x^2+2x}$

12-50.   Find the point(s) of intersection of the line and parabola below. Be sure to check each point by substituting it back into both equations.

$$y = 3x^2 - 5x + 2$$
$$y = 4x + 2$$

12-51.   Solve the following quadratic equations by completing the square, if possible. Leave your answers in *exact* form. Check your solution(s).

a. $x^2 - 14x = -24$ b. $x^2 + 6x - 9 = 0$

c. $x^2 - 198x + 9797 = 0$ d. $x^2 - 9x = 15.75$

12.3.1 How can I derive it?

$$x = \frac{-b \pm \sqrt{b^2 - 4ac}}{2a}$$

Deriving the Quadratic Formula

In Chapter 9 you learned how to solve quadratic equations with the Quadratic Formula and the Zero Product Property. At the time, you had not yet learned how to complete the square of a quadratic equation and thus were not able to derive the Quadratic Formula by completing the square. You now have the tools to derive the Quadratic Formula by completing the square. To do this, you will start with the equation $ax^2 + bx + c = 0$ and will solve for x to prove that:

$$x = \frac{-b \pm \sqrt{b^2 - 4ac}}{2a}$$

12-52.   DERIVATION OF THE QUADRATIC FORMULA

The steps below outline a proof that if

$$ax^2 + bx + c = 0, \text{ then } x = \frac{-b \pm \sqrt{b^2 - 4ac}}{2a}.$$

Fold a piece of lined paper in half
vertically, make a crease, and then
unfold the paper. Copy the algebraic
steps shown below onto the left-hand
side of your paper. Write your answer
to each question to the right of the
corresponding algebraic step.

Problem: Solve the equation $ax^2 + bx + c = 0$.

1. $ax^2 + bx = -c$ What was done to get this?

2. $x^2 + \frac{b}{a}x = -\frac{c}{a}$ What was done to get this?

Now complete the square.

3. $x^2 + \frac{b}{a}x + \frac{b^2}{4a^2} = \frac{b^2}{4a^2} - \frac{c}{a}$ Why did we choose $\frac{b^2}{4a^2}$?

4. $(x + \frac{b}{2a})^2 = \frac{b^2}{4a^2} - \frac{c}{a}$ What was done to get this?

5. $(x + \frac{b}{2a})^2 = \frac{b^2 - 4ac}{4a^2}$ What was done to get this?

You're very close! Now solve for x.

6. $x + \frac{b}{2a} = \pm \frac{\sqrt{b^2 - 4ac}}{2a}$ Why is there a $\pm$ symbol?

7. $x = -\frac{b}{2a} \pm \frac{\sqrt{b^2 - 4ac}}{2a}$ What was done to get this?

Finally, simplify the result.

8. $x = \frac{-b \pm \sqrt{b^2 - 4ac}}{2a}$ What was done to get this result?

12-53.   Use the Quadratic Formula to solve the following quadratic equations. Be sure to
check your solutions, if possible.

a. $8x^2 + 14x - 15 = 0$ b. $5m + 0.5m^2 - 3 = 0$

c. $k^2 - 10k = -30$ d. $4x^2 - 25 = 0$

12-54.   Solve the quadratics below by first completing the square. Leave your solutions in exact form.

a. $x^2 - 10x + 22 = 0$ b. $x^2 + 2x = 18$

12-55.   Ms. Speedi's favorite recipe for fruit punch requires 12% apple juice. How much pure apple juice should she add to 2 gallons of punch that has 8% apple juice to meet her standards?

12-56.   Graph the function $g(x) = \sqrt{x-3} + 1$ on graph paper. Describe its domain and range.

12-57.   Use the graph of $f(x)$ at right to find the following values.

a. $f(1)$ b. $f(-6)$

c. $f(0)$ d. $f(-3)$

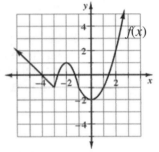

12-58.   Factor the quadratics below using any method.

a. $x^2 - 81$ b. $x^2 + 12x + 36$

c. $4x^2 - 4x - 3$ d. $16x^2 - 25$

12-59.   Where do the two parabolas below intersect? Show how you know.

$$y = x^2 + 4x - 2$$
$$y = x^2 - 3x + 5$$

12-60.   Write three different single-term expressions that are equivalent to x^{-2}. At least one expression should use division and another should use multiplication. Show how you know that your expressions are equivalent.

12.4.1 How can I make a prediction?

Using Data and Trend Lines to Make Predictions

In today's activity, you will use data to make a prediction. As you work, remember to find all the **connections** you can between different representations.

12-61.   THE BURNING CANDLE

Today is your friend's birthday. You want to surprise her by walking into the room carrying a piece of cake with a lit candle. However, you only have one candle and you are not sure it will stay lit long enough. Can you predict when the candle will burn out?

Your Task: Collect data for your burning candle that will help you predict when it will burn out. Collect data for at least two minutes (but no more than three minutes to save the candle for the surprise!). Then analyze the data and make a prediction. Your analysis must include:

- At least three representations of the data.

- An explanation of how you can use the equation to determine when the candle will burn out.

Discussion Points

What data should be collected as the candle burns?

What should the graph of the data look like?

Which representation can help you determine the most accurate prediction?

Further Guidance

12-62.   Start by collecting data from the burning candle. Record its weight at various times after it has started to burn. (The candle's weight is easier and safer to measure than its height.) Make sure you let the candle burn for at least two minutes, but no more than three minutes. Also be sure you get at least five data points. When all the data is collected, blow the candle out.

12-54.   Solve the quadratics below by first completing the square. Leave your solutions in exact form.

a. $x^2 - 10x + 22 = 0$ b. $x^2 + 2x = 18$

12-55.   Ms. Speedi's favorite recipe for fruit punch requires 12% apple juice. How much pure apple juice should she add to 2 gallons of punch that has 8% apple juice to meet her standards?

12-56.   Graph the function $g(x) = \sqrt{x-3} + 1$ on graph paper. Describe its domain and range.

12-57.   Use the graph of $f(x)$ at right to find the following values.

a. $f(1)$ b. $f(-6)$

c. $f(0)$ d. $f(-3)$

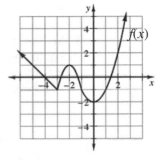

12-58.   Factor the quadratics below using any method.

a. $x^2 - 81$ b. $x^2 + 12x + 36$

c. $4x^2 - 4x - 3$ d. $16x^2 - 25$

12-59.   Where do the two parabolas below intersect? Show how you know.

$$y = x^2 + 4x - 2$$
$$y = x^2 - 3x + 5$$

12-60.   Write three different single-term expressions that are equivalent to x^{-2}. At least one expression should use division and another should use multiplication. Show how you know that your expressions are equivalent.

12.4.1   How can I make a prediction?

Using Data and Trend Lines to Make Predictions

In today's activity, you will use data to make a prediction. As you work, remember to find all the **connections** you can between different representations.

12-61.   THE BURNING CANDLE

Today is your friend's birthday. You want to surprise her by walking into the room carrying a piece of cake with a lit candle. However, you only have one candle and you are not sure it will stay lit long enough. Can you predict when the candle will burn out?

Your Task: Collect data for your burning candle that will help you predict when it will burn out. Collect data for at least two minutes (but no more than three minutes to save the candle for the surprise!). Then analyze the data and make a prediction. Your analysis must include:

- At least three representations of the data.

- An explanation of how you can use the equation to determine when the candle will burn out.

Discussion Points

What data should be collected as the candle burns?

What should the graph of the data look like?

Which representation can help you determine the most accurate prediction?

Further Guidance

12-62.   Start by collecting data from the burning candle. Record its weight at various times after it has started to burn. (The candle's weight is easier and safer to measure than its height.) Make sure you let the candle burn for at least two minutes, but no more than three minutes. Also be sure you get at least five data points. When all the data is collected, blow the candle out.

12-63.   Let x represent the time (in seconds) since the candle started to burn, and let y represent the weight of the candle. Make an $x \rightarrow y$ table showing the data you collected for the burning candle.

12-64.   With your team, decide how the axes should be scaled for a graph of the candle data. Then graph the data you have collected. Agree with your teammates on a trend line that best fits the data, and add it to your graph.

12-65.   Use your trend line to determine when the candle will burn out as you answer the questions below.

    a.   Write the equation for your trend line.

    b.   What do you know about the point on the graph at which the candle burns out? Do you know the value of either x or y at this point?

    c.   Use your equation and your answer to part (b) to solve for the time when the candle will burn out.

12-66.   Aura thinks the solution to the systems of equations at right is $(-2, 4)$ while Edison thinks the solution is $(2, -2)$. Teresito thinks they are both wrong. Who is correct? **Justify** your answer.

$$3x + 2y = 2$$
$$5x - 12 = y$$

12-67.   Evaluate the expression below when $x = 27$ and $y = 16$.

$$6x^{2/3}y^{1/4} \cdot x^{-1}y^{1/2}$$

12-68.   Graph the function $h(x) = -\sqrt{3-x}$. Use inequalities to describe its domain and range.

12-69.   If $f(x) = \frac{-5}{x+2}$ and $g(x) = (x-2)^3$, find each output value below (if possible). If it is not possible, explain why not.

    a. $f(-2)$ b. $g(-1)$ c. $g(4)$ d. $f(-7) + g(1)$ e. $f(3) - g(2)$

12-70.   James used the Distributive Property and got $6m - 12$. Find an expression that he could have started with.

12-71.   Find all of the points at which the parabolas below intersect. Write your solution(s) in (x, y) form.

$$y = x^2 - x + 12$$
$$y = 2x^2 + 3x + 7$$

12.4.2   What do I know about the pattern?

Analyzing Non-linear Tile Patterns

Remember tile patterns? When you first studied tile patterns, most of the patterns you studied grew linearly. You now have the tools to analyze more complex patterns and can apply what you know about non-linear equations. Today your team will use multiple representations to analyze and make predictions about a complex tile pattern.

12-72.   **TEAM PATTERN CHALLENGE**

Your teacher will assign your team one of the tile patterns below to analyze.

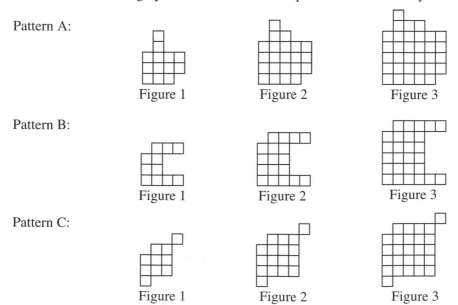

Pattern A:

Figure 1   Figure 2   Figure 3

Pattern B:

Figure 1   Figure 2   Figure 3

Pattern C:

Figure 1   Figure 2   Figure 3

Your Task: With your team, analyze your pattern completely. Create a stand-alone poster that shows all the things you discovered about your tile pattern. Your poster must also include the information described below.

Problem continues on next page →

Algebra Connections

12-72.   *Problem continued from previous page.*

Pattern Analysis:

- Figures 0 through 4.

- An $x \to y$ table.

- A graph.

- A sketch and description of the 100th figure.

- A rule for the xth figure.

Using the Rule:

- How can you rewrite your rule? Use algebra to simplify your rule.

- Use your rule to make predictions about figures in your pattern that you cannot draw.

  - How many tiles are in Figure 538?

  - *Pattern A*: Which figure will have 555,022 tiles?
    Pattern B: Which figure will have 491,403 tiles?
    Pattern C: Which figure will have 608,401 tiles?

12-73.   If a tile pattern can be described by the equation $y = (x-1)(x+1) + x + 2$, where x represents the figure number and y represents the number of tiles, find each of the following.

a.   The number of tiles in Figure 307.

b.   The number of the figure that contains 169,333 tiles.

12-74.   Solve the equations and inequalities below. Write your solutions in exact form.

a. $\frac{3}{4} - \frac{x}{3} = \frac{7-x}{4}$ b. $(b-4)^2 < 12$

c. $|3+x| - 9 \le 21$ d. $5n^2 - 11n + 2 = 0$

12-75.   Graph the parabola described by the following equation by finding its x-intercepts and vertex.

$$y = 3x^2 - 10x + 2$$

12-76. For $f(x) = \frac{x^2}{x+5}$ and $g(x) = \sqrt{3x-2}$, find the following, if possible.

    a. $f(6)$ b. $g(17)$ c. $f(-5)$ d. $g(-2)$

    e. $g(-1) - f(2)$ f. $f(4) + g(2)$ g. $g(x+2)$ h. $f(x-1)$

12-77. Add or subtract the following rational expressions. Then simplify your solutions, if possible.

    a. $\dfrac{x-4}{2x^2+9x-5} + \dfrac{x+3}{x^2+5x}$ b. $\dfrac{4x^2-11x+6}{2x^2-x-6} - \dfrac{x+2}{2x+3}$

12-78. **Multiple Choice:** Which of the following expressions is equivalent to $x^2 - 12x + 40$?

    a. $(x-6)^2 + 4$ b. $(x-6)^2 + 28$

    c. $(x-12)^2 + 4$ d. $(x-12)^2$

12-79. Examine the graph of the relation at right.

    a.   Use inequalities to name its domain and range.

    b.   Is this relation a function? How can you tell?

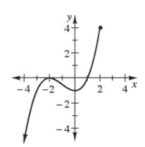

12-80. If a tile pattern can be described by the equation $y = (x-1)(x+2) + x$, where x represents the figure number and y represents the number of tiles, find each of the following.

    a.   The number of tiles in Figure 211.

    b.   The number of the figure that contains 6558 tiles.

12-81. Erika can mow her family's lawn in 3 hours. Her little brother can do it in 5 hours. How long will it take them to mow the lawn if they work together?

12-82. Find the equation of the line parallel to $3x + 2y = 10$ that goes through the point $(4, -7)$.

12-83. Rich has $1,268,714 and is spending $2,742 per day. Fred, on the other hand, has $231,384 and is saving $100 per day. When will they have the same amount of money saved? How much will each have at that time?

12-84.   **Multiple Choice:** For which of the following equations or inequalities is $x = -1$ a solution?

a. $(x+3)^2 > 4$ b. $\frac{x+5}{2} = 2x^2$ c. $\sqrt{x+6} = 25$ d. $x^2 + 5x + 6 = 0$

12.4.3   What do I know about the inequality?

Investigating a Complex Function

Over the course of this year, you have studied many different kinds of functions and inequalities: linear, quadratic, absolute values, square roots, and others. Today you will use the tools you have learned to analyze a new and interesting inequality.

12-85.   FUNKY FUNCTION

The following relation combines two functions you have studied to make a new kind of graph.

$$f(x) = \left| 3 - 2x - x^2 \right| + 2$$

Your Task: With your team, create a *complete* description of the graph of $f(x)$.

Discussion Points

What does a complete description of a graph include?

How can you graph a relation when
you have no idea what it will look like?

Apply and Extend

12-86.   For the function $f(x) = \left| 3 - 2x - x^2 \right| + 2$, find $f(14)$.

12-87.   Use your graph and rule to find every x-value for which $\left| 3 - 2x - x^2 \right| + 2 = 6$.

12-88.   What if the equation in problem 12-85 were an inequality instead? Consider the inequality $y > \left| 3 - 2x - x^2 \right| + 2$. How would you need to change your graph to represent the solutions for $y > \left| 3 - 2x - x^2 \right| + 2$? **Justify** your conclusion.

12-89.   Is $(-5, 7)$ a solution to $y < \sqrt{x^2 + 24}$? Show how you know.

12-90.   The graphs of several relations are shown below. Decide if each is a function. If the relation is not a function, explain why not.

a. 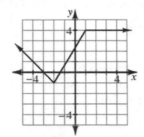   b. 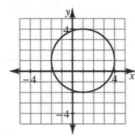   c.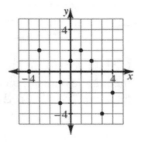

12-91.   Solve the quadratics below by completing the square. Leave your solutions in exact form.

a. $x^2 - 6x - 12 = 0$ b. $x^2 - 3 = 4x$

12-92.   Determine the number of solutions for each of the quadratics below. Note: You do not need to solve the quadratics.

a. $(x - 5)^2 = -6$ b. $312x^2 + 514x + 181 = 0$

c. $(x + 3)^2 - 10 = 0$ d. $4x^2 + 49 = 28x$

12-93.   Jeremiah inherited his grandmother's very large coin collection at the end of the year 2000. Since then, he has been giving away or selling the coins from the collection. The table at right shows the decreasing number of coins in his collection for the past six years.

Year	# of Coins
2000	1617
2001	1552
2002	1498
2003	1453
2004	1401
2005	1344

a.   Find the equation of a line that best fits Jeremiah's data.

b.   At this rate, when should Jeremiah expect to be out of coins?

12-94.   If $f(-1) = 7$ and $f(3) = 8$, and if the graph of $f(x)$ is a line:

a.   Graph the line on graph paper.

b.   Find the equation for $f(x)$.

c.   If $g(x)$ is a line that is perpendicular to $f(x)$, what is its slope?

12.4.4   What is the largest area?

Using Algebra to Find a Maximum

In this final activity, you will **connect** and **apply** much of your knowledge from throughout the course to solve a challenging problem.

12-95.   FENCING LESSONS

Lucy wants to be a farmer, just like her dad. Her father says he will give her some cows to raise if she can build them a good pen. Lucy saves her money and buys 30 meters of fencing material. She will use it to build a rectangular pen against one wall of her family's barn, as shown in the picture at right.

Lucy has come to you for help. She wants to build a pen for her cows that gives them as much possible area to roam. How long should each side of the fence be to give the cows as much roaming area as possible? How can you convince Lucy that the pen is the largest?

Your Tasks:

- Create a poster showing all four representations of this situation.

- On your poster, include a drawing of the pen with the largest possible area. State its dimensions (width and height) and its area.

- Use multiple representations to **justify** your conclusion that this is the largest pen.

Discussion Points

What is the goal of this problem?

What can *x* and *y* represent in this situation?

What are the possible dimensions
of the rectangular pen?

How can you collect and represent data
about the different-sized pens?

Further Guidance

12-96.   MAKING A TABLE

Start by trying out some different-sized pens to see which ones appear to give the largest area. Your teacher will show you how to use string to make models of possible pens.

a.   Start an $x \rightarrow y$ table for this situation. Let x be the length of the sides of the pen that are attached to the barn and let y represent the enclosed area. Use your string model to try out at least four other sets of pen dimensions. Calculate the area for each pen you try and enter your data into your table.

b.   Of all the pens you have tried so far, which dimensions have created the largest possible roaming area for the cows? Do you think this is the largest area possible? Why or why not?

12-97.   MAKING A GRAPH

A graph can help you analyze the data.

a.   Graph the data from problem 12-96. Be careful about how you scale your axes, so that all the possible pens will fit on your graph.

b.   Is there a point on the graph where x is almost as big as it can possibly be? Do you have a point on your graph where x is almost as small as it can possibly be? If you are missing pens like these, build an example of each one using your string, enter the lengths and areas in your table, and plot the points on your graph.

c.   Should the x-intercepts be included on your graph? Discuss this with your team and **justify** your conclusions. What do the x-intercepts of this graph represent?

12-98.   ANALYZING THE GRAPH

a.   Looking at the points you have plotted so far, can you see what the general shape of the graph will be? If so, sketch in what you think the whole graph should look like. If not, build some more pens with your string to fill in the sections of the graph where you do not have enough points. When you see the general shape of the graph, sketch it.

b.   Find the point on your graph representing the pen with the greatest area. What are the dimensions of this pen?

c.   Use your graph to approximate the greatest possible enclosed area.

Algebra Connections

12-99.   WRITING AN EQUATION

   a.   If length of the sides that are attached to the barn are x meters long, and if she has only 30 meters of barbed wire, write an expression for the width of the pen in terms of x.

   b.   Now write an equation for y, the area of the space enclosed by the fence, in terms of x. Simplify your equation.

   c.   What kind of graph should this equation have? Does it match your graph?

   d.   In your equation from part (b), set $y = 0$ and find the roots of the resulting equation. Does your graph from problem 12-98 confirm these roots?

   e.   Use your equation to find the vertex of the graph. Does your graph confirm this result?

   f.   Use your new results to find the largest possible roaming area Lucy can give her cows. What are the dimensions of this pen? Is this answer more precise than the one you got from your graph? How do you know?

12-100.   SHOWING YOUR WORK

   Finally, put together a poster showing your work on this problem. Be sure to include all four representations of the situation. Use the equation and the graph to **justify** to Lucy which dimensions the pen should have.

12-101.   Find the lowest point of the graph of the function $f(x) = 3x^2 + 15x - 18$. Explain how you know it is the lowest.

12-102.   Solve each equation.

   a. $\sqrt{y^2 + 5} = 3$ b. $\frac{x^2 + x - 6}{x + 3} = 6$

12-103.   Find the point(s) of intersection of the system of equations below. Show all your work.

$$y = 5x - 22$$
$$y = x^2 - 6x + 8$$

12-104. Graph the function $f(x) = \frac{5}{x-2}$. Use inequalities to describe its domain and range.

12-105. How much candy costing $8 a pound should be mixed with 6 pounds of candy costing $10 a pound to create a mixture costing $8.50 a pound?

12-106. Andrew and Charles were each asked to find the value of $(x^2)^{1/2}$ when $x = 10$. Their work is shown below.

Andrew: "When I tried other values of x for a different problem, I found that $(1^2)^{1/2} = 1$, $(2^2)^{1/2} = 2$, and $(3^2)^{1/2} = 3$. So, I predict that $(10^2)^{1/2}$ must equal 10."

Charles: "Since $(x^a)^b = x^{ab}$, then $(x^2)^{1/2}$ must equal $x^{2 \cdot (1/2)}$. I can simplify this to become $x^{2/2} = x$. Therefore $(x^2)^{1/2}$ must be x and when $x = 10$, $(10^2)^{1/2} = 10$."

a. Who used inductive reasoning? Who used deductive reasoning? For each person, explain how you know.

b. What is the difference between inductive and deductive reasoning?

c. Without a calculator, find the value of $(x^2)^{1/2}$ when $x = 312$ and when $x = 7344$.

12-107. Find the point of intersection of the two functions below using any method. Describe how you found your solution.

$$y = 2x + 9$$
$$y = x^2 - 2x - 3$$

12-108. Find the equation of the line perpendicular to $3x - y = 4$ that goes through the point $(-12, 4)$.

12-109. Graph the inequality $y > |x - 2| + 1$ on graph paper.

12-110. Determine the number of solutions for each of the quadratics below. *Note:* You do not need to solve the quadratics.

a. $(x - 2)^2 = -3$

b. $6x^2 - x - 2 = 0$

c. $4x^2 - 4x + 1 = 0$

d. $427x^2 + 731x - 280 = 0$

Additional California Topics 1.1

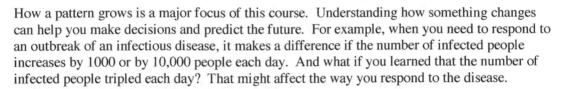

Investigating the Growth of Patterns

This lesson is designed to follow Lesson 1.1.4.

How a pattern grows is a major focus of this course. Understanding how something changes can help you make decisions and predict the future. For example, when you need to respond to an outbreak of an infectious disease, it makes a difference if the number of infected people increases by 1000 or by 10,000 people each day. And what if you learned that the number of infected people tripled each day? That might affect the way you respond to the disease.

Today you will work with your study team to analyze this and other situations that involve different types of relationships. As you work together, ask each other the following questions to start and continue productive mathematical discussions.

What is the pattern? How is it changing? How can you describe it?

How does it grow (or get smaller)?

How can we organize the data?

ACT-1. DATA LABS

Today your team will collect and analyze data from three labs, which are described below. At each station, read the directions carefully, and collect and record your data. While you may visit the stations in any order, do not split your team members between stations. Instead, make sure you visit each station as a team so that every team member understands what the data represents and how each pattern is changing.

Once your data is collected, move on to problems ACT-2 and ACT-3 to analyze your data.

Lab A: Hot Tub Design

Perry is designing a hot tub that he will locate behind his house. He has 36 square designer tiles to use for the bottom of his hot tub. He wants to use all of the tiles, but he does not yet know how he will arrange them to form the hot tub. If his hot tub will be rectangular, how many different rectangles with an area of 36 square units does he have to choose from?

Use the square tiles provided to find as many rectangular configurations as you can. Remember to record the length and the width of each rectangle you find. Assume that Perry's yard is big enough to accommodate any rectangular design you create and that it matters which dimension is the width and which is the length.

Problem continues on next page →

ACT-1.   *Problem continued from previous page.*

Lab B: Local Crisis

Health officials in Parsnipville are concerned about the recent outbreak of the flu. While scientists are working hard to find a vaccine, the town leaders are turning to you to predict how many people will be sick over time. They hope to find a vaccine in a week. Here are the facts: The epidemic started when Velma and Stanley returned from their exotic vacation with symptoms of the flu. Then, each day, the number of sick people has multiplied by three. The town of Parsnipville has 3800 citizens.

Use the beans (or other material) provided by your teacher to represent the people infected with the flu. Start with two beans to represent Velma and Stanley. Then carefully replace each bean with three beans to represent the growth of the disease. Collect (and record) data for the first few days until you understand how the disease is growing.

Lab C: Sign On the Dotted Line

Certain legal documents, such as those used when buying property, sometimes require up to 50 signatures! How long do you think that might take? To find out, collect data as one person of your team signs his or her first name. Have a team member use a stop watch to time how long it takes to sign his or her first name 2, 3, 5, 7, and 10 times. In order to collect good, clean data, be sure to have your team member practice signing his or her first name before you start.

ACT-2.   REPRESENTING DATA

In problem ACT-1, you collected data for three different situations. Now your team will work together to find ways of representing the data to help answer questions in problem ACT-3. Obtain an ACT2 Resource Page from your teacher.

a.   For each lab, complete the corresponding table below on the resource page. Use patterns to complete your table for any values in the top row not already included in your data from problem ACT-1. Some entries are started for you.

Lab A: Hot Tub Design

Width of Hot Tub	1	2	3	4	6	9	12	18	36
Length of Hot Tub	36								

Lab B: Local Crisis

Day	0	1	2	3	4	5	6	7
# of Infected People	2							

Lab C: Sign On the Dotted Line

# of Signatures	0	1	2	3	4	5	6	7	8	9	10
Time (in seconds)											

Problem continues on next page →

ACT-2.   *Problem continued from previous page.*

    b.   Now plot your data from each lab on the set of axes provided on the resource page. Note that some data points may not fit on the given axes. Then describe each graph. What does each graph look like? Should the points be connected?

    c.   For each graph, find the point where $x = 4$ and label it with its coordinate. Then explain what that point represents in each context.

ACT-3.   ANALYSIS

    Graphs and tables not only represent data, but they also allow you to answer questions about the data. Use your tables and graphs on the resource page from problem ACT-2 to answer the questions below.

    a.   Which data appears to be linear? That is, when graphed, which data forms a line? Explain why it makes sense for this context to have a linear graph.

    b.   The town of Parsnipville will have a vaccine on Day 7. Since the town has 3800 citizens, how many people will need the vaccine on that day? Is it easier to answer this question with your graph or with your table? Explain.

    c.   Now that Perry knows his options for the design of his hot tub, he wants to pick the hot tub that has the smallest perimeter. What do you recommend?

    d.   Why isn't there a point when $x = 0$ for your graph for Lab A? Could there be? Explain.

METHODS AND MEANINGS

Direct and Inverse Variation

There are several special relationships that you will study in this course. One of these is called **direct variation** (also called **direct proportion**). The data you gathered in the "Sign on the Dotted Line" lab (in problem ACT-1) is an example of direction variation.

Another relationship you will study about in this course is **inverse variation** (also called **inverse proportion**). The data collected in the "Hot Tub Design" lab (in problem ACT-1) is an example of inverse variation.

While direct and inverse variation will be formally defined in a later lesson, examples of graphs of both types of variation are shown at right.

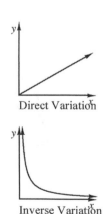

Direct Variation

Inverse Variation

ACT-4. Consider the situation described below.

a. Meredith lives 24 blocks from her friend's house. If she travels 1 block every minute, how many minutes will it take her to reach her friend's house? What if she travels 2 blocks every minute? Show how you calculated each answer.

b. Copy and complete the table below to represent the amount of time it would take Meredith to get to her friend's house.

Speed (in blocks per minute)	1	2	3	4	6	8	10	12	24
Time to Get to Her Friend's House (in mins)									

c. What happens to the time it takes to get to her friend's house as Meredith's speed increases? Explain.

ACT-5. In December of 2003, the average price for a gallon of regular gas in the United States was $1.50.

a. At that time, what did it cost to buy 12 gallons of gas?

b. Gerald paid $12.60 for a tank of gas. How many gallons did he buy?

c. At right is a graph of this situation. Predict how the line would change to represent the average cost of gas in December of 2005, when gas cost $2.20 per gallon on average.

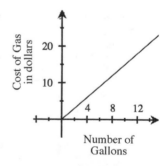

d. Review the Math Notes box for this lesson. Does the cost of gas vary directly with the number of gallons or inversely? Explain how you know.

ACT-6. Marilee has a collection of three football jerseys with the numbers 2, 5, and 14 on them. One way to represent a set (or collection) of numbers on the jerseys is with **set notation**. Using set notation, Marilee's set of jerseys numbers can be written $\{2, 5, 14\}$. The "curly" brackets indicate that it is the set of objects that are listed inside the brackets.

a. If she decides to pack only one jersey for a trip, one choice is $\{2\}$. What other choices could she make? Use set notation to represent your solutions.

b. How many ways could she choose two jerseys? Use set notation to list all the ways Marilee could select two jerseys to take on her trip.

Algebra Connections

ACT-7. Consider the statement, "The sum of two odd numbers is odd." Is this statement true or false? Explain your reasoning. If the statement is false, produce a **counterexample** (an example that shows at least one exception).

ACT-8. If a and b are any positive integers, decide if each statement below is sometimes true, always true, or never true. **Explain** how you made your decision.

a. $a + b = b + a$ b. $a - b = b - a$

c. $a \cdot b = b \cdot a$ d. $a \div b = b \div a$

Additional California Topics 1.2

Algebraic Properties

This lesson is designed to follow Lesson 2.1.9.

One of the Ways of Thinking used in this course is **Justifying**. Up until now, you have justified your conclusions using explanations and reasoning to convince others. Another way to demonstrate valid conclusions is to use algebraic properties (sometimes referred to as "laws"). During this lesson, you will use the Commutative, Associative, Identity, and Inverse Properties of addition and multiplication to justify conclusions and determine if other conclusions are valid.

ACT-9. Use algebra tiles and an expression comparison mat to show that the expressions below are equivalent.

$$3 + (2x^2 + 3x) \text{ and } (3 + 2x^2) + 3x$$

a. State the algebraic property that justifies that they are equivalent.

b. Use the same property to rewrite the expression $(4 + y) + 2y$. Then simplify the expression as much as possible.

c. What if the terms are not being added? Does the Associative Property still hold? Use algebra tiles and an expression comparison mat to compare $2x^2 - (3x - 8)$ with $(2x^2 - 3x) - 8$. Are these expressions equivalent? Explain.

d. Your work for part (c) answered the question "What if the terms are not being added?" What is another question you could ask about the Associative Property? Create another test for the Associative Property that will help you better understand the conditions under which it holds true. Be creative. When you are finished, be prepared to share your results with your class.

ACT-10. When finding the perimeter of the shape at right for part (b) of problem 2-13, Kiet and Corvell saw the shape differently. Their resulting expressions are shown below.

Kiet: $2+2x+2$ Corvell: $2+x+3+x-1$

a. Examine each expression. Is each expression valid for the perimeter of the shape? **Justify** your conclusion.

b. Show that the expressions are equivalent. What algebraic properties can be used to demonstrate that Kiet's expression is equivalent to Corvell's expression?

ACT -11. Examine the work below of a student simplifying the expression $9-(3-5y)$. Is the work valid? If so, **justify** your conclusion by naming the algebraic properties. If not, explain which statement (or statements) is incorrect and provide a valid strategy to simplify the expression.

Note: This stoplight icon will appear periodically throughout the text. Problems with this icon display common errors that can be made. Be sure not to make the same mistakes yourself!

a. $9-(3-5y)$
b. $(9-3)-5y$
c. $(6+3-3)-5y$
d. $(6+0)-5y$
e. $6-5y$

ACT-12. Using algebra tiles, Brad and Donis each used different steps to simplify the expression $-5+2x+8$. Their work is show below. For each student's work, justify each step by naming the property that was used or other valid reasoning. Then compare their strategies.

Donis's work

Statement	Reason
1. $-5+2x+8$	Given
2. $2x+8+(-5)$	a.
3. $2x+3+5+(-5)$	b.
4. $2x+3+0$	c.
5. $2x+3$	d.

Brad's work

Statement	Reason
1. $-5+2x+8$	Given
2. $-5+2x+5+3$	e.
3. $-5+5+2x+3$	f.
4. $0+2x+3$	g.
5. $2x+3$	h.

ACT-13. Determine if the following statements are always true, sometimes true, or never true. **Justify** your conclusion.

    a. $3x^2 + 7 = 7 + 3x^2$ b. $2x - 1 = 5$

    c. $-(-18) = 18$ d. $-2 + 8 = -10$

    e.   A rectangle with perimeter of 10 units has an area of 6 square units.

ACT-14. Using the pattern shown at right, copy and complete the following Diamond Problems. Then answer parts (e) and (f) below.

    a.   b.   c.   d.

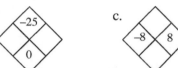

    e.   What property guarantees that (a) and (c) have the same solutions? Justify your answer.

    f.   Use the same property to find another solution to (b) above.

ACT -15. Examine the work below that shows one way to simplify the expression $-8 + 0 + (1 \cdot 5x + 13)$. Is the work valid? If so, **justify** your conclusion by naming the algebraic property for each step. If not, explain which statement (or statements) is incorrect and provide a valid strategy to simplify the expression.

    a. $-8 + 0 + (1 \cdot 5x + 13)$
    b. $-8 + (1 \cdot 5x + 13)$
    c. $-8 + (5x + 13)$
    d. $-8 + (13 + 5x)$
    e. $(-8 + 13) + 5x$
    f. $(-8 + 8 + 5) + 5x$
    g. $5 + 5x$

ACT-16. Review the algebraic properties found in the Math Notes boxes for Chapter 2. Then identify which property is being used below.

a. $1 \cdot (3y) = 3y$

b. $16 + 2x = 2x + 16$

c. $-4 + 4 = 0$

d. $3 + (6 + 2x) = (3 + 6) + 2x$

e. $18x^2 + 0 = 18x^2$

f. $\frac{3}{4} \cdot \frac{4}{3} = 1$

ACT-17. Decide if the following statements are true or false. **Justify** your conclusion.

a. $\frac{1}{2}(18) = 18 \div 2$

b. If $a + 2 = b$, then $a + 3 = b + 1$

c. $10 - 2 \cdot 5 = 40$

d. If $2x - 5 = 7$, then $x = 6$

ACT-18. The set of integers can be represented with the notation below.

$$\{..., -3, -2, -1, 0, 1, 2, 3, ...\}$$

Note that the "..." symbol indicates that the numbers continue to follow the pattern without end. Use set notation to represent the set of numbers described below.

a. The set of even numbers

b. The set of natural numbers (i.e., integers greater than or equal to zero)

ACT-19. Decide if the following statements are always, sometimes, or never true. Explain your answer.

a. When a number is squared, the result is always positive.

b. The product of two negative numbers is positive.

c. If a and b are integers, then $\frac{a}{b}$ is an integer.

d. If the number x is an even integer, then $x + 2$ must be odd.

Additional California Topics 1.3

Modeling Data

This lesson is designed to follow Lesson 3.2.4.

To find out if a roller coaster was safe, you collected data comparing a person's reach height with his or her height and found out that this data is roughly linear. What other types of graphs and rules can model a situation? Today you will examine a new situation in which data can help to answer a question.

ACT-20. BIRTHDAY PARTY

Kate is planning to ride her bike across town to attend her grandmother's 65th birthday party. The distance between her home and the party is 10 blocks. Assume that Kate will ride her bike at a constant rate.

a. If Kate takes 10 minutes to ride to the party, how fast does she need to travel in blocks per minute (bpm)? Explain how you found your answer.

b. How fast does Kate need to travel if she takes 5 minutes to ride from home to the party? 2 minutes? *1 minute?*

c. *Complete the table below. What is the relationship between the input (time it takes her to get from home to the party) and her corresponding speed?*

Traveling Time (min)	¼	½	1	2	4	5	10	15	20
Speed (blocks per min)									

d. Examine the data in the table. Is it linear? How can you tell?

ACT-21. GRAPHING THE DATA

Return to your data from part (c) of problem ACT-20. Carefully graph the points on graph paper. As you graph, answer the questions below. You may answer the questions in any order.

- What scale should you use so that you can plot all of the points and so that your graph is as large as possible?

- Can Kate's traveling time be exactly zero minutes? Why or why not? Adjust your graph to reflect your conclusion.

- Is the graph linear? If not, describe the shape formed by the data.

- What happens to Kate's speed as her traveling time increases?

- Does it make sense to connect the data? Why or why not?

- Have you seen this type of graph before? If so, in what circumstances (i.e., what was the situation or problem in which this type of graph appeared)?

ACT-22.   WRITING A RULE

While graphing your data in problem ACT-21, you may have noticed that you graphed a similar relationship in problem 3-103. Find your graph and table from problem 3-103 to learn more about this type of relationship.

a.   List four different points from the table in problem 3-103 in (x, y) form.

b.   What is the relationship between the x- and y-coordinates of each point from part (a)? How can you write this relationship algebraically?

c.   The relationship in problem 3-103 is an example of **inverse variation**. Any relationship for which the product of the x- and y-values is a constant is an example of inverse variation. The rule for this type of relationship is often written as $y = \frac{constant}{x}$ or as $xy = constant$. In the case of problem 3-103, the rule could be written as $y = \frac{24}{x}$ or $xy = 24$.

Examine your data from the Birthday Party, problem ACT-20. Does the product of the corresponding x- and y-values remain constant? If so, write a rule in the form $y = \frac{constant}{x}$.

d.   If Kate wants to get to her grandmother's party in 3 minutes, how fast does she need to travel? Confirm your answer using your graph and your rule. Which representation provides the most accurate answer?

ACT-23.   EXTENSION

Obtain a grapher from your teacher.

a.   Enter the points of your data from part (c) of problem ACT-20 into your grapher and plot the data. Choose an appropriate viewing window that will allow you to see all of the data points.

b.   Now graph the rule from part (c) of problem ACT-22 on top of the data. Does your rule seem to "fit" the data? If not, adjust your rule by changing the constant to find a better fit.

METHODS AND MEANINGS

More on Direct and Inverse Variation

When the product of each input and its corresponding output is a constant, the relationship is said to **vary inversely**. The relationship between Kate's traveling time and her speed in problem ACT-20 is an example of inverse variation.

If the product of x and y equals a constant (not equal to 0), then x **and** y **vary inversely**. Formally, x and y vary inversely (or, said differently, x and y are **inversely proportional**) if $xy = k$ *or* $y = \frac{k}{x}$ for a constant $k \neq 0$.

An example, $y = \frac{12}{x}$, is graphed at right. In the case of the Birthday Party problem (ACT-20), negative values of x and y are inappropriate. However, the rule $y = \frac{12}{x}$ does allow for negative and positive values for x and y, thus producing a portion of the graph in Quadrant III. Also note that the graph has no y-intercept, since $12 \div 0$ is undefined.

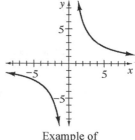

Example of
Inverse Variation

Another type of relationship is called **direct variation**. If the graph of a set of points is linear and passes through the point (0, 0), then y **varies directly with** x. Formally, x and y vary directly (or, said differently, are **directly proportional**) if for a constant k, not equal to zero, $y = kx$.

An example of direct variation, $y = \frac{1}{2}x$, is graphed at right. Notice that this example includes the portion of $y = \frac{1}{2}x$ in Quadrant III. However, in some direct variation situations, this portion of the graph may not make sense.

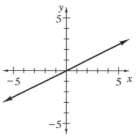

Example of
Direct Variation

ACT-24. On graph paper, draw at least three different rectangles with an area of 36 square units.

    a. Complete the table below for rectangles with an area of 36 square units.

Base	1	2	3	4	6	9	12	18	36	x
Height										

    b. Based on the data in the table, what type of relationship do x and y have? How can you tell?

    c. Write the rule you described in part (b) in algebraic symbols.

    d. Use the points in your table to graph this rule on graph paper.

ACT-25. In problems ACT-20 and ACT-24, you considered situations involving inverse variation. But what if y varies *directly* with x? Consider the situation where y is twice the value of x.

    a. How can you write this relationship algebraically? How is this rule different than an inverse variation relationship? You may want to review the Math Notes box from this lesson for more information.

    b. Create a table for this relationship.

    c. On graph paper, graph this relationship. Describe the resulting shape.

ACT-26. The amount of money Rachelle earns for babysitting varies directly with the number of hours she works. This means that the amount of money she earns is proportional to how many hours she works.

    a. If Rachelle earns $42 after babysitting 7 hours, how much does she earn per hour? How much should she earn if she babysits for 5 hours? Show how you found your answers.

    b. Rachelle decided to raise her rate to $9 per hour. How much will Rachelle earn if she babysits 3 hours? How many hours would she need to work to earn $45?

         Algebra Connections

ACT-27. During a trip to the Midwest, Mr. Presley spent the same amount each day. He kept records of his available money and created the graph at right.

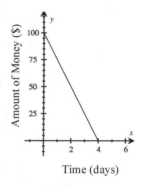

Amount of Money ($)

Time (days)

    a. How much money did Mr. Presley have at the start of his trip? How can you tell?

    b. How much did Mr. Presley spend each day? Explain how you know.

    c. What if Mr. Presley started with $150 but followed the same spending pattern. How would that change his graph? Explain.

    d. What if Mr. Presley spent less per day? Predict how that would change his graph.

ACT-28. Use your pattern-finding skills to copy and complete the table below.

IN (x)	−1	½	1	2	3	4	5	10
OUT (y)	−20	40	20	10				

    a. Explain any patterns you found in your table. How did you find each y-value?

    b. Examine the data in the table. Without graphing the data, predict whether the graph would be linear or not. **Justify** your conclusion.

    c. Write a rule for the data in the table. Use your rule to find y when $x = 100$.

Additional California Topics 1.4

Polynomial Division

This lesson is designed to follow Lesson 8.3.3.

In Chapter 5, you developed a strategy to multiply polynomials. Today, you will **reverse your thinking** to develop a strategy to divide polynomials. As you work today, use the questions below to stimulate mathematical conversation:

How can we represent it?

Will this strategy always work? If not, is there another strategy?

How can we verify our solution?

ACT-29. Use a generic rectangle to multiply $(x+2)(3x-5)$.

    a.   What is $(3x^2 + x - 10) \div (x+2)$? How do you know?

    b.   Likewise, determine $(3x^2 + x - 10) \div (3x - 5)$.

ACT-30. Now consider the problem $(2x^2 + 11x + 12) \div (x+4)$. How can you use a generic rectangle to find this **quotient** (the result of division)? With your team, find a way to complete the generic rectangle set up for you at right. As you work, answer the questions below in any order to help you make sense of the process.

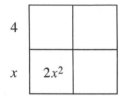

- Why are the terms x and 4 placed outside the generic rectangle, while the term $2x^2$ was placed inside the rectangle?

- What is the quotient? That is, what is $(2x^2 + 11x + 12) \div (x+4)$?

- How can you verify your solution?

ACT-31. What if the expression in problem ACT-30 were instead $(2x^2 + 11x + 13) \div (x+4)$?

    a.   How would that change your result? Discuss this with your team and be ready to share your **conjecture** (educated guess) with the class.

    b.   Now predict the result for $(2x^2 + 11x + 10) \div (x+4)$. Then, as a class, find a way to verify your prediction.

    c.   Compare your strategy of dividing polynomials with that of long division, as presented in the Math Notes box in this lesson. In your Learning Log, describe the similarities and differences of the different strategies. Title this entry "Division of Polynomials" and include today's date.

ACT-32. Find each quotient below. Verify your work.

    a. $\frac{4x^2+4x-35}{2x+7}$ b. $(10x^3 + 13x^2 - 3x) \div (5x - 1)$

    c. $(3m^2 + 20m + 10) \div (3m + 2)$ d. $(9x^2 - 3x + 1) \div (3x)$

Methods and Meanings

Dividing Polynomials

In Chapter 5, you developed a strategy to multiply polynomials. To divide polynomials, such as dividing $(3x^2 + 31x + 41)$ by $(x + 9)$ you must **reverse** the process.

Two strategies for dividing polynomials are demonstrated below.

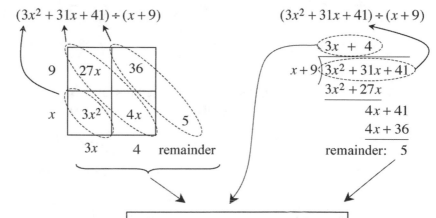

Using a Generic Rectangle:

$(3x^2 + 31x + 41) \div (x + 9)$

Using Long Division:

$(3x^2 + 31x + 41) \div (x + 9)$

Result: $(3x + 4)$ with remainder 5

Thus, $(3x^2 + 31x + 41) \div (x + 9) = (3x + 4)$ with remainder 5 or $3x + 4 + \frac{5}{x+9}$.

ACT-33. Use the strategies that you developed in this lesson to divide the following polynomials.

a. $(x^2 + 6x - 16) \div (x - 2)$

b. $(x^2 + 6x - 14) \div (x - 2)$

c. $(3n^2 + 10n + 7) \div (3n + 1)$

d. $\frac{y^2 - 9y + 14}{y - 3}$

ACT-34. Use your knowledge of the properties of numbers to determine if the following assertions are true or false.

a. $\sqrt{4}\sqrt{9} = \sqrt{4 \cdot 9}$

b. $\sqrt{64} - \sqrt{1} = \sqrt{64 - 1}$

c. $\sqrt{16} + \sqrt{4} = \sqrt{16 + 4}$

d. $\sqrt{100} \div \sqrt{25} = \sqrt{100 \div 25}$

e. Based on your work in parts (a) through (d), write a conjecture (a statement based on your observations) about which operations allow you to combine square roots.

ACT-35. Test your conjecture from part (e) of problem ACT-34 by rewriting the following expressions, if possible. Confirm your answer with a calculator. If necessary, alter your conjecture.

a. $\sqrt{10}\sqrt{3}$

b. $\sqrt{2} + \sqrt{1}$

c. $\sqrt{18} \div \sqrt{2}$

d. $\sqrt{6} - \sqrt{2}$

e. $\sqrt{19} + \sqrt{3}$

f. $\sqrt{24}\sqrt{6}$

g. $4\sqrt{9} - 2\sqrt{9}$

h. $\frac{\sqrt{28}}{\sqrt{7}}$

ACT-36. Determine if the following statements are sometimes, always, or never true. **Justify** your conclusion. For each, assume that x and y are each positive or zero.

a. $\sqrt{x} + \sqrt{y} = \sqrt{x + y}$

b. $\sqrt{x}\sqrt{y} = \sqrt{xy}$

c. $(\sqrt{x})^2 = x$

d. x is greater than $\sqrt{x}$

ACT-37. While diving from a platform which is 10 meters (roughly 32.8 feet) above the pool below, Hu's height above water was $h = -16t^2 + 4t + 32.8$ (where t is measured in seconds and h is measured in feet).

a. For how many seconds was Hu in the air after he left the platform? Write and solve an equation to find your answer.

b. How high was Hu in the air one second after he left the platform? Show how you got your answer.

ACT-38. While working on a problem, Jed wrote the equation of a line below.

$$y - (-8) = \tfrac{3}{4}(x - 1)$$

a. What is the slope of his line?

b. Name at least one point this line must pass through. Explain how you found your answer.

c. Change his equation so that the result is perpendicular to Jed's line, and through the point $(-5, 6)$.

Glossary

absolute value   The absolute value of a number is the distance of the number from zero. Since the absolute value represents a distance, without regard to direction, it is always non-negative. Thus the absolute value of a negative number is its opposite, while the absolute value of a non-negative number is just the number itself. The absolute value of x is usually written "$|x|$". For example, $|-5| = 5$ and $|22| = 22$. (p. 389)

Additive Identity Property   The Additive Identity Property states that adding zero to any expression leaves the expression unchanged. That is, $a + 0 = a$. For example, $-2xy^2 + 0 = -2xy^2$. (p. 53)

Additive Inverse Property   The Additive Inverse Property states that for every number a there is a number $-a$ such that $a + (-a) = 0$. For example, the number 5 has an additive inverse of -5; $5 + (-5) = 0$. The additive inverse of a number is often called its opposite. For example, 5 and -5 are opposites. (p. 72)

Additive Property of Equality   The Additive Property of Equality states that equality is maintained if the same amount is added to both sides of an equation. That is, if $a = b$, then $a + c = b + c$. For example, if $y = 3x$, then $y + 1.5 = 3x + 1.5$. (p. 249)

algebra tiles   An algebra tile is a manipulative whose area represents a constant or variable quantity. The algebra tiles used in this course consist of large squares with dimensions x-by-x and y-by-y; rectangles with dimensions x-by-1, y-by-1, and x-by-y; and small squares with dimensions 1-by-1. These tiles are named by their areas: x^2, y^2, x, y, xy, and 1, respectively. The smallest squares are called "unit tiles." In this text, shaded tiles will represent positive quantities while unshaded tiles will represent negative quantities. (p. 41)

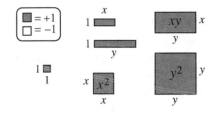

area   For this course, area is the number of square units needed to fill up a region on a flat surface. In later courses, the idea will be extended to cones, spheres, and more complex surfaces. (p. 5)

Area = 15 square units

Associative Property of Addition   The Associative Property of Addition states that if a sum contains terms that are grouped, the sum can be grouped differently with no effect on the total. That is, $a + (b + c) = (a + b) + c$. For example, $3 + (4 + 5) = (3 + 4) + 5$. (p. 53)

Associative Property of Multiplication   The Associative Property of Multiplication states that if a product contains terms that are grouped, the product can be grouped differently with no effect on the result. That is, $a(bc) = (ab)c$. For example, $2 \cdot (3 \cdot 4) = (2 \cdot 3) \cdot 4$. (p. 53)

asymptote   A line that a graph of a curve approaches as closely as you wish. An asymptote is often represented by a dashed line on a graph. For example, the graph at right has an asymptote at $y = -3$. (p. 472)

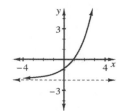

average   See "mean."

axes   In a coordinate plane, two number lines that meet at right angles at the origin (0, 0). The x-axis runs horizontally and the y-axis runs vertically. See the example at right. (p. 10)

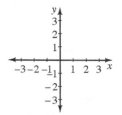

b   When the equation of a line is expressed in $y = mx + b$ form, the constant b gives the y-intercept of the line. For example, the y-intercept of the line $y = -\frac{1}{3}x + 7$ is 7. (p. 149)

base (1) When working with an exponential expression in the form a^b, a is called the base. For example, 2 is the base in 2^5. (5 is the exponent, and 32 is the value.) (Also see "exponent.") (p. 452) (2) When working with geometric figures, the term "base" may be applied to a side of a triangle, rectangle, parallelogram, or trapezoid. "Base" may also be applied to the face of a prism, cylinder, pyramid, or cone.

binomial   An expression that is the sum or difference of exactly two terms, each of which is a monomial. For example, $-2x + 3y^2$ is a binomial. (pp. 193, 329)

boundary line or curve   A line or curve on a two-dimensional graph that divides the graph into two regions. A boundary line or curve is used when graphing inequalities with two variables. For example, the inequality $y < \frac{2}{3}x + 2$ is graphed at right. The dashed boundary line has equation $y = \frac{2}{3}x + 2$. A boundary line is also sometimes called a "dividing line." (p. 393)

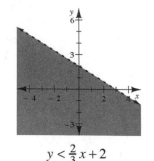

$$y < \frac{2}{3}x + 2$$

boundary point   The endpoint of a ray or segment on a number line where an inequality is true. For strict inequalities (that is, inequalities involving < or >), the point is not part of the solution. We find boundary points by solving the equality associated with our inequality. For example, the solution to the equation $2x + 5 = 11$ is $x = 3$, so the inequality $2x + 5 \geq 11$ has a boundary point at 3. The solution to that inequality is illustrated on the number line at right. A boundary point is also sometimes called a "dividing point." (p. 386)

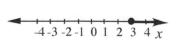

closure properties of rational numbers   The closure properties of rational numbers state that the product or sum of two rational numbers is a rational number. For example, $\frac{1}{2}$ and $\frac{3}{4}$ are both rational numbers; $\frac{1}{2} + \frac{3}{4}$ is $\frac{5}{4}$; and $\frac{5}{4}$ is a rational number. Also, 2.2 and 0.75 are both rational numbers; $2.2 \cdot 0.75$ is 1.65; and 1.65 is a rational number. (p. 214)

coefficient (numerical)   A number multiplying a variable or product of variables. For example, -7 is the coefficient of $-7xy^2$. (p. 255)

coincide   Two graphs coincide if they have all their points in common. For example, the graphs of $y = 2x + 4$ and $3y = 6x + 12$ coincide; both graphs are lines with a slope of 2 and a y-intercept of 4. When the graphs of two equations coincide, those equations share all the same solutions and have an infinite number of intersection points. (p. 252)

combining like terms   Combining two or more like terms simplifies an expression by summing constants and summing those variable terms in which the same variables are raised to the same power. For example, combining like terms in the expression $3x + 7 + 5x - 3 + 2x^2 + 3y^2$ gives $8x + 4 + 2x^2 + 3y^2$. When working with algebra tiles, combining like terms involves putting together tiles with the same dimensions. (p. 57)

common denominator   A common denominator of a group of fractions is an expression that has the denominators of each of the fractions as a factor. For example, if we are simplifying the sum $\frac{2}{x+3} + \frac{5x}{7} + \frac{3x-8}{2}$, we might use $14(x+3)$ as a common denominator for all three terms. (p. 503)

common factor   A common factor is a factor that is the same for two or more terms. For example, x^2 is a common factor of $3x^2$ and $-5x^2y$. (p. 338)

Commutative Property of Addition   The Commutative Property of Addition states that if two terms are added, the order can be reversed with no effect on the total. That is, $a + b = b + a$. For example, $7 + 12 = 12 + 7$. (p. 45)

Commutative Property of Multiplication   The Commutative Property of Multiplication states that if two expressions are multiplied, the order can be reversed with no effect on the result. That is, $ab = ba$. For example, $5 \cdot 8 = 8 \cdot 5$. (p. 45)

complete graph   A complete graph includes all the necessary information about a line or a curve. To be complete, a graph must have the following components: (1) the x-axis and y-axis labeled, clearly showing the scale; (2) the equation of the graph written near the line or curve; (3) the line or curve extended as far as possible on the graph with arrows if the line or curve continues beyond the axes; (4) the coordinates of all special points, such as x- and y-intercepts, shown in (x, y) form. (p. 120)

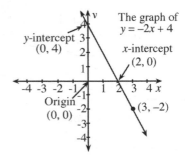

completing the square   In this course, we use completing the square to convert a quadratic equation in standard form into perfect square form. To complete the square, we add (or subtract) a constant to (or from) both sides of the equation so that the quadratic expression can be factored into a perfect square. For example, when given the quadratic equation $x^2 - 6x + 4 = 0$, we can complete the square by adding 5 to both sides. The resulting equation, $x^2 - 6x + 9 = 5$, has a left-hand side we can factor, resulting in the perfect square form quadratic equation $(x - 3)^2 = 5$. (p. 444)

conclusion   In an "If...then..." statement, the "then" portion is called the conclusion. For example, in the statement "*If* $x = 3$, *then* $x^2 = 9$," the conclusion is "$x^2 = 9$." (Also see "hypothesis.") (p. 241)

consecutive numbers   Integers that are in order without skipping any of them. For example, 8, 9, and 10 are consecutive numbers. (p. 256)

congruent   Two shapes are congruent if they have exactly the same size and shape. For example, the two triangles at right are congruent.

constant   A symbol representing a value that does not change. For example, in the equation $y = 2x + 5$, the number 5 is a constant. (p. 255)

continuous graph   A graph whose points are connected with an unbroken line or curve is called a continuous graph. A continuous graph can be traced with a pencil without ever lifting the pencil to move from one point on the graph to another point. For example, the graphs shown below are both continuous. (Also see "discrete.") (p. 102)

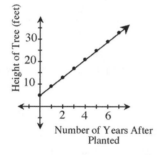
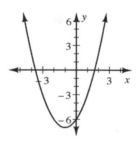

coordinate(s)   The number corresponding to a point on the number line or an ordered pair (x, y) that corresponds to a point in a two-dimensional coordinate system. In an ordered pair, the x-coordinate appears first and the y-coordinate appears second. For example, the point $(3, 5)$ has an x-coordinate of 3. (pp. 8, 10)

coordinate plane   A flat surface defined by two number lines meeting at right angles at their zero points. A coordinate plane is also sometimes called a "Cartesian Plane." (p. 10)

coordinate system   A system of graphing ordered pairs of numbers on a coordinate plane. An ordered pair represents a point, with the first number giving the horizontal position relative to the x-axis and the second number giving the vertical position relative to the y-axis. For example, the diagram at right shows the point $(3, 5)$ graphed on a coordinate plane. (p. 8)

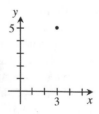

counterexample An example showing that a statement has at least one exception; that is, a situation in which the statement is false. For example, the number 4 is a counterexample to the hypothesis that all even numbers are greater than 7. (p. 192)

deductive reasoning See "justify."(p. 448)

degree (1) The degree of a monomial is the sum of the exponents of its variables. For example, $3x^2y^5$ has degree 7, because the sum of the exponents (5+2) is 7. (2) The degree of a polynomial in one variable is the degree of the term with the highest exponent. For example, $3x^5 - 4x^2 - x + 7$ has degree 5, because the highest exponent to which x is raised is 5. (3) The degree of a polynomial in more than one variable is the highest sum of the exponents among the terms. For example, $2x^5y^3 - 4x^2y^4z^3 - xy^5 + 3y^2z - 12$ has degree 9, because the sum of the exponents in the second term is 9 and no term has a higher exponent sum.

dependent variable When one quantity depends for its value on one or more others, it is called the dependent variable. For example, we might relate the speed of a car to the amount of force you apply to the gas pedal. Here, the speed of the car is the dependent variable; it depends on how hard you push the pedal. The dependent variable appears as the output value in an $x \rightarrow y$ table, and is usually placed relative to the vertical axis of a graph. We often use the letter y for the dependent variable. When working with functions or relations, the dependent variable represents the output value. (Also see "independent variable.") (pp. 110, 473)

difference of squares A polynomial that can be factored as the product of the sum and difference of two terms. The general pattern is $x^2 - y^2 = (x + y)(x - y)$. Most of the differences of squares found in this course are of the form $a^2x^2 - b^2 = (ax + b)(ax - b)$, where a and b are nonzero real numbers. For example, the difference of squares $4x^2 - 9$ can be factored as $(2x + 3)(2x - 3)$. (p. 497)

dimensions The dimensions of a flat region or space tell how far it extends in each direction. For example, the dimensions of a rectangle might be 16 cm wide by 7 cm high. (p. 22)

discrete graph A graph that consists entirely of separated points is called a discrete graph. For example, the graph shown at right is discrete. (Also see "continuous.") (p. 102)

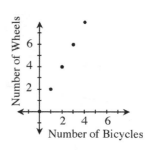

discriminant For quadratic equations in standard form $ax^2 + bx + c = 0$, the discriminant is $b^2 - 4ac$. If the discriminant is positive, the equation has two roots; if the discriminant is zero, the equation has one root; if the discriminant is negative, the equation has no real-number roots. For example, the discriminant of the quadratic equation $2x^2 - 4x - 5$ is $(-4)^2 - 4(2)(-5) = 56$, which indicates that that equation has two roots (solutions).

Distributive Property We use the Distributive Property to write a product of expressions as a sum of terms. The Distributive Property states that for any numbers or expressions a, b, and c, $a(b + c) = ab + ac$. For example, $2(x + 4) = 2 \cdot x + 2 \cdot 4 = 2x + 8$. We can demonstrate this with algebra tiles or in a generic rectangle. (p. 198)

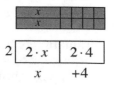

dividing line   See "boundary line."

dividing point   See "boundary point."

domain   The set of all input values for a relation or function. For example, the domain of the function graphed at right is $x \geq -3$. (p. 473) For variables, the domain is the set of numbers the variable may represent. (Also see "range.")

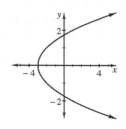

Elimination Method   A method for solving a system of equations. The key step in using the Elimination Method is to add or subtract both sides of two equations to eliminate one of the variables. For example, the two equations in the system at right can be added together to get the simplified result $7x = 14$. We can solve this equation to find x, then substitute the x-value back into either of the original equations to find the value of y. (pp. 250, 264)

$$5x + 2y = 10$$
$$2x - 2y = 4$$

equal   Two quantities are equal when they have the same value. For example, when $x = 4$, the expression $x + 8$ is equal to the expression $3x$ because their values are the same. (p. 68)

Equal Values Method   A method for solving a system of equations. To use the Equal Values Method, take two expressions that are each equal to the same variable and set those expressions equal to each other. For example, in the system of equations at right, $-2x + 5$ and $x - 1$ each equal y. So we write $-2x + 5 = x - 1$, then solve that equation to find x. Once we have x, we substitute that value back into either of the original equations to find the value of y. (p. 176)

$$y = -2x + 5$$
$$y = x - 1$$

equation   A mathematical sentence in which two expressions appear on either side of an "equals" sign (=), stating that the two expressions are equivalent. For example, the equation $7x + 4.2 = -8$ states that the expression $7x + 4.2$ has the value –8. In this course, an equation is often used to represent a rule relating two quantities. For example, a rule for finding the area y of a tile pattern with figure number x might be written $y = 4x - 3$. (p. 68)

equation mat   An organizing tool used to visually represent two equal expressions using algebra tiles. For example, the equation mat at right represents the equation $2x - 1 - (-x + 3) = 6 - 2x$. (p. 69)

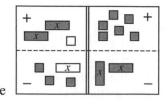

equivalent   Two expressions are equivalent if they have the same value. For example, $2 + 3$ is equivalent to $1 + 4$. (p. 19) Two equations are equivalent if they have all the same solutions. For example, $y = 3x$ is equivalent to $2y = 6x$. Equivalent equations have the same graph. (p. 205)

evaluate   To evaluate an expression, substitute the value(s) given for the variable(s) and perform the operations according to the order of operations. For example, evaluating $2x + y - 10$ when $x = 4$ and $y = 3$ gives the value 1. (p. 49)

exponent   In an expression of the form a^b, b is called the exponent. For example, in the expression 2^5, 5 is called the exponent. (2 is the base, and 32 is the value.) The exponent indicates how many times to use the base as a multiplier. For example, in 2^5, 2 is used 5 times: $2^5 = 2 \cdot 2 \cdot 2 \cdot 2 \cdot 2 = 32$. For exponents of zero, the rule is: for any number $x \neq 0$, $x^0 = 1$. For negative exponents, the rule is: for any number $x \neq 0$, $x^{-n} = \frac{1}{x^n}$, and $\frac{1}{x^{-n}} = x^n$. (Also see "laws of exponents.") (p. 452)

expression   An expression contains one or more numbers and/or variables. Each part of the expression separated by addition or subtraction signs is called a "term." For example, each of these is an expression: $6xy^2$, 24, $2.5q - 7$, $\frac{y-3}{4+x}$. (p. 47)

expression comparison mat   An expression comparison mat puts two expression mats side-by-side so they can be compared to see which represents the greater value. For example, in the expression comparison mat at right, the left-hand mat represents –3, while the right-hand mat represents –2. Since $-2 > -3$ the expression on the right is greater. (p. 55)

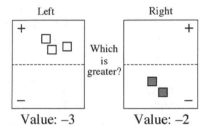

expression mat   An organizing tool used to visually represent an expression with algebra tiles. An expression mat has two regions, a positive region at the top and a negative region at the bottom. The tiles on the expression mat at right represent a value of -3. (p. 47)

Value: –3

factor   (1) In arithmetic: When two or more integers are multiplied, each of the integers is a factor of the product. For example, 4 is a factor of 24, because $4 \cdot 6 = 24$. (2) In algebra: When two or more algebraic expressions are multiplied together, each of the expressions is a factor of the product. For example, x^2 is a factor of $-17x^2y^3$, because $(x^2)(-17y^3) = -17x^2y^3$. (3) To factor an expression is to write it as a product. For example, the factored form of $x^2 - 3x - 18$ is $(x-6)(x+3)$. (p. 329)

factored completely   A polynomial is factored completely if none of the resulting factors can be factored further using integer coefficients. For example, $-2(x+3)(x-1)$ is the completely factored form of $-2x^2 - 4x + 6$. (p. 337)

factored form   A quadratic equation in the form $a(x+b)(x+c) = 0$, where a is nonzero, is said to be in factored form. For example, $-7(x+2)(x-1.5) = 0$ is a quadratic equation in factored form. (p. 438)

Fibonacci Sequence The sequence of numbers 1, 1, 2, 3, 5, 8, 13, …. Each term of the Fibonacci sequence (after the first two terms) is the sum of the two preceding terms. (p. 95)

Figure 0   The figure that comes before Figure 1 in a tile pattern. When representing a tile pattern with a graph, the y-intercept of the graph is the number of tiles in Figure 0. When representing a tile pattern with an equation in $y = mx + b$ form, b gives the number of tiles in Figure 0. (p. 142)

F.O.I.L. An approach for multiplying two binomials. "F.O.I.L." stands for "First, Outer, Inner, Last." It describes the order in which to multiply the terms of two binomials to be sure to get all the products. For example, the equation below shows how to apply the F.O.I.L. method to multiply $(2x+3)(x-4)$.

$$(2x+3)(x-4) = \underbrace{(2x)(x)}_{firsts} + \underbrace{(2x)(-4)}_{outers} + \underbrace{(3)(x)}_{inners} + \underbrace{(3)(-4)}_{lasts} = 2x^2 - 5x - 12$$

fraction buster "Fraction busting" is a method of simplifying equations involving fractions that uses the Multiplicative Property of Equality to rearrange the equation so that no fractions remain. To use this method, multiply both sides of an equation by the common denominator of all the fractions in the equation. The result will be an equivalent equation with no fractions. For example, when given the equation $\frac{x}{7} + 2 = \frac{x}{3}$, we can multiply both sides by the "fraction buster" 21. The resulting equation, $3x + 42 = 7x$, is equivalent to the original but contains no fractions. (p. 419)

function A relation in which for each input value there is one and only one output value. For example, the relation $f(x) = x + 4$ is a function; for each input value (x) there is exactly one output value. In terms of ordered pairs (x, y), no two ordered pairs of a function have the same first member (x). (p. 473)

function notation When a rule expressing a function is written using function notation, the function is given a name, most commonly "f," "g," or "h." The notation $f(x)$ represents the output of a function, named f, when x is the input. It is pronounced "f of x." For example, $g(2)$, pronounced "g of 2", represents the output of the function g when $x = 2$. If $g(x) = x^2 + 3$, then $g(2) = 7$. (p. 464)

generic rectangle A type of diagram used to visualize multiplying expressions without algebra tiles. Each expression to be multiplied forms a side length of the rectangle, and the product is the sum of the areas of the sections of the rectangle. For example, the generic rectangle at right can be used to multiply $(2x+5)$ by $(x+3)$. (p. 218)

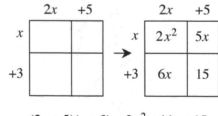

$$(2x+5)(x+3) = 2x^2 + 11x + 15$$

area as a product   area as a sum

graph A graph represents numerical information spatially. The numbers may come from a table, situation (pattern), or rule (equation or inequality). Most of the graphs in this course show points, lines, and/or curves on a two-dimensional coordinate system like the one at right (pp. 8, 10) or on a single axis called a number line (see below). (p. 21) (See "complete graph.")

greater than   One expression is greater than another if its value is larger. We indicate this relationship with the greater than symbol ">". For example, $4+5$ is greater than $1+1$. We write $4+5>1+1$. (pp. 55, 377)

greatest common factor (GCF)   (1) For integers, the greatest positive integer that is a common factor of two or more integers. For example, the greatest common factor of 28 and 42 is 14.   (2) For two or more algebraic monomials, the product of the greatest common integer factor of the coefficients of the monomials and the variable(s) in each algebraic term with the smallest degree of that variable in every term. For example, the greatest common factor of $12x^3y^2$ and $8xy^4$ is $4xy^2$. (3) For a polynomial, the greatest common monomial factor of its terms. For example, the greatest common factor of $16x^4+8x^3+12x$ is $4x$.

growth   One useful way to analyze a mathematical relationship is to examine how the output value grows as the input value increases. We can see this growth on a graph of a linear relationship by looking at the slope of the graph. (p. 142)

growth factor   When two quantities are in a linear relationship, the growth factor describes how much the output value changes when the input value increases by 1. For example, the $x \rightarrow y$ table at right shows a linear relationship with a growth factor of 6. The growth factor is equal to the slope of the line representing a linear relationship. The growth factor is also equal to the value of m when the relationship is represented with an equation in $y=mx+b$ form. (p. 205)

x	y
1	7
2	13
3	19
4	25

growth number   See "growth factor."

Guess and Check   A strategy for solving problems that starts with making a guess and then checking whether that guess is a correct solution to the problem. If the guess is not correct, the checking process helps suggest a closer next guess. The second guess is then checked. This process is repeated until a correct solution is found. Being organized is critical to using Guess and Check successfully. A table is one good way to organize your work. The Guess and Check process leads to writing equations to represent and solve word problems. (pp. 22, 65)

horizontal lines   Horizontal lines are "flat" and run left to right in the same direction as the x-axis. Horizontal lines have equations of the form $y=b$, where b can be any number. For example, the graph at right shows the horizontal lines $y=3$ and $y=-2$. The slope of any horizontal line is 0. The x-axis has the equation $y=0$ because $y=0$ everywhere on the x-axis. (p. 291)

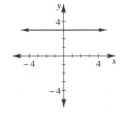

hypothesis   (1) A term scientists use to mean an "educated guess" (or what mathematicians call a conjecture), based on data, patterns, and relationships. For instance, having looked at many multiples of five, you might form a hypothesis that every multiple of five ends in the digit 0 or the digit 5.   (2) In an "If...then..." statement, the "if" portion is called the hypothesis. For example, in the statement "*If* $x=3$, *then* $x^2=9$," the hypothesis is "$x=3$." (Also see "conclusion.") (p. 241)

identity element for addition 0 is the identity element for addition because adding 0 to an expression leaves the expression unchanged. That is, $a + 0 = 0$. (Also see "Additive Identity Property.") (p. 53)

identity element for multiplication 1 is the identity element for multiplication because multiplying an expression by 1 leaves the expression unchanged. That is, $a(1) = a$. (Also see "Multiplicative Identity Property.") (p. 53)

Identity Property of Addition See "Additive Identity Property."

Identity Property of Multiplication See "Multiplicative Identity Property."

independent variable When one quantity changes in a way that does not depend on the value of another quantity, the value that changes independently is represented with the independent variable. For example, we might relate the speed of a car to the amount of force you apply to the gas pedal. Here, the amount of force applied may be whatever the driver chooses, so it represents the independent variable. The independent variable appears as the input value in an $x \rightarrow y$ table, and is usually placed relative to the horizontal axis of a graph. We often use the letter x for the independent variable. When working with functions or relations, the independent variable represents the input value. (Also see "dependent variable.") (pp. 110, 473)

inductive reasoning Drawing a conclusion based on a pattern. For example, having seen many multiples of 5 that end in the digit 0 or 5, you might use inductive reasoning to make a hypothesis or conjecture that *all* multiples of 5 end in the digit 0 or 5. (p. 448)

inequality An inequality consists of two expressions on either side of an inequality symbol. For example, the inequality $7x + 4.2 < -8$ states that the expression $7x + 4.2$ has a value less than 8. (p. 352)

inequality symbols The symbol $\leq$ read from left to right means "less than or equal to." The symbol $\geq$ read from left to right means "greater than or equal to." The symbols $<$ and $>$ mean "less than" and "greater than," respectively. For example, "7<13" means that 7 is less than 13. (p. 377)

input value The input value is the independent variable in a relation. We substitute the input value into our rule (equation) to determine the output value. For example, if we have a rule for how much your phone bill will be if you talk a certain number of minutes, the number of minutes you talk is the input value. The input value appears first in an $x \rightarrow y$ table, and is represented by the variable x. When working with functions, the input value, an element of the domain, is the value put into the function. (pp. 97, 464)

integers The set of numbers { . . . $-3, -2, -1, 0, 1, 2, 3, \ldots$ }. (p. 15)

intersection See "point of intersection."

irrational numbers The set of numbers that cannot be expressed in the form $\frac{a}{b}$, where a and b are integers and $b \neq 0$. For example, π and $\sqrt{2}$ are irrational numbers. (p. 365)

justify   To use facts, definitions, rules, and/or previously proven statements in an organized way to convince an audience that a claim (or an answer) is valid or true. For example, you might justify your claim that $x = 2$ is a solution to $3x = 6$ by pointing out that when you multiply 3 by 2, you get 6. (p. 88)

lattice points   The points on a coordinate grid where the grid lines intersect. The diagram at right shows two lattice points. The coordinates of lattice points are integers. (p. 283)

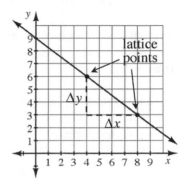

laws of exponents   The laws of exponents we study in this course are: (p. 452)

Law	Examples	
$x^m x^n = x^{m+n}$ for all x	$x^3 x^4 = x^{3+4} = x^7$	$2^5 \cdot 2^{-1} = 2^4$
$\frac{x^m}{x^n} = x^{m-n}$ for $x \neq 0$	$x^{10} \div x^4 = x^{10-4} = x^6$	$\frac{5^4}{5^7} = 5^{-3}$
$(x^m)^n = x^{mn}$ for all x	$(x^4)^3 = x^{4 \cdot 3} = x^{12}$	$(10^5)^6 = 10^{30}$
$x^0 = 1$ for $x \neq 0$	$\frac{y^2}{y^2} = y^0 = 1$	$9^0 = 1$
$x^{-1} = \frac{1}{x}$ for $x \neq 0$	$\frac{1}{x^2} = (\frac{1}{x})^2 = (x^{-1})^2 = x^{-2}$	$3^{-1} = \frac{1}{3}$
$x^{m/n} = \sqrt[n]{x^m}$ for $x \geq 0$	$\sqrt{k} = k^{1/2}$	$y^{2/3} = \sqrt[3]{y^2}$

least common multiple (LCM)   (1) The smallest common multiple of a set of two or more integers. For example, the least common multiple of 4, 6, and 8 is 24. (2) For two or more algebraic monomials, the product of the least common integer multiples of the coefficients of the monomials and the variable(s) in each algebraic term with the greatest degree of that variable in every term. For example, the least common factor of $12x^3y^2$ and $8xy^4$ is $24x^3y^4$. (p. 503)

"legal" moves   When working with an equation mat or expression comparison mat, there are certain "legal" moves you can make with the algebra tiles that keep the relationship between the two sides of the mat intact. For example, removing an x tile from the positive region of each side of an equation mat is a legal move; it keeps the expressions on each side of the mat equal. The legal moves are those justified by the properties of the real numbers. (p. 54)

less than   (1) One expression is less than another if its value is not as large. We indicate this relationship with the less than symbol "<". For example, $1+1$ is less than $4+5$. We write $1+1 < 4+5$. (p. 377) (2) We sometimes say that one amount is a certain quantity less than another amount. For example, a student movie ticket might cost two dollars *less than* an adult ticket. (p. 28)

"let" statement   A "let" statement is written at the beginning of our work to identify the variable that will represent a certain quantity. For example, in solving a problem about grilled cheese sandwiches, we might begin by writing "Let s = the number of sandwiches eaten." It is particularly important to use "let" statements when writing mathematical sentences, so that your readers will know what the variables in the sentences represent. (p. 233)

like terms   Two or more terms that contain the same variable(s), with corresponding variables raised to the same power. For example, $5x$ and $2x$ are like terms. (Also see "combining like terms.") (p. 57)

line of symmetry   A line that divides a shape into two pieces that are mirror images of each other. If you fold a shape over its line of symmetry, the shapes on both sides of the line will match perfectly. A shape with a line of symmetry is shown at right. (p. 342)

line of symmetry

linear equation   An equation in two variables whose graph is a line. For example, $y = 2.1x - 8$ is a linear equation. The standard form for a linear equation is $ax + by = c$, where a, b, and c are constants and a and b are not both zero. Most linear equations can be written in $y = mx + b$ form, which is more useful for determining the line's slope and y-intercept. (p. 205)

looking inside   "Looking inside" is a method of solving one-variable equations containing parentheses or an absolute value symbol. To use "looking inside," we first determine what the value of the entire expression inside the parentheses (or absolute value symbol) must be. We then use that fact to solve for the value of the variable. For example, to use "looking inside" to solve the equation $4(x + 2) = 36$, we first determine that $x + 2$ must equal 9. We then solve the equation $x + 2 = 9$ to find that $x = 7$. (p. 424)

m   When the equation of a line is expressed in $y = mx + b$ form, the constant m gives the slope of the line. For example, the slope of the line $y = -\frac{1}{3}x + 7$ is $-\frac{1}{3}$. (p. 149)

mathematical sentence   A mathematical sentence is an equation that uses variables to represent unknown quantities. For example, the mathematical sentence $b + g = 23$ might represent the fact that the total number of boys and girls in the class is 23. It is helpful to define variables using "let" statements before using them in a mathematical sentence. (Also see " 'let' statement.") (p. 232)

mean   The mean, or average, of several numbers is one way of defining the "middle" of the numbers. To find the average of a group of numbers, add the numbers together then divide by the number of numbers in the set. For example, the average of the numbers 1, 5, and 6 is $(1 + 5 + 6) \div 3 = 4$. (p. 11)

monomial   An expression with only one term. It can be a number, a variable, or the product of a number and one or more variables. For example, 7, $3x$, $-4ab$, and $3x^2y$ are each monomials. (p. 329)

multiple representations   See "representation" and "representations web."

Multiplicative Identity Property   The Multiplicative Identity Property states that multiplying any expression by 1 leaves the expression unchanged. That is, $a(1) = a$. For example, $437x \cdot 1 = 437x$. (p. 53)

Multiplicative Inverse Property   The Multiplicative Inverse Property states that for every nonzero number a there is a number $\frac{1}{a}$ such that $a \cdot \frac{1}{a} = 1$. For example, the number 6 has a multiplicative inverse of $\frac{1}{6}$; $6 \cdot \frac{1}{6} = 1$. The multiplicative inverse of a number is usually called its reciprocal. For example, $\frac{1}{6}$ is the reciprocal of 6. For a number in the form $\frac{a}{b}$, where a and b are non-zero, the reciprocal is $\frac{b}{a}$. (p. 72)

Multiplicative Property of Equality   The Multiplicative Property of Equality states that equality is maintained if both sides of an equation are multiplied by the same amount. That is, if $a = b$, then $a \cdot c = b \cdot c$. For example, if $y = 3x$, then $2(y) = 2(3x)$.

negative   A negative number is a number less than zero. Negative numbers are graphed on the negative side of a number line. (p. 15)

non-commensurate   Two measurements are called non-commensurate if no whole number multiple of one measurement can ever equal a whole number multiple of the other. For example, measures of 1 cm and $\sqrt{2}$ cm are non-commensurate, because no combination of items 1 cm long will ever have exactly the same length as a combination of items $\sqrt{2}$ cm long. (p. 42)

numeral   A symbol that names a number. For example, each of these is a numeral: 22.6, -19, 0.

numerical coefficient   See "coefficient."

opposite   Two numbers are opposites if they are the same distance from zero, but one is positive and one is negative. For example, 5 and -5 are opposites. The opposite of a number is sometimes called its additive inverse, indicating that the sum of a number and its opposite is zero. (p. 72)

order of operations   The specific order in which certain operations are to be carried out to evaluate or simplify expressions. The order is: parentheses (or other grouping symbols), exponents (powers or roots), multiplication and division (from left to right), and addition and subtraction (from left to right). (p. 49)

ordered pair Two numbers written in order as follows: (x, y). The primary use of ordered pairs in this course is to represent points in an x-y coordinate system. The first coordinate (x) represents the horizontal distance and direction from the origin; the second coordinate (y) represents the vertical distance and direction from the origin. For example, the ordered pair (3, 5) represents the point shown in bold at right. (p. 10)

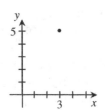

origin   The point on a coordinate plane where the x- and y-axes intersect is called the origin. This point has coordinates $(0, 0)$. The point assigned to zero on a number line is also called the origin. (p. 120)

output value   The output value is the dependent variable in a relation. When we substitute the input value into our rule (equation), the result is the output value. For example, if we have a rule for how much your phone bill will be if you talk a certain number of minutes, the amount of your phone bill is the output value. The output value appears second in an $x \rightarrow y$ table, and is represented by the variable y. When working with functions, the output value, an element of the range, is the value that results from applying the rule for the function to an input value. (pp. 97, 464)

parabola   A parabola is a particular kind of mathematical curve. In this course, a parabola is always the graph of a quadratic function $y = ax^2 + bx + c$ where a does not equal 0. The diagram at right shows some examples of parabolas. The highest or lowest point on the graph is called the vertex. (p. 106)

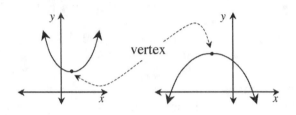

parallel   Two or more straight lines on a flat surface that do not intersect (no matter how far they are extended) are parallel. If two lines have the same slope and do not coincide, they are parallel. For example, the graphs of $y = 2x + 3$ and $y = 2x - 2$ are parallel (see diagram at right). When two equations have parallel graphs, the equations have no solutions in common. (p. 252)

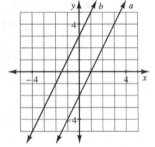

pattern   A pattern is a set of things in order that change in a regular way. For example, the numbers 1, 4, 7, 10, … form a pattern, because each number increases by 3. The numbers 1, 4, 9, 16, … form a pattern, because they are squares of consecutive integers. (p. 96) In this course, we often look at tile patterns, whose figure numbers and areas we represent with a table, a rule (equation), or a graph. (pp. 18, 93)

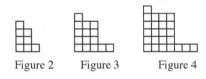

Figure 2   Figure 3   Figure 4

percent   A ratio that compares a number to 100. Percents are often written using the "%" symbol. For example, 0.75 is equal to $\frac{75}{100}$ or 75%. (p. 19)

perfect square form   A quadratic equation in the form $a(x + b)^2 = c$, where a is nonzero, is said to be in perfect square form. For example, $3(x - 12)^2 = 19$ is a quadratic equation in perfect square form. (p. 438)

perfect square trinomials Trinomials of the form $a^2x^2 + 2abx + b^2$, where a and b are nonzero real numbers, are known as perfect square trinomials and factor as $(ax+b)^2$. For example, the perfect square trinomial $9x^2 - 24x + 16$ can be factored as $(3x-4)^2$. (p. 497)

perimeter The distance around a figure on a flat surface. (p. 5)

Perimeter =
$5 + 8 + 4 + 6 = 23$ units

perpendicular Two lines or segments that meet (intersect) to form a 90° angle. For example, the lines shown on the graph at right are perpendicular. If two perpendicular lines are graphed in an x, y-coordinate system, their slopes are opposite reciprocals. (p. 308)

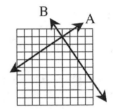

point of intersection A point of intersection is a point that the graphs of two equations have in common. For example, (3, 4) is a point of intersection of the two graphs shown at right. Two graphs may have one point of intersection, several points of intersection, or no points of intersection. The ordered pair representing a point of intersection gives a solution to the equations of each of the graphs. (pp. 165, 252)

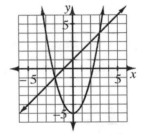

point-slope form The point-slope form of the equation of a line is $y - k = m(x - h)$, where (h, k) are the coordinates of a point on the line, and m is the slope of the line. For example, a line with slope –4 passing through the point (5, 8) has the equation $y - 8 = -4(x - 5)$. To find the equation of the line in $y = mx + b$ form, we solve the point-slope form equation for y. (p. 314)

polygon A two-dimensional closed figure of straight line segments ("edges" or "sides") connected end to end. Each side (or edge) intersects only the endpoints of its two adjacent sides (or edges). For example, the shape at right is a polygon.

polynomial An expression that is the sum or difference of two or more monomials (terms). For example, $x^8 - 4x^6y + 6x^4y^2$ is a polynomial. (p. 329)

power A number or variable raised to an exponent in the form x^n. See "exponent."

prediction A rule (equation), table, or graph can be used to make a prediction about the value(s) a quantity will take that we have not yet seen. For example, we might analyze data about the height of a tree in each of its first three years of growth to predict how tall it will be at the end of year 4. (p. 97)

prime number   A positive integer with exactly two factors. The only factors of a prime number are 1 and itself. For example, the numbers 2, 3, 17, and 31 are all prime. 31 has no factors other than 1 and 31. (p. 241)

problem-solving strategies   This course incorporates several problem-solving strategies, specifically, making a guess and checking it, using manipulatives (such as algebra tiles), making systematic lists, collecting data, graphing, drawing a diagram, breaking a large problem into smaller subproblems, working backward, and writing and solving equations. For example, a student given the details of a cell-phone pricing plan and asked how many minutes would cost $29.95 might approach the problem by writing an equation and solving it, making a table of times and prices, graphing the relationship, or guessing and checking various numbers of minutes. (p. 2)

product   The result of multiplying. For example, the product of 4 and 5 is 20; the product of $3a$ and $8b^2$ is $24ab^2$. (p. 28)

proportion   An equation stating that two ratios (fractions) are equal. For example, the equation below is a proportion. A proportion is a useful type of equation to set up when solving problems involving proportional relationships. (p. 211)

$$\frac{68 \text{ votes for Mr. Mears}}{100 \text{ people surveyed}} = \frac{34 \text{ votes for Mr. Mears}}{50 \text{ people surveyed}}$$

quadrants   The coordinate plane is divided by its axes into four quadrants. The quadrants are numbered as shown in the first diagram at right. When graphing data that has no negative values, we sometimes use a graph showing only the first quadrant. (p. 10)

4-quadrant graph:

II | I

III | IV

1st-quadrant graph:

quadratic equation   An equation that can be written in the form $ax^2 + bx + c = 0$, where a, b, and c are real numbers and a is nonzero. A quadratic equation written in this form is said to be in standard form. For example, $3x^2 - 4x + 7.5 = 0$ is a quadratic equation. (p. 348)

quadratic expression   An expression that can be written in the form $ax^2 + bx + c$, where a, b, and c are real numbers and a is nonzero. For example, $3x^2 - 4x + 7.5$ is a quadratic expression. (p. 329)

Quadratic Formula   The Quadratic Formula states that if $ax^2 + bx + c = 0$ and $a \neq 0$, then $x = \frac{-b \pm \sqrt{b^2 - 4ac}}{2a}$. For example, if $5x^2 + 9x + 3 = 0$, then $x = \frac{-9 \pm \sqrt{9^2 - 4(5)(3)}}{2(5)} = \frac{-9 \pm \sqrt{21}}{10}$. (p. 357)

quadrilateral A polygon with four sides. For example, the shape at right is a quadrilateral.

radical   An expression in the form $\sqrt{a}$, where $\sqrt{a}$ is the positive square root of a. For example, $\sqrt{49} = 7$. (Also see "square root.") (p. 365)

radicand   The expression under a radical sign. For example, in the expression $3+2\sqrt{x-7}$, the radicand is $x-7$.

range   The set of all output values for a function or relation. For example, the range of the function graphed at right is $y>-2$. (Also see "domain.") (p. 473)

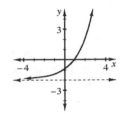

ratio   A ratio compares two quantities by division. A ratio can be written using a colon, but is more often written as a fraction. For example, we might be interested in the ratio of female students in a particular school to the total number of students in the school. This ratio could be written as 1521:2906 or as the fraction shown at right. (p. 211)

$$\frac{1521 \text{ female students}}{2906 \text{ total students}}$$

rational expression   An expression in the form of a fraction in which the numerator and/or denominator contain polynomials. For example, $\frac{x+2}{x^2+8x+12}$ is a rational expression. (pp. 409, 413)

rational numbers   Numbers that can be expressed in the form $\frac{a}{b}$, where a and b are integers and $b \neq 0$. For example, 0.75 is a rational number because it can be expressed in the form $\frac{3}{4}$. (p. 214)

real numbers   Irrational numbers together with rational numbers form the set of the real numbers. For example, the following are all real numbers: 2.78, -13267, 0, $\frac{3}{7}$, π, $\sqrt{2}$. All real numbers are represented on the number line. (p. 365)

reciprocal   The reciprocal of a nonzero number is its multiplicative inverse; that is, the reciprocal of x is $\frac{1}{x}$. For a number in the form $\frac{a}{b}$, where a and b are non-zero, the reciprocal is $\frac{b}{a}$. The product of a number and its reciprocal is 1. For example, the reciprocal of 12 is $\frac{1}{12}$, and $12 \cdot \frac{1}{12} = 1$. (Also see "Multiplicative Inverse Property.") (p. 72)

Reflexive Property   The Reflexive Property states that any expression is always equal to itself. That is, $a = a$. For example, $1627x^2 - 2 = 1627x^2 - 2$.

relation   An equation that relates inputs to outputs. For example, $y = \frac{4x}{x-3}$ and $x^2 + y^2 = 18$ are both relations. The set of input values to a relation is the domain, and the set of output values is the range. A relation can also be thought of as a set of ordered pairs. (p. 473)

representation   A representation expresses a relationship between quantities in a particular way. In this course, we emphasize four different ways of representing a numerical relationship: with a graph, table, situation (pattern), or rule (equation or inequality). (Also see "representations web.") (p. 161)

representations web The representations web, or just "the web," is an organizational tool we use to keep track of connections between the four representations of numerical relationships emphasized in this course. As we learn how to move from one representation of a particular type of pattern to another, we record this by drawing an arrow on the web. For example, an arrow from "rule" to "graph" in the web might record our ability to draw the graph for a given equation. (Also see "representation.") (p. 161)

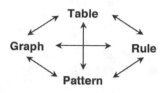

rewriting To rewrite an equation or expression is to write an equivalent equation or expression. In this course, "rewriting" also refers to a method of solving one-variable equations. In "rewriting," we use algebraic techniques to write an equation equivalent to the original. This will often involve using the Distributive Property to eliminate parentheses. We then solve the equation using various solution methods, including perhaps rewriting again. For example, to solve the equation $4(x+2) = 36$ by "rewriting," we use the Distributive Property to rewrite the equation as $4x + 8 = 36$. We then solve this equation to find that $x = 7$. (p. 424)

root A root of an equation is a solution of the equation. For example, the roots of $(x-4)(2x+3) = 0$ are $x = 4$ and $x = -\frac{3}{2}$. When working with a function $f(x)$, the x-intercepts of the function's graph are the roots of the equation $f(x) = 0$. (p. 344)

rule A rule is an equation or inequality that represents the relationship between two numerical quantities. We often use a rule to represent the relationship between quantities in a table, a pattern, a real-world situation, or a graph. For example, the rule $y = 0.4x + 25$ might tell us how to find the total cost y in cents of talking on a pay phone for x minutes. (p. 93)

scale on axes The scale on an axis tells you what number each successive mark on the axis represents. A complete graph has the scale marked with numbers on each axis. Each axis should be scaled so that each interval represents the same amount. (p. 105)

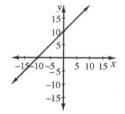

scientific notation A number is expressed in scientific notation when it is in the form $a \cdot 10^n$, where $1 \le a < 10$ and n is an integer. For example, the number 31,000 can be expressed in scientific notation as $3.1 \cdot 10^4$. (p. 451)

similar figures Similar figures have the same shape but are not necessarily the same size. For example the two triangles at right are similar. In similar figures, the measures of corresponding angles are equal and the lengths of corresponding sides are proportional. (p. 78)

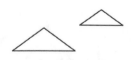

simple radical form A number $r\sqrt{s}$ is in simple radical form if no square of an integer divides s and s is not a fraction; that is, there are no perfect square factors (square numbers such as 4, 9, 16, etc.) under the radical sign and no radicals in the denominator. For example, $5\sqrt{12}$ is not in simple radical form since 4 (the square of 2) divides 12. But $10\sqrt{3}$ is in simple radical form and is equivalent to $5\sqrt{12}$. (p. 365)

simplify   To simplify an expression is to write a less complicated expression with the same value. A simplified expression has no parentheses and no like terms. For example, the expression $3 - (2x + 7) - 4x$ can be simplified to $-4 - 6x$. When working with algebra tiles, a simplified expression uses the fewest possible tiles to represent the original expression. (p. 55)

slope   A ratio that describes how steep (or flat) a line is. Slope can be positive, negative, or even zero, but a straight line has only one slope. Slope is the ratio $\frac{\text{vertical change}}{\text{horizontal change}}$ or $\frac{\text{change in } y \text{ value}}{\text{change in } x \text{ value}}$, sometimes written $\frac{\Delta y}{\Delta x}$. When the equation of a line is written in $y = mx + b$ form, m is the slope of the line. Some texts refer to slope as the ratio of the "rise over the run." A line has positive slope if it slopes upward from left to right on a graph, negative slope if it slopes downward from left to right, zero slope if it is horizontal, and undefined slope if it is vertical. (p. 291)

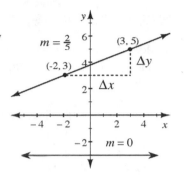

slope-intercept form   See "$y = mx + b$."

slope triangle   A slope triangle is a right triangle drawn on a graph of a line so that the hypotenuse of the triangle is part of the line. The vertical leg length is the change in the y-value (Δy); the horizontal leg length is the change in the x-value (Δx). We use the lengths of the legs in the triangle to calculate the slope ratio $\frac{\Delta y}{\Delta x}$. For example, the diagram at right shows a slope triangle with $\Delta y = 2$, $\Delta x = 4$. The slope of the line in the example is $\frac{2}{4}$, or $\frac{1}{2}$. (Also see "slope.") (p. 282)

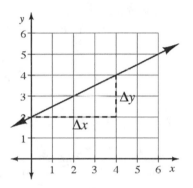

solution   The number or numbers that when substituted into an equation or inequality make the equation or inequality true. For example, $x = 4$ is a solution to the equation $3x - 2 = 10$ because $3x - 2$ equals 10 when $x = 4$. A solution to a two-variable equation is sometimes written as an ordered pair (x, y). For example, $x = 3$ and $y = -2$ is a solution to the equation $y = x - 5$; this solution can be written as $(3, -2)$. (pp. 128, 201, 245, 252)

solve   (1) To find all the solutions to an equation or an inequality (or a system of equations or inequalities). For example, solving the equation $x^2 = 9$ gives the solutions $x = 3$ and $x = -3$. (pp. 68, 119, 170) (2) Solving an equation for a variable gives an equivalent equation that expresses that variable in terms of other variables and constants. For example, solving $2y - 8x = 16$ for y gives $y = 4x + 8$. The equation $y = 4x + 8$ has the same solutions as $2y - 8x = 16$, but $y = 4x + 8$ expresses y in terms of x and some constants. (p. 203)

square numbers   The numbers in the pattern 1, 4, 9, 16, 25, ... That is, the squares of the counting numbers 1, 2, 3, 4, 5, ... are known as square numbers.

square root A number a is a square root of b if $a^2 = b$. For example, the number 9 has two square roots, 3 and –3. A negative number has no real square roots; a positive number has two; and zero has just one square root, namely, itself. Other roots, such as cube root, will be studied in other courses. (Also see "radical.") (p. 365)

standard form for a number   See "standard notation."

standard form for quadratics A quadratic expression in the form $ax^2 + bx + c$ is said to be in standard form. For example, the following are all expressions in standard form: $3m^2 + m - 1$, $x^2 - 9$, and $3x^2 + 5x$. (p. 335)

standard form of a linear equation The standard form for a linear equation is $ax + by = c$, where a, b, and c are real numbers and a and b are not both zero. For example, the equation $2.5x - 3y = 12$ is in standard form. When you are given the equation of a line in standard form, it is often useful to write an equivalent equation in $y = mx + b$ form to find the line's slope and y-intercept. (p. 205)

standard notation A number written out completely, showing all digits and without use of exponents is written in standard notation. For example, 31,000 is the standard notation for the number expressed by $3.1 \cdot 10^4$. Standard notation is also sometimes called "standard form."

starting value In certain situations, the dependent variable has a starting value where the situation described in a problem begins. For example, if we are measuring the population of a town over time, that population will have some starting value when we begin our measurements. (p. 203)

substitution Replacing one symbol with a number, a variable, or another algebraic expression of the same value. Substitution does not change the value of the overall expression. For example, suppose we are trying to evaluate the expression $13x - 6$ when $x = 4$. Since x has the value 4, we can substitute 4 into the expression wherever x appears, giving us the equivalent expression $13(4) - 6$. (p. 248)

Substitution Method A method for solving a system of equations by replacing one variable with an expression involving the remaining variable(s). For example, in the system of equations at right the first equation tells you that y is equal to $-3x + 5$. We can substitute $-3x + 5$ in for y in the second equation to get $2(-3x + 5) + 10x = 18$, then solve this equation to find x. Once we have x, we substitute that value back into either of the original equations to find the value of y. (pp. 242, 248)

$$y = -3x + 5$$
$$2y + 10x = 18$$

Substitution Property The Substitution Property states that if $a = b$, a can be replaced by b in any expression without changing the value of the expression. For example, if $x = 4$, $13x - 6$ has the same value as $13(4) - 6$.

sum The result of adding two or more numbers. For example, the sum of 4 and 5 is 9. (p. 28)

Symmetric Property of Equality   The Symmetric Property states that if two expressions are equal, it does not matter which is stated first. That is, if $a = b$ then $b = a$. For example, $56 \div 8 = 7$, and $7 = 56 \div 8$.

symmetry   See "line of symmetry."

system of equations   A system of equations is a set of equations with the same variables. Solving a system of equations means finding one or more solutions that make each of the equations in the system true. A solution to a system of equations gives a point of intersection of the graphs of the equations in the system. There may be zero, one, or several solutions to a system of equations. For example, $(1.5, -3)$ is a solution to the system of equations at right; setting $x = 1.5$, $y = -3$ makes both of the equations true. Also, $(1.5, -3)$ is a point of intersection of the graphs of these two equations. (p. 165)

$$y = 2x - 6$$
$$y = -2x$$

system of inequalities   A system of inequalities is a set of inequalities with the same variables. Solving a system of inequalities means finding one or more regions on the coordinate plane whose points represent solutions to each of the inequalities in the system. There may be zero, one, or several such regions for a system of inequalities. For example, the shaded region at right is a graph of the system of inequalities that appears below it. (p. 391)

$$y \leq x^2 + x - 6$$
$$y > \tfrac{2}{3}x$$

table   The tables used in this course represent numerical information by organizing it into columns and rows. The numbers may come from a graph, situation (pattern), or rule (equation). Many of the tables in this course are x-y tables like the one shown at right. (pp. 13, 23)

IN (x)	−2	4	1	6	−5
OUT (y)	6	−2	−3	2	−9

term   A term is a single number, variable, or the product of numbers and variables. In an expression, terms are separated by addition or subtraction signs. For example, in the expression $1.2x - 45 + 3xy^2$, the terms are $1.2x$, -45, and $3xy^2$. (p. 57)

tile pattern   See "pattern."

Transitive Property of Equality   The Transitive Property of Equality states that if $a = b$ and $b = c$, then $a = c$. For example, if $x = 2y$ and $2y = 13$, then x must equal 13. (p. 448)

trend line   A line that represents a set of data. The trend line does not necessarily intersect each data point; it attempts to approximate the data, as in the example at right. Trend lines are often used to make predictions about future, unobserved data points. (p. 279)

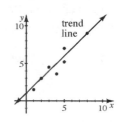

trinomial   A polynomial that is the sum or difference of exactly three terms, each of which is a monomial. For example, $x^2 + 6x + 9$ is a trinomial. (pp. 329)

twice   Two times as much. For example, a twenty-dollar bill has *twice* the value of a ten-dollar bill. (p. 28)

undoing   In this course, "undoing" refers to a method of solving one-variable equations. In "undoing," we undo the last operation that was applied to an expression by applying its inverse operation. We then solve the resulting equation using various solution methods, including perhaps undoing again. For example, in the equation $4(x+2) = 36$, the last operation that was applied to the left-hand side was a *multiplication* by 4. So to use "undoing," we *divide* both sides of the equation by 4, giving us $x+2=9$. We then solve the equation $x+2=9$ (perhaps by "undoing" again and subtracting 2 from both sides) to find that $x=7$. (p. 424)

variable   A symbol used to represent one or more numbers. In this course, letters of the English alphabet are used as variables. For example, in the expression $3x-(8.6xy+z)$, the variables are x, y, and z. (p. 41)

vertex (of a parabola)   The vertex of a parabola is the highest or lowest point on the parabola (depending on the parabola's orientation). (p. 106)

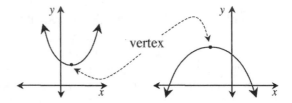

vertical lines   Vertical lines run up and down in the same direction as the y-axis and are parallel to it. All vertical lines have equations of the form $x=a$, where a can be any number. For example, the graph at right shows the vertical lines $x=4$ and $x=-1$. The y-axis has the equation $x=0$ because $x=0$ everywhere on the y-axis. Vertical lines have undefined slope. (p. 291)

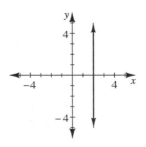

Ways of Thinking   This course emphasizes five Ways of Thinking about mathematical ideas: justifying (explaining and verifying your ideas), generalizing (predicting behavior for any situation), making connections (connecting your ideas to other ways of seeing or to past or future learning), reversing thinking (solving problems "backward and forward"), and applying and extending (applying your knowledge to new contexts and extending it to help solve new problems). For example, when confronted with a new type of mathematical problem, you might solve it by reversing your thinking to work backwards or by trying to make connections to problems you have seen before. Once you have a solution, you might be asked to justify your solution or generalize it to a broader class of problems. Finally, you might then apply what you have learned on this problem to the next new type of problem that comes along. (p. 2)

web   See "representations web."

x-axis   See "axes."

x-coordinate   See "coordinate."

x-intercept(s)   The point(s) where a graph intersects the x-axis. A graph may have several x-intercepts, no x-intercepts, or just one. We sometimes report the x-intercepts of a graph with coordinate pairs, but since the y-coordinate is always zero, we often just give the x-coordinates of x-intercepts. For example, we might say that the x-intercepts of the graph at right are (0, 0) and (2, 0), or we might just say that the x-intercepts are 0 and 2. (pp. 119, 301)

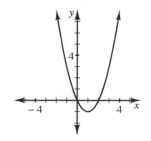

x→y table   An x→y table, like the one at right, represents pairs of values of two related quantities. The input value (x) appears first, and the output value (y) appears second. For example, the x→y table at right tells us that the input value 10 is paired with the output value 18 for some rule. (p. 94)

IN (x)	OUT (y)
	8
0	-2
-4	-10
10	18
-2	
	198
0.5	

y-axis   See "axes."

y-coordinate   See "coordinate."

y-intercept(s)   The point(s) where a graph intersects the y-axis. A function has at most one y-intercept; a relation may have several. The y-intercept of a graph is important because it often represents the starting value of a quantity in a real-world situation. For example, on the graph of a tile pattern the y-intercept represents the number of tiles in Figure 0. We sometimes report the y-intercept of a graph with a coordinate pair, but since the x-coordinate is always zero, we often just give the y-coordinate of the y-intercept. For example, we might say that the y-intercept of the graph at right is (0, 2), or we might just say that the y-intercept is 2. When a linear equation is written in $y = mx + b$ form, b tells us the y-intercept of the graph. For example, the equation of the graph at right is $y = x + 2$ and its y-intercept is 2. (pp. 119, 298, 301)

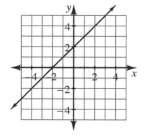

$y = mx + b$ When two quantities x and y have a linear relationship, that relationship can be represented with an equation in $y = mx + b$ form. The constant m is the slope, and b is the y-intercept of the graph. For example, the graph at right shows the line represented by the equation $y = 2x + 3$, which has a slope of 2 and a y-intercept of 3. This form of a linear equation is also called the slope-intercept form. (p. 149)

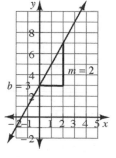

zero   A number often used to represent "having none of a quantity." Zero is neither negative nor positive. Zero is the identity element for addition. (pp. 51, 53, 346, 348)

Zero Product Property   The Zero Product Property states that when the product of two or more factors is zero, one of these factors must equal zero. That is, if $a \cdot b = 0$, then either $a = 0$ or $b = 0$ (or both). For example, if $(x + 4)(2x - 3) = 0$, then either $x + 4 = 0$ or $2x - 3 = 0$ (or both). The Zero Product Property can be used to solve factorable quadratic equations. (p. 349)

List of Symbols

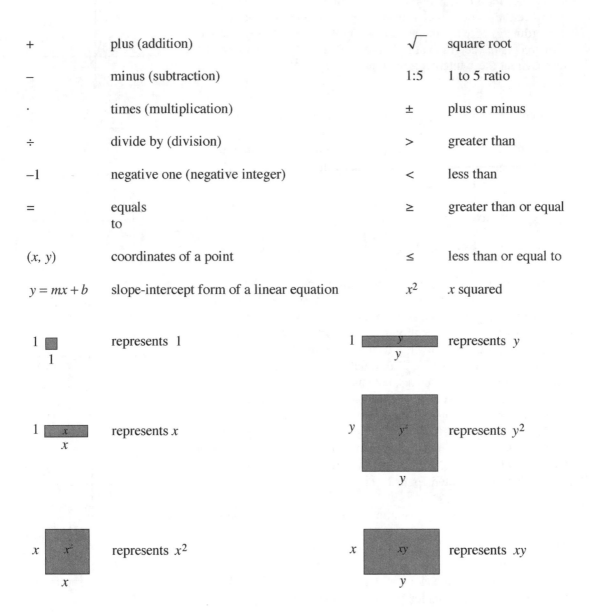

+	plus (addition)	$\sqrt{}$	square root
−	minus (subtraction)	1:5	1 to 5 ratio
·	times (multiplication)	±	plus or minus
÷	divide by (division)	>	greater than
−1	negative one (negative integer)	<	less than
=	equals to	≥	greater than or equal
(x, y)	coordinates of a point	≤	less than or equal to
$y = mx + b$	slope-intercept form of a linear equation	x^2	x squared

1 □ represents 1

1 □ represents y

1 □ represents x

y □ represents y^2

x □ represents x^2

x □ represents xy

Note: For this text, all unshaded tiles will represent negative quantities. For example, the tile □ represents −1.

Index
Student Version

Many of the pages referenced here contain a definition or an example of the topic listed, often within the body of a Math Notes box. Others contain problems that develop or demonstrate the topic. It may be necessary to read the text on several pages to fully understand the topic. Also, some problems listed here are good examples of the topic and may not offer any explanation. The page numbers below reflect the pages in the Student Version. References to Math Notes boxes are bolded.

Symbols

$\leq, <, >, \geq$ symbols, 350
Δ (delta), 282, 283
$\pm$ (plus or minus), 357, **358**
$\sqrt{}$ (square root), 365

A

Absolute value, 388, **389**
  solving equations with, **430**
  solving inequalities with, 432
Adding and subtracting rational
  expressions, 499, 502, **503**
Adding integers, **15**
Additive Identity, **53**
Additive Inverse Property, **72**
Algebra tiles, 41, 42, 44, **198**
  building a square, **427**
  multiplying binomials, **192**
  naming, 41
  on an equation mat, 68, **69**
  on an expression comparison mat, 55
  on an expression mat, 47, 52, **60**
  solving equations, 68
  to combine like terms, 42, **57**
  to simplify expressions, 52, **57**, **60**
Algebra, properties of
  Associative Properties, **53**
  Commutative Properties, **45**
  Distributive Property, 194, **198**
  Identity Properties, **53**, **410**
  Inverse properties, **72**
  Transitive Property, **448**

All numbers solution, **127**
Apartment problem, the, 22
Applying and extending, 224
Approximate form, 426
Approximating square roots, 365
Area
  as a product, 191, **192**, **218**, 327
  as a sum, 191, **192**, **218**, 327
  of a figure, **5**
  of a rectangle, **5**, 7
  of a square, 336
Associative Property
  of Addition, **53**
  of Multiplication, **53**
Average (mean), 11, 25
Axes, **10**
  independent and dependent, **110**
  scaling, 14, 105, 115
  x- and y-axes, **10**

B

b, 149, 150, **298**
Base, **452**
Big Cs problems, 100, 101, 124
Big Race problems, 296, 298, **300**
Binomial, **329**
Boundaries, system of inequalities, 392, **393**
Boundary point, 376, **377**, **386**
Burning Candle problem, the, 512

C

Calculator check, 67
Cartesian plane, **10**
Checking a solution, **201**
Chubby Bunny problems, 169, 170
Closure Properties, **214**, 215
Coefficient, **255**
Coincide, **252**, **258**
Cola Machine problem, 467
Combining like terms, **57**
Common factor, 338
Commutative Property, **45**
Complete Graph, **119**
Completing the square, 436, 437, 438, 440, **444**
    deriving the Quadratic Formula, 510
Conclusion, **241**, 384
Consecutive numbers, 256
Constant, 149, **255**
Continuous, 101, **102**, 147
Coordinates, 8, **10**, 46, **119**
Counterexample, 192, 284, 527
Cube root, 450

D

Decimal, **19**
Deductive reasoning, **448**
Delta, 282, 283
Dependent, 13, **110**, **473**
Deriving the Quadratic Formula, 510
Diamond problems, 6, 16, 331, 332
    factoring, 331, 338
Difference of squares, 497
Dimensions, 7, 27, 46
Direct proportion. *See* Direct Variation
Direct variation, **525**, 532, **533**
Discrete, 101, **102**
Distributive Property, 194, **198**
Dividing integers, **24**
Dizzyland problem, 311
Domain, 470, **473**

E

Elimination Method, 250, **264**
Ellipsis, 530
Endpoint
    solid, 376, **377**, **386**
    unfilled, 376, **377**, **386**
Equal Values Method, 170, **171**, **176**
Equation of line
    point-slope form, **314**
    slope-intercept form, 150, **298**
    through two points, 310
Equations, 68, **69**
    approximating from data, 279
    equivalent, 411, 416, 418, **419**
    from a pattern, 93, 139
    from a table, 94, 98, 150
    from a situation, 108
    from word problems, **234**
    linear. *See* Linear equations
    proportional, 209, 210, **211**
    quadratic, **335**, 348, **349**
    quadratic application, 360, 364
    quadratic, from a graph, 354
    quadratic, in perfect square form, 426, **427**
    quadratic, solving with the Quadratic Formula, 357, **358**, **361**
    quadratic, solving with the Zero Product Property, **361**
    of a line, 149
    solving. *See* Solving equations
    solving by looking inside, 422, **424**
    solving by rewriting, 411, 414, 415, 416, 418, 422, **424**
    solving by undoing, 422, **424**
    solving with absolute value, **430**
    solving without algebra tiles, **171**
    systems. *See* Systems of equations
Equation mat, 68, **69**
Equivalent, 16
    equations, 399, **416**, 418, **419**
    expressions, 48
    fractions, 212
Estimating Fish problem, 216
Eucalyptus Grove problem, 8

H

Highest point, 106
Horizontal change (delta x), **291**
Hypothesis, **241**, 384

I

Identity Properties, **53**
Iditarod Trail Sled Dog Race problem, 163
If ... then ... statement, **241**
Independent, 13, **110, 473**
Inductive reasoning, **448**
Inequalities, 375
   boundary point, 376, **377, 386**
   from word problems, 380
   solving by graphing, 432
   with absolute value, 432
   with one variable, 376, **386**
Inequality symbols, 350, **352, 377**
Infinite solutions, **127**
Input, 464, **473**
Integers, **15**
Intercepts, 113, 119, 483
   shortcuts, 362
Intersection, 163, 165, **258**, 483
Inverse properties, **72**
Inverse proportion. *See* Inverse Variation
Inverse variation, **525**, 532, **533**
Irrational numbers, 365

J

John's Giant Redwood problems, 98, 126
Justification, algebraic, 241
Justifying, 88

L

Lattice points, 283
Learning Logs, 24
Less than, **28**
Let statement, 233
Line Factory problems
   Line Factory Logo, 313
   Quality Control, 275
   Slope Walk, 293
   Take A Walk, 297
   Walk The Walk, 294

Linear equations
   finding the intercepts, 362
   from a graph, 156
   from a table, 150
   point-slope form, **314**
   slope-intercept form, 150, 203,
      205, 298
   solving. *See* Solving equations
   standard form, 203, **205**
   through two points, 310
   $y = mx + b$ form, 203, **205**
Linear inequality
   boundary, 382
   graph, 382, 385
   solutions of, 382, 385
Lines of symmetry, **342**
Literal equations, 203
Logical conclusions, **241**, 384
Looking inside, 422, **424**
Lowest point, 106

M

m, 149, 150, 283, 285, 286, 290, **291,**
   298
Machine, relation, 464, 465, 467,
   473
Making connections, 36
Mathematical sentences, 231, 232,
   234, 236, 375
Mathography problem, 6
Mean, 11, 25
Minus, meaning of, 47
Mixture problems, 508
Mode, 70
Moe's Yo problem, 364
Monomial, **329**
More than, **28**
Motion detector, 293, 297
Multiple representations, 139, **161**
   connections between, 139, 152
   quadratic, 344
   quadratic web, 345
   web, 144, 173
Multiplicative Identity, **53**
Multiplicative Identity Property, **410**
Multiplicative Inverse Property, **72**
Multiplying binomials
   with algebra tiles, **192**
   with generic rectangles, 197, **218**
Multiplying integers, **24**

R

Range, 471, **473**
Ratio, 210, **211**
  slope, **291**
Rational expressions, 409
  adding and subtracting, 499, 502, **503**
  multiplying and dividing, 412, **413**
  simplifying, 410, **413**
Rational Numbers, **214**, 365
Ratios, equal, 212
Real numbers, 365
Reasoning
  deductive, **448**
  inductive, **448**
Reciprocal, **72**
Recorder/Reporter, 4
Rectangle
  area, **5**, 7, 191
  area as a product, **218**
  area as a sum, **218**
  building with algebra tiles, 193
  dimensions, **7**, 27, 46, 191
  generic, 197, **198**, **218**
  perimeter, **5**
Regions, 392
Relations, 465, 475
  domain, 470, 471, **473**
  function, 467
  input and output, 464
  range, **473**
  transformations, 479
Representations
  connections between, 139, 152
  multiple, **161**
  numeric, 11, 16, **19**
  web, 144, 159, **161**, 173
Resource Manager, 4
Reversing thinking, 184
Rewriting, solving by, 415, 416, 422, **424**
Rewriting expressions
  Distributive Property, 194, **198**
  multiplying binomials, **192**
  with exponents, **452**
Roots, 450
  of a parabola, 344, 350

Rule, 161
  from a graph, 149, 156
  from a pattern, 100, 139, 143, 148
  from a situation, 108
  from a table, 94, 97, 98, 150
  quadratic, from a graph, 354
  quadratic, from a situation or
    pattern, 345
  quadratic, from a table, 351

S

Saint Louis Gateway Arch problem,
  360
Sampling, 80, 81, 216
Save the Earth problem, 316
Scaling axes, 105, 115
Scatterplot, 163, 278
Scientific notation, 451
Search and Rescue problem, 395
Set notation, 526, 530
Sierpinski Triangle, **82**
Silent Board Game, 97
Similar figures, **78**, 280
Simplifying expressions, 52, 60, 64
  by combining like terms, **57**
  on an expression mat, **60**
  recording your work, 64
  with algebra tiles, **60**
Slope, 281, 282, 283, **291**, **298**
  as a rate, 293
  negative, 285, 286, **291**
  of parallel lines, 288, 290, 308
  of perpendicular lines, 307, 308
  positive, 286, **291**
  triangles, 282, 285, 286, **298**, **314**
  undefined, **291**
  without a slope triangle, 290
  zero, 286, **291**
Slope-intercept form, 150, **205**, **298**
Solution, **127**
  checking, 118, **201**
  exact and approximate forms, 426
  infinite solutions, **127**
  no solution, **127**
  of a linear equation, 118, 382
  of a one-variable inequality, 376,
    386
  of a system of equations, **252**
  of a system of inequalities, 391,
    399

Algebra I

California Mathematics Content Standards

Symbolic reasoning and calculations with symbols are central in algebra. Through the study of algebra, a student develops an understanding of the symbolic language of mathematics and the sciences. In addition, algebraic skills and concepts are developed and used in a wide variety of problem-solving situations.

1.0 Students identify and use the arithmetic properties of subsets of integers and rational, irrational, and real numbers, including closure properties for the four basic arithmetic operations where applicable:

    1.1 Students use properties of numbers to demonstrate whether assertions are true or false.

2.0 Students understand and use such operations as taking the opposite, finding the reciprocal, taking a root, and raising to a fractional power. They understand and use the rules of exponents.

3.0 Students solve equations and inequalities involving absolute values.

4.0 Students simplify expressions before solving linear equations and inequalities in one variable, such as $3(2x-5) + 4(x-2) = 12$.

5.0 Students solve multistep problems, including word problems, involving linear equations and linear inequalities in one variable and provide justification for each step.

6.0 Students graph a linear equation and compute the x- and y- intercepts (e.g., graph $2x + 6y = 4$). They are also able to sketch the region defined by linear inequality (e.g., they sketch the region defined by $2x + 6y < 4$).

7.0 Students verify that a point lies on a line, given an equation of the line. Students are able to derive linear equations by using the point-slope formula.

8.0 Students understand the concepts of parallel lines and perpendicular lines and how those slopes are related. Students are able to find the equation of a line perpendicular to a given line that passes through a given point.

9.0 Students solve a system of two linear equations in two variables algebraically and are able to interpret the answer graphically. Students are able to solve a system of two linear inequalities in two variables and to sketch the solution sets.

10.0 Students add, subtract, multiply, and divide monomials and polynomials. Students solve multistep problems, including word problems, by using these techniques.

11.0 Students apply basic factoring techniques to second-and simple third-degree polynomials. These techniques include finding a common factor for all terms in a polynomial, recognizing the difference of two squares, and recognizing perfect squares of binomials.

12.0 Students simplify fractions with polynomials in the numerator and denominator by factoring both and reducing them to the lowest terms.

13.0 Students add, subtract, multiply, and divide rational expressions and functions. Students solve both computationally and conceptually challenging problems by using these techniques.

14.0 Students solve a quadratic equation by factoring or completing the square.

15.0 Students apply algebraic techniques to solve rate problems, work problems, and percent mixture problems.

16.0 Students understand the concepts of a relation and a function, determine whether a given relation defines a function, and give pertinent information about given relations and functions.

17.0 Students determine the domain of independent variables and the range of dependent variables defined by a graph, a set of ordered pairs, or a symbolic expression.

18.0 Students determine whether a relation defined by a graph, a set of ordered pairs, or a symbolic expression is a function and justify the conclusion.

19.0 Students know the quadratic formula and are familiar with its proof by completing the square.

20.0 Students use the quadratic formula to find the roots of a second-degree polynomial and to solve quadratic equations.

21.0 Students graph quadratic functions and know that their roots are the x- intercepts.

22.0 Students use the quadratic formula or factoring techniques or both to determine whether the graph of a quadratic function will intersect the x-axis in zero, one, or two points.

23.0 Students apply quadratic equations to physical problems, such as the motion of an object under the force of gravity.

24.0 Students use and know simple aspects of a logical argument:

24.1 Students explain the difference between inductive and deductive reasoning and identify and provide examples of each.

24.2 Students identify the hypothesis and conclusion in logical deduction.

24.3 Students use counterexamples to show that an assertion is false and recognize that a single counterexample is sufficient to refute an assertion.

25.0 Students use properties of the number system to judge the validity of results, to justify each step of a procedure, and to prove or disprove statements:

25.1 Students use properties of numbers to construct simple, valid arguments (direct and indirect) for, or formulate counterexamples to, claimed assertions.

25.2 Students judge the validity of an argument according to whether the properties of the real number system and the order of operations have been applied correctly at each step.

25.3 Given a specific algebraic statement involving linear, quadratic, or absolute value expressions or equations or inequalities, students determine whether the statement is true sometimes, always, or never.

Mathematics Content Standards for California Public Schools reproduced by permission, California Department of Education, CDE Press, 1430 N Street, Suite 3207, Sacramento, CA 95814.